KB160379

의사·치과의사·간호사를 위한

진료 영어 Handbook

임창석 지음

군자출판사

의사, 치과의사, 간호사를 위한
진료 영어 Handbook

첫째판 1쇄 인쇄 | 2004년 9월 25일
첫째판 1쇄 발행 | 2004년 9월 30일
첫째판 2쇄 발행 | 2007년 10월 10일

지 은 이   임창석
발 행 인   장주연
편집디자인   송정현
표지디자인   고경선
발 행 처   군자출판사
등   록   제 4-139호(1991. 6. 24)

본   사   (110-717) 서울특별시 종로구 인의동 112-1 동원회관 BD 3층
              Tel. (02) 762-9194/5   Fax. (02) 764-0209
대 구 지 점   Tel. (053) 428-2748   Fax. (053) 428-2749
광 주 지 점   Tel. (062) 228-0252   Fax. (062) 228-0251
부 산 지 점   Tel. (051) 893-8989   Fax. (051) 893-8986

ISBN 89-7089-521-3

정가 25,000원

임창석

1964년 광주 출생.
전남대학교 의과대학 및 대학원 졸업.
정형외과 전문의 및 박사과정 수료.
미국 Ohio College of Podiatric Medicine 객원교수.
현재 한전의료재단 한일병원 정형외과 과장.
 1996년 「문학사상」 신인상에 <가을 삽화>가 당선되어 소설가로 등단.
작품 : 삽화소설 <빨간 일기장>
장편소설 <정도령>
<의료인을 위한 100가지 기본 영어>

Prologue

한국에서 흔히 접하는 질환들을 중심으로,
의료인들이 병원에서 쉽게 가지고 다니며 쓸 수 있는,
진료 영어 Handbook을 만들었다.
몇 년 동안 의협 신문에 연재했던 글들을 모으고,
추가로 각과별로 자주 접하는 질병들의 설명을 덧붙여,
Holistic Medicine을 다루는 책이 되게끔 노력하였다.
비록 각 분야의 전문적인 개념을 깊이 다루질 못했더라도,
이 책에서 다루는 기본적이면서도 간결한 영어 표현들이,
한국을 찾은 외국인들을 진료하는데,
작은 보탬이 되었으면 하는 바램이다.

(N : Nurse, D : Doctor or Dentist, P : Patient or Patient's Family)

의사, 치과의사, 간호사를 위한
진료 영어 Handbook

1 *Medical Interview 7 Steps*
(진료 인터뷰 7단계)

1) Greeting & Chief Complaint

(1) Greeting(인사)

Good morning. Good afternoon.
Hi. Hi there. Hi dear.
Hello. Hello again.
How are you? How are you doing?
How are you now? How are you today?
How have you been?
How's it going?
Nice to see you. Good to see you.
I'm glad to meet you.
Nice to meet you.
I'm glad you came in today.
It's nice to see you again.
It's good to see you back.
안녕하세요. 반갑습니다.

(2) 초진환자

Are you having any problem?
Why did you come in today?
What's your problem?
What's the trouble?

What sorts of troubles have you been having?
What sort of trouble brings you to me?
What is your main complaint?
What brings you today?
What brought you to this hospital?
What symptoms made you decide to come to this hospital?
What can I do for you?
Can you tell me your problem?
Can you describe your symptoms?
Can I help you?
How can I help you today?
Tell me why you came today?
Tell me why you came in?
Tell me about your symptoms.
Please describe your problems
I would like to hear about your symptoms.
Would you like to describe to me what the problem is?
Maybe you can start by telling me what brought you to the hospital?

무슨 일로 병원에 오셨죠?

(3) 재진 환자

How are you feeling today?
How do you feel today?

오늘은 어떠세요?

How are you feeling these days?
How do you feel these days?
How have you been feeling since I last saw you?
How have things been going for you?

요즘은 어떠세요?

Do you feel much better?

Feeling better?
좀 더 나으세요?

Are you still having problem?
아직도 문제가 있나요?

Are you still having pain?
Are you still getting the pain?
아직도 아프세요?

Seems like it's been a long time.
I haven't seen you for a long time.
I haven't seen you for a while.
Long time no see.
It's been quite a while.
오랜만에 보는 것 같군요.

It's been almost 3 months since I last saw you.
당신을 본 지가 3개월이 되었군요.

(4) Dialogue

D : Hi. I am Dr. Kim. Are you Mr. Morris?
안녕하세요. 닥터 김입니다. 모리스씨죠?

P : Yes, I am glad to know you.
예 당신을 알게되어 반갑습니다.

D : Thank you, I am glad to know you too.
Come and sit down.
고맙습니다. 저도 당신을 알게되어 반갑습니다. 앉으세요.

P : Thank you.
감사합니다.

D : Why did you come in today?
오늘 무슨 이유로 오셨죠?

P : I've had the flu symptom.
독감 증상이 있습니다.

D : How long have you had it?
얼마나 오랫동안 아팠어요?

P : 2 days.
이틀 되었습니다.

D : What exactly is the trouble?
어떤 점이 가장 문제죠?

P : Cough seems to be getting worse.
기침이 더 나빠지는 것 같습니다.

My head is killing me.
머리가 너무 아파요.

2) Present Illness & Other Current Problems

(1) Site (부위)

Where is your pain?
Where does it hurt?
Where do you hurt?
Where do you experience the pain?
Where is the pain located?
Which part is aching?
Show me where?
어디가 아프시죠?

Where exactly is it located?

정확히 어디가 아프시죠?

Where does it hurt most?

What is the worst part?

어디가 가장 아프시죠?

What is your major concern?

가장 걱정되는 것이 무엇이지요?

Could you point out the pain site?

아픈 곳을 가리켜 줄래요?

Could you point out the site where it is worst?

Could you point to where it hurts most?

Could you show me with your finger the point where it hurts
    you most?

가장 아픈 곳을 가리켜 줄래요?

(2) Cause (원인)

How did this happen?

What happened to you?

어떻게 된 것이죠?

How did this symptom occur?

Why do you think this symptom occur?

Why do you think you have this problem?

어떻게 이 증상이 생겼죠?

How did you hurt?

How did you get hurt?

How did you get injury?

어떻게 다치셨죠?

I need to ask you a few questions about how to get hurt?
어떻게 다쳤는지 몇 마디 묻고 싶군요.

Does anything special bring it on?
이것이 발생된 특별한 이유가 있나요?

Is there anything you can think of that triggers these symptoms?
이러한 증상들을 야기 시킨 특별한 것들이 있다고 생각되십니까?

What makes the pain?
What triggers your pain?
무엇이 아프게 하죠?

Where did you get hurt?
어디서 다치셨죠?

(3) Time (시간)

When did this symptom begin?
When did your pain start?
When did you first notice this symptom?
언제 증상이 시작되었죠?

When does this symptom seem to come on?
When does it occur?
When does it hurt?
When do you get this symptom?
언제 증상이 나타나죠?

How long have you had it?
How long did it last?
증상이 얼마나 되었죠?

When did accident happen?
When did you hurt?
When did you get injury?
언제 다쳤죠?

(4) Frequency (빈도)

How often does this symptom occur?
How frequently do you have symptoms?
How often do you get symptoms?
How often does the symptom come?
증상이 얼마나 자주 발생되죠?

Is this the first time?
Is this the first time you ever had this symptom?
이번이 첫 번째인가요?

Do you have pain all the time?
하루종일 아픈가요?

Does it come and go?
증상이 있다 없다 하나요?

Have you ever had the similar pain?
Have you had this pain before?
Have you ever experienced the same kind of pain before?
비슷한 통증을 가졌던 적이 있나요?

(5) Character (특징)

How do you feel your pain?
What does your pain feel like?
What kind of pain is it?

What is your quality of pain?

어떤 통증이 느껴지죠?

Is it constant or intermittent?

계속 아픈가요 아니면 간간이 아픈가요?

Is it sharp or dull?

찌르듯이 아픈가요 묵직하게 아픈가요?

Could you describe the pain?
(beating? biting? boring? burning?
colicky? cramping? dull? gripping?
heavy? numb? piercing? pressing?
prickling? pulling? sharp? shooting?
sore? stabbing? tearing? throbbing?
tingling? twisting?)

통증의 느낌이 어떻던가요?

Describe your pain intensity using a scale of 0 (representing no
pain) to 10 (representing the worst pain imaginable).

당신의 통증 정도를 0에서 10까지의 숫자를 이용하여 말해줄래요?

What makes the pain worse?

어쩔 때 통증이 심해지죠?

Do you think the pain has been getting worse?

통증이 더 나빠지고 있다고 생각되나요?

What makes the pain better?

어쩔 때 통증이 좋아지죠?

Does the pain wake you up?

통증이 잠을 깨웁니까?

Is the pain worse at night?
통증이 밤에 더 심해지나요?

Is the pain radiating anywhere?
Does this pain go to any other place?
다른 곳으로 퍼지지는 않습니까?

How does your symptom change with time?
증상의 변화가 시간에 따라 다른 가요?

Does the movement make any difference to the symptom?
움직임에 따라 변화가 있는 가요?

How would you rate the severity of your symptoms?
증상이 얼마나 자주 심해지던가요?

Are your symptom getting worse?
증상이 더 나빠지나요?

What other symptoms are associated with the pain?
통증과 함께 다른 증상들은 어떠합니까?

(6) Other Medical Problems (다른 의학적 문제)

Can you think of other problems that you've had recently?
최근 당신에게 문제가 되는 것들이 있나요?

Has anything problems been bothering you?
당신을 괴롭히는 문제들이 있나요?

Do you have any other medical problems?
다른 의학적인 문제를 가지고 있나요?

Are you still being treated?

지금도 치료받고 있나요?

Have you ever had any medical attention to your problem?

병에 대해 의학적인 주의를 받은 적이 있나요?

Are you currently under the care of a doctor for any health condition?

어떤 건강 문제로 의사의 치료를 받고 있나요?

Do you have any other illnesses that you see a doctor for?

의사에게 진료를 받은 다른 질병이 있나요?

Have you seen another doctor?

다른 의사에게 진료 받은 적이 있나요?

Do you become fatigued easily?

쉽게 피곤해지나요?

Is there anything else you'd like to tell me?

나에게 말하고 싶은 것이 있나요?

I'd like to take a full medical history.

병력에 대해 전부 듣고 싶습니다.

(7) Other Medication (다른 약물 복용)

Are you on any medication?
Are you taking any medication?
Are you currently taking any medicines?
Do you take any medication?
Have you taken any medicine?
다른 약을 복용하고 있나요?

What medications do you take?
What medications are you currently taking?

어떤 약을 복용하고 계시죠?

Why are you taking it?
Why do you take that?
What are you taking that for?

왜 약을 복용하고 계시죠?

How much are you taking?

얼마나 복용하고 계시죠?

How long have you been taking the medication?

얼마나 오래 약을 복용하고 있으시죠?

How often do you take the medication?

얼마나 자주 복용하시죠?

When do you take it?

언제 약을 복용하시죠?

Did you take it today?

오늘도 약을 드셨나요?

Do you take pain-killers sometimes?

진통제를 가끔씩 먹나요?

(8) Dialogue 1.

D : Where does it hurt?

어디가 아프시죠?

P : My left hip hurts.
제 왼쪽 고관절이 아픕니다.

It's killing me.
너무 아파요.

D : Did you have any trauma?
다치셨나요?

P : I fell and broke my hip 2 years ago.
2년 전에 넘어져 고관절이 부러졌었습니다.

I had hip surgery.
고관절 수술을 받았습니다.

But the pain started without any reason 2 days ago.
그런데 통증이 2일 전부터 아무 이유 없이 시작되었습니다.

D : How frequently do you have pain?
얼마나 자주 통증을 느끼시죠?

P : Every moment of the day.
하루종일 아픕니다.

D : It would be better to take an X-ray.
X-ray를 찍어보는 것이 좋겠습니다.

And then I will give you a little something for pain.
그리고 나서 통증을 줄이도록 조치를 해 드리겠습니다.

(9) Dialogue 2.

D : Do you have any problem?
어떤 문제가 있나요?

P : I've had flu for more than 5 days.
독감이 5일 이상 가는군요.

I've been running a fever.
열이 나는군요.

And I have a sore throat.
그리고 목이 아픕니다.

Nothing seems to be working right.
모든 것이 좋지 않은 것 같아요.

D : There is something going around.
지금 유행입니다.

P : Yes, I know.
예 알고 있습니다.

I'm coming down with something.
뭔가 더 안 좋아지는 것 같아요.

D : Have you seen another doctor?
다른 의사에게 진료 받은 적이 있나요?

P : No.
아닙니다.

D : Have you taken any medication?
어떤 약을 복용하셨나요?

P : No. Doc.
아닙니다. 의사 선생님.

D : Do you have any other medical problems?
다른 의학적인 문제를 가지고 있나요?

P : Something is wrong with my hearing.

청력에 문제가 있습니다.

D : Can you hear me whispering.

속삭이면 들을 수는 있나요?

P : I can't hear well.

잘 들을 수가 없습니다.

3) Past Medical History & Family History

(1) Past Health (과거 건강 상태)

How has your health been?
How about your health in the past?
Tell me about how your health been in the past?

과거 건강 상태는 어떠했습니까?

Have you been in good health before you became ill this time?

이번에 아프기 전까지는 건강하셨나요?

Tell me about any serious illnesses you have had in the past?
Have you had any serious illness before?

과거에 크게 아팠던 적이 있나요?

Have you ever had any accidents or injuries?

과거에 다친 적이 있나요?

Have you ever had an operation?
Have you ever had surgery before?
Have you had any operation in the past?

수술 받은 적이 있나요?

When were you operated on?
When did you have surgery?
언제 수술을 받았죠?

Have you ever had any serious illnesses or operations?
과거에 아프거나 수술했던 적이 있나요?

Have you ever been in hospital for any reason?
어떤 이유로 입원한 적이 있나요?

Have you ever been hospitalized due to any serious illnesses or
  operation?
Were you ever hospitalized due to any disease or surgery?
어떤 병이나 수술로 병원에 입원했던 적이 있나요?

Do you know what the diagnosis was?
진단이 무엇이었는지 압니까?

When were you hospitalized?
언제 입원하셨죠?

What kind of operations have you had?
어떤 종류의 수술을 받으셨죠?

When was the date of operation?
수술 날짜가 언제죠?

Is there anything else about your past history that you would like
  to tell me about?
저에게 말하고 싶은 과거병력이 있나요?

Do you have any known allergy?
본인이 알고 있는 알러지가 있습니까?

Have you ever had an allergic reaction to any drug?

어떤 약에 알러지가 있었던 적이 있나요?

Is there anything in your past history, such as diabetes, hypertension, tuberculosis, hepatitis and allergy?

과거에 당뇨병이나 고혈압, 결핵, 간염, 알러지 등에 걸린 적이 있나요?

Could you have been exposed to tuberculosis?

결핵에 노출되었던 적이 있나요?

Did you have any kinds of childhood disease?

어렸을 때 어린이 질환에 걸렸던 적이 있습니까?

What was the diagnosis when you were seen by the doctor last time?

최근에 의사에게 진료를 받고 나서 진단이 무엇이었습니까?

I'd like to check your old chart and films.

당신의 구 챠트와 필름을 확인하고 싶군요.

(2) Family Health (가족 건강 상태)

Could you tell me a little bit about your family?
I would like to know a little about your family.

가족에 대해 말씀해 주실래요?

Is there anything else about your family's health that you would like to tell me about?

저에게 말하고 싶은 가족에 관한 건강에 대한 이야기가 있나요?

Are there any similar problems that you think run in your family?

당신 가족 중에 비슷한 증상을 가진 사람들이 있나요?

Are there any illnesses that seem to run in your family?
Are there any illnesses that your family members have had?
당신 가족들이 가진 병들이 있나요?

Has anyone in your family been seriously ill?
Has anyone else sick in your family?
당신 가족 중에 누가 많이 아프나요?

Have any of them been sick? fever?
그들 중 누가 아프거나 열이 나지는 않나요?

Is there any history of cancer, hypertension or diabetes in your family?
당신 가족 중에 암이나 고혈압, 당뇨를 가진 적이 있나요?

Does asthma run in your family?
천식이 가족들에게 있나요?

Does anyone in your home have medical problems that you are aware of?
가족 중에 당신이 알고 있는 질환이 있나요?

How are your parents?
부모님은 어떠신가요?

Are your parents in good health?
Are your parents well?
당신의 부모님 건강하신가요?

Are your parents still alive?
당신의 부모님들은 아직 살아 계신가요?

What did your parents pass away from?
부모님이 무엇으로 돌아가셨죠?

Do you have any children?
아이가 있나요?

How old are they?
그들은 몇 살이죠?

(3) Dialogue 1.

D : Tell me more about how you are feeling.
　　당신이 느끼는 것에 대해서 더 말해 주세요.

P : I get pain in the night.
　　밤에 통증을 느낍니다.

D : How often do you get pain?
　　얼마나 자주 아프시죠?

P : Nearly every day.
　　거의 매일이죠.

D : Do you get pain just after eating?
　　식사 후에 통증을 느끼지는 않습니까?

P : No.
　　아닙니다.

D : Maybe you get pain in bed.
　　아마도 당신은 잠을 자려 할 때 통증을 느끼는가 보군요.

P : Yes. Night stomach pain wakes me up frequently.
　　맞습니다. 밤에 발생되는 위통 때문에 자주 깹니다.

D : Does anything special bring it on?
　　그 증상을 일으킨 어떤 원인이 있었습니까?

P : Nothing special.
특별한 것이 없습니다.

D : Do you suffer from indigestion?
소화가 잘 안되시나요?

P : Yes.
예.

D : Do you have nausea or vomiting?
오심이나 구토 증상이 있습니까?

P : Sometimes I feel nauseous.
가끔씩 메스껍습니다.

D : What about your bowel movements?
화장실 습관은 어떻죠?

P : I am constipated.
변비가 있어요.

D : Do you ever have blood in your bowel movements?
대변에 피가 섞인 적은 없었나요?

P : No.
없었습니다.

D : Do you have a history of previous abdominal surgery?
전에 복부 수술을 받은 적이 있습니까?

P : No
아닙니다.

(4) Dialogue 2.

D : I'd like to review your history.
당신의 과거력을 알고 싶군요.

Have you ever had any serious illnesses or operations in the past?
과거에 크게 아픈 적이나 수술을 받은 적이 있습니까?

P : I had an appendectomy 10 years ago.
10년 전에 충수돌기 절제술을 받았습니다.

D : Have you ever been told that you have high blood pressure, diabetes, allergy or any other disease?
당신은 고혈압이나 당뇨병, 알러지 같은 어떤 질환이 있다고 진단을 받은 적이 있습니까?

P : Not that I know of.
없습니다.

D : Are you married?
결혼은 했나요?

P : Yes.
예.

D : Could you tell me a little bit about your family?
당신의 가족에 대해서 말씀 좀 해주실래요?

P : What would you like to know?
무엇을 알고 싶으시죠?

D : How long have you been together?
결혼한 지 얼마나 오래 되었지요?

P : 8 years.

8년 되었습니다.

D : How many people are there in your family?

가족이 모두 몇 명이지요?

P : Three.

3 명입니다.

D : Do you have only one child?

애가 한 명밖에 없나요?

P : Yes. One boy.

예. 아들 하나입니다.

D : How old is he?

아이가 몇 살이지요?

P : 7 years old. He goes elementary school.

7살입니다. 초등학교에 다녀요

D : Is your wife in good health?

당신의 부인은 건강하십니까?

P : Yes. We've all been fine.

예. 모두가 지금까지 건강했습니다.

D : Are your parents still alive?

당신의 부모님은 모두 살아 계신가요?

P : My mother is living.

어머니는 살아 계십니다.

But my father passed away when he was 60.

하지만 아버지는 60세에 돌아가셨습니다.

D : What did he pass away from?

왜 돌아가셨지요?

P : Liver cancer.

간암으로 돌아가셨습니다.

D : How about your mother?

어머니는 어떠시죠?

P : She is in good health and looks young for her age.

그녀는 건강하시고, 나이에 비해 젊어 보이십니다.

But she suffers from intermittent headache.

하지만 어머니께서는 가끔씩 두통을 앓고 계십니다.

4) Social, Emotional and Habitual Status

(1) Occupation (직업)

What do you do for a living?
What kind of work do you do?
What kind of work are you doing?
What business are you in?
What's your job?
What's your occupation?
What is your work?

직업이 무엇이지요?

What other jobs have you held in the past?

과거의 직업은 무엇이지요?

Do you think anything at work is affecting your symptoms?
당신의 증상에 영향을 준 직장에서의 일이 있나요?

How have things been going for you?
하는 일들은 다 어떠십니까?

(2) Exercise (운동)

Do you take any exercise?
운동을 하시나요?

Do you have time for exercise?
운동할 시간은 가지나요?

Do you exercise regularly?
규칙적으로 운동을 하시나요?

Tell me what you do for exercise?
운동을 위해 무엇을 하시죠?

How often do you excercise?
얼마나 자주 운동을 하시죠?

How much do you excercise?
얼마나 많이 운동하시죠?

What kind of exercise do you usually do?
What kind of exercise do you like?
어떤 운동을 좋아하나요?

Do you play any sports?
What kind of sports do you play?
어떤 스포츠를 하시죠?

What sports do you enjoy?
What's your favorite sports?
어떤 스포츠를 좋아하시죠?

Have you ever tried to excercise?
운동을 하시려고 노력한 적은 있습니까?

(3) Weight (체중)

How much do you weigh?
Tell me about your present weight.
Tell me what's happening with your weight.
체중이 얼마죠?

Have you lost or gained weight recently?
Any recent weight gain or loss?
Have you lost or gained weight for no clear reason?
최근에 체중이 불거나 줄어든 적이 있나요?

Is there any change in your weight?
체중의 변화가 있나요?

Has it changed in the past year?
지난 1년 동안 체중의 변화가 있습니까?

How much did you weigh a year ago?
1년 전에는 체중이 얼마였죠?

What is the most you have ever weighed?
가장 체중이 많이 나갔던 게 얼마죠?

Why has it changed, do you think?
왜 변했다고 생각을 하죠?

Have you ever tried any medication to lose weight?
체중을 줄이려고 약물을 사용한 적이 있습니까?

How tall are you?
키가 얼마죠?

(4) Smoking (흡연)

Do you smoke?
담배를 피우나요?

How much do you smoke?
담배를 얼마나 피시죠?

Is that as much as you've always smoked?
그 정도가 항상 피운 양인가요?

Have you ever smoked more than that?
그보다 더 피운 적은 있나요?

How many cigarettes do you smoke a day?
하루에 담배를 몇 가치 피시죠?

What do you smoke?
어떤 것을 피시죠?

When did you start smoking?
언제 흡연을 시작하셨죠?

How old were you when you started?
몇 살 때 시작하셨죠?

How many years have you smoked?
몇 년 동안 담배를 피웠죠?

Have you ever attempted to cut down smoking?
흡연을 줄이려고 한 적이 있나요?

(5) Drinking (음주)

Do you drink?
술을 마시나요?

Are you a heavy drinker?
술을 많이 마시나요?

Do you drink every day?
매일 술을 마시나요?

Are you a steady drinker?
꾸준히 술을 마시나요?

How much do you drink on average?
보통 얼마나 마시죠?

Do you have any more than that?
그 보다 많이 마시기도 하나요?

Have you ever tried to cut down drinking?
술을 줄이려 노력한 적은 있나요?

Do you think you are a normal drinker?
일반적인 애주가라고 생각하나요?

Do you ever feel bad about your drinking?
음주가 싫은 적이 있었나요?

Have you ever had a drinking problem?
술 때문에 문제가 있은 적이 있나요?

Have you ever been in a hospital because of drinking?

음주 때문에 입원한 적이 있나요?

Is there something that would be hard for you to give up?

포기하기 어려운 다른 이유가 있나요?

Have you ever been injured after drinking?

음주 후 다친 적은 있나요?

(6) Stress (스트레스)

Do you ever feel under stress?

스트레스를 받은 적이 있나요?

How about your stress at work?

일할 때 스트레스는 어떻습니까?

What kind of things make you stressed?

어떤 것들이 스트레스를 주죠?

How have your spirit been?
What sort of mood have you been?

당신의 기분은 어떠했습니까?

Did you ever suffer from depression?

우울증을 경험한 적이 있나요?

Are you feeling blue?

지금 우울 한가요?

Has there been a recent tragedy or very stressful event in your
life?

최근 당신에게 슬픔이나 스트레스를 준 일이 있나요?

Do you feel helpless or hopeless about certain things in your life?

당신의 삶에서 희망이 없다고 느끼는 일이 있나요?

Is there a fluctuation or seasonality to your feelings?

계절이나 상황에 따라 감정의 변화가 있나요?

Do you become easily irritated?

쉽게 화를 내게 됩니까?

What do you do to prevent stress in your life?

스트레스를 방지하기 위해 무엇을 하죠?

(7) Life (생활)

Have you had any trouble sleeping?

잠자는 데 문제가 있나요?

Are you able to sleep when you want to sleep?

잠자고 싶을 때 잠을 잘 수 있나요?

How is your appetite?

식욕은 어떤가요?

Have you had any trouble with your appetite?

식욕에 문제가 있나요?

Do you diet regularly?

규칙적으로 식사를 하나요?

Are you currently on a restricted diet?

식사 제한을 하고 있는 중입니까?

Tell me about your diet.
먹는 것에 대해 이야기 해보세요.

How often do you pass your bowels now?
현재 얼마나 자주 화장실을 가시죠?

How do you spend your free time?
여가시간은 어떻게 보내죠?

What do you do for relaxation?
휴식을 위해 무엇을 하지요?

Do you have good friends?
좋은 친구들을 가지고 있나요?

Have you any hobbies?
취미가 있나요?

Is there any problems in your marriage?
결혼 생활에 문제는 없나요?

Are things OK with work, your family, your life?
일이나 가족, 생활은 다 괜찮나요?

Is there any stress or problems with your family?
가족들과 어떤 스트레스나 문제는 없나요?

Do you have any concerns about your family?
당신 가족들에 대한 어떤 걱정이 있나요?

Tell me about your habits.
습관에 대해서 말해 주실래요?

Have you any animals at home?
집에 애완동물을 기르나요?

Do you have any religion?
종교가 있나요?

Do you live in an apartment?
아파트에서 사나요?

(8) Sex (성)

How about your sexual relationship?
섹스관계는 어떤가요?

When did you first have sex?
언제 처음 섹스를 했죠?

How frequently do you have sex?
얼마나 자주 섹스를 하죠?

Are you having any sexual problems?
섹스에 어떤 문제가 있나요?

When did you have last sex?
마지막 섹스를 한 적이 언제죠?

Are you sexually active now?
지금도 섹스를 하시나요?

Do you use any form of contraception?
Are you using any contraception?
피임을 하시나요?

Have you had sex with anyone other than your regular partner?
다른 파트너와 섹스를 한 적이 있나요?

Do you have any questions about sex?

성에 대해 물어볼 것이 있나요?

(9) Dialogue

D : What is your work?

무슨 일을 하시죠?

P : I am out of work at present.

지금은 실직상태입니다.

D : How long have you been out of work?

직업이 없는 지 얼마나 되셨죠?

P : 2 years.

2 년 되었습니다.

D : Have you ever had any medical attention to your problem?

당신의 증상에 대해 의학적인 주의를 받은 적이 있나요?

P : No.

없습니다.

D : How has your health been in the past?

당신의 과거 건강 상태는 어떠했습니까?

P : I used to get sick a lot when I was a kid.

어렸을 때는 자주 아팠습니다.

D : Please describe your symptoms.

증상을 말해 주실래요?

P : Maybe a little bit trouble with my wind.

아무래도 숨을 쉬는데 문제가 있는 것 같습니다.

I don't breath as well as I used to.
평상시처럼 숨을 쉴 수가 없습니다.

It's probably just the cigarettes.
아마도 담배 때문이겠지요.

D : How much do you smoke?
담배를 얼마나 많이 피시죠?

P : Not too much.
많이 안 피웁니다.

I smoke a pack a day.
하루 한 갑 피웁니다.

D : Is that as much as you have always smoked?
그 양이 당신이 항상 피우는 양입니까?

P : Sometimes more, sometimes less.
때론 많이 피기도 하고 때론 적게 핍니다.

D : Have you any pets at home?
집에 애완동물을 기르고 있나요?

P : No.
아닙니다.

D : Do you exercise regularly?
규칙적으로 운동을 하십니까?

P : No.
아닙니다.

D : Have you lost or gained weight recently?
최근에 체중에 어떤 변화가 있었습니까?

P : I have lost weight recently.

최근에 몸무게가 줄었어요.

D : What did you weigh 6 months ago?

6달 전에는 몸무게가 얼마였죠?

P : Sixty-nine kilogram.

69kg이었습니다.

D : And now?

지금은 얼마죠?

P : Sixty kilogram.

60kg입니다.

D : What about your bowel movements?

배변 습관은 어떻지요?

P : I go once a day, in the morning.

아침에 한 번씩 갑니다.

D : I'm going to do your physical examination.

이학적 검사를 하겠습니다.

5) Physical Examination

(1) 아픈 부위를 잠간 살펴볼 때

Let me take a look.
Let me have a look.
Let's take a look.
Let me see.
Let me look.

I'll take a look.
잠깐 살펴보겠습니다.

Let me look at your - .
Let's look at -.
I need to have a look at your - .
I'd like to see your -.
-을 살펴보겠습니다.

(2) 혈압, 체온, 체중을 잴 때

Let's check your blood pressure.
I'll take your blood pressure.
I want to check your blood pressure.
I am just going to take your blood pressure.
혈압을 측정하겠습니다.

Can I have your arm?
팔 좀 주실래요?

Will you roll up your sleeve?
소매를 올려 주실래요?

Don't grip your hand and relax.
손을 쥐지 말고 푸세요.

Blood pressure is 120 over 80.
혈압이 120에 80이군요.

I'll check your temperature by mouth.
구강으로 체온을 측정해보겠습니다.

Please hold the thermometer under your tongue.
체온계를 혀 아래에 물고 계세요.

I'll check your body weight.
몸무게를 측정하겠습니다.

Please, step on the scale.
체중계 위로 올라가 줄래요?

Okay, step off.
됐습니다. 내려오세요.

You weigh - kilogram.
- Kg 나가는군요.

(3) Physical Examination 중 필요한 표현

I would like to examine you.
I'm going to examine you.
I'm going to do physical examination.
검사를 해보겠습니다.

Do you have any questions before we do your exam?
검사하기 전 물어볼 것이 있나요?

Let me examine you now.
I need to examine now.
지금 검사하겠습니다.

Would you please lie down on the bed?
진료대 위로 올라가 누울래요?

Lie down on your back on the bed.
등을 대고 진료대에 누우세요.

Bend your knees and relax your arms.
무릎을 구부리고 팔에 긴장을 푸세요.

Try to relax.
Just relax.
Let yourself go loose.
긴장하지 마세요.

I'm going to loosen your clothes.
옷을 느슨하게 하겠습니다.

Don't be so stiff.
몸을 뻣뻣하게 하지 마세요.

Would you sit up for me?
일어나 앉으세요.

Please, take off your shirt.
윗옷을 벗어주세요.

Please take off everything to your underwear.
Please get undressed down to your underwear.
Please take off your dress except pants and bra.
Slip everything off except your pants and bra.
Could I ask you now to slip your clothes off down to your
  underwear?
속옷만 남겨두고 벗어주세요.

Put on this gown.
이 가운을 입으세요.

Are you OK?
Are you comfortable?
Is this comfortable?
Is this Okay?
괜찮으세요?

Please tell me if I hurt you.

아프게 하면 말해 주세요.

I'm going to ask you to hold your breath for a moment.

잠깐만 숨을 참아 줄래요?

Please tell me if it hurts.
Tell me if there is any tender point.
Tell me if I hit any sore places?

아프면 말해주세요.

Does it hurt where I touch?
Do you have pain here?
Do you feel any pain?
Any tenderness here?

이곳이 아픈가요?

Almost over.

거의 끝났습니다.

All done.
We are done.
It's finished.

끝났습니다.

You can get dressed now.
You can put your clothes back on.
Please put on your clothes.
Would you like to get dressed?

옷을 입으셔도 됩니다.

(4) Head & Neck (두경부)

I am going to examine your fundus with ophthalmoscope.
검안경으로 안저 검사를 할 것입니다.

Stare up at the ceiling.
천장을 봐주세요.

I will hold your ear lobe to insert otoscope into the ear.
귀 안으로 이경을 넣기 위해 귀를 잡겠습니다.

Please tip the head slightly toward the shoulder.
머리를 어깨 쪽으로 기울여 줄래요?

I am adjusting the position of the otoscope to get a better view of
your ear eardrum.
고막이 잘 보이도록 이경의 위치를 바꾸고 있습니다.

I would like to check your mouth and throat.
입과 인후를 검사하겠습니다.

Open your mouth.
입을 벌리세요.

Stick out your tongue to examine the back of the throat.
인후를 보게 혀를 내밀어 주세요.

Say Ah.
아 하고 말해주세요.

I will place the tongue blade at the back on the tongue and press
down.
설압자를 혀 뒤에 대고 누를 것입니다.

This may cause gag.

구토가 나올 수 있습니다.

Now I am checking the size of your thyroid gland.

이제 갑상선 크기를 검사해 보겠습니다.

Okay, Try to relax.

됐습니다. 긴장을 푸세요.

It feels normal.

정상인 것 같군요.

Next I will just feel under your arms to palpate for lymph nodes.

다음은 임파선을 보기 위해 액와 부위를 검사할 것입니다.

I can't detect any abnormal lymph node.

이상한 임파선은 없군요.

(5) Chest (흉부)

I'm going to listen to your heart and lung.

이제 심장과 폐를 청진 해보겠습니다.

Let me listen to your chest.
Let me take a listen.

가슴을 청진 하겠습니다.

Would you roll up your shirts?

셔츠를 올려 줄래요?

Please, take off your shirt.

셔츠를 벗어주세요.

My stethoscope will feel cold.
청진기가 아마 차가울 거예요.

Let yourself go loose.
편안하게 하세요.

Take a normal breath.
정상으로 숨을 쉬세요.

I am going to listen your heart.
심장 소리를 들어 보겠습니다.

Take a deep breath and hold.
숨을 들이쉬었다가 참으세요.

Okay. Good. Breathe out.
좋습니다. 숨을 내쉬세요.

Another big breath.
다시 숨을 들이키세요.

Breathe out.
내 쉬세요.

All right. Try again.
좋습니다. 다시 한 번 반복해 주세요.

Take a deep breath and hold it.
숨을 깊게 들이쉬고 멈추세요.

Breathe out.
숨을 내쉬세요.

Good. Your heart sound is pretty good.
좋습니다. 당신의 심장소리는 정상이군요.

I am going to check your breath sound.
호흡소리를 들어 보겠습니다.

Take a deep breath in and out.
숨을 깊이 들이 쉬었다가 내 쉬세요.

Okay.
좋습니다.

Take a deep breath again.
숨을 깊이 들이쉬세요.

Breathe out.
내 쉬세요.

Breathe in again.
다시 숨을 들이쉬세요.

Breathe out.
숨을 내쉬세요.

Please, lean forward.
앞으로 몸을 숙여 주실래요?

Another deep breath.
다시 숨을 깊이 쉬세요.

Breathe through your mouth.
입으로 숨을 쉬세요.

OK.
됐습니다.

Your breathing sounds are clear.
소리가 정상이군요.

I'll feel under your arm for lymph nodes.
임파선을 검사하기 위해 팔 아래를 만져볼게요.

(6) Breast (유방)

Now, I am going to have a look at your breast.
자, 이제 당신의 유방을 검사하겠습니다.

Please tell me if I hurt you.
만약 내가 아프게 하면 말해주세요.

Lift your right arm up.
오른쪽 손을 올려 주실래요?

I'm just going to look at them to see if there are any lumps.
혹시 혹 같은 것이 있는 지 살펴보겠습니다.

Put your left arm up over your head.
왼손을 머리 위로 올려 주실래요?

Okay, your breast feel normal.
됐습니다. 당신의 유방은 정상인 것 같군요.

I can't detect any lumps.
어떤 혹도 발견되지 않는군요.

But examine your breasts the same time every months and seven to ten days after your menstrual cycle ends.
하지만 당신의 가슴을 월경 주기 마지막 7내지 10일 후에 매 달 검사하십시오.

And woman should have a mammogram from the ages of 35.
그리고 여성들은 35세부터는 유방 X선 검사를 시행하여야 합니다.

(7) Abdomen (복부)

I'm just going to have a look.
지금부터 검사해 보겠습니다.

Would you please lie down on the table?
진료대 위로 올라가 누우실래요?

Lie on your back with your knee bent.
등을 대고 눕고 무릎을 구부리실래요?

Do you get pain right here?
이곳이 아픈가요?

Can you feel tenderness?
아픈가요?

Abdomen is soft, non-tender.
복부는 아프지 않고 정상이군요.

OK. Please turn over and lie on your stomach.
됐습니다. 몸을 돌아서 엎드려 주세요.

I will try to be as gentle as possible.
가능한 부드럽게 하겠습니다.

OK. Roll over and lie down on your left side.
됐습니다. 왼쪽으로 돌아누워 주세요.

Bend your knees.
무릎을 구부려 주세요.

Please tell me if you feel any tender point.
아픈 곳이 있으시면 말해 주세요.

OK. Lie on your right side.
알겠습니다. 오른쪽으로 돌아 누우실래요?

Any tenderness here?
이곳이 혹시 아픈가요?

OK, please turn over and lie on your back?
됐습니다. 몸을 돌아서 누우세요.

Good. Would you sit up for me?
좋습니다. 앉아 주실래요?

(8) Female Organ (여성 기관)

I would now like to do vaginal examination.
이제 질 검사를 해보겠습니다.

Please, take off your dress behind the curtain.
커튼 뒤에서 옷을 벗어 줄래요?

I will examine you 2 minutes later.
2분 뒤에 검사하겠습니다.

Please lie down on the table.
진찰대에 올라가 누워주세요.

Could you please put your legs into stirrups.
두 발을 다리 받침대 위에 올려 주세요.

OK. I want to you to pull yourself down to the end of the table.
예, 이제 몸을 진찰대 아래까지 오도록 내려주세요.

That's fine.
좋습니다.

I am now introducing the speculum.

자 이제 검사기구를 넣겠습니다.

You are going to feel the cold metal but it won't harm you.

이제 차가운 금속을 느낄 것인데 해는 없습니다.

Try to relax.

긴장을 푸세요.

I will try to be as gentle as possible.

가능한 부드럽게 하겠습니다.

That seems all right.

괜찮은 것 같군요.

Now I want to do the Pop test.

자 이제 팝 테스트 검사를 시행하겠습니다.

I will send this sample to the laboratory.

이 샘플을 검사실로 보낼 것입니다.

We will do a culture for infection at the same time.

동시에 감염 여부를 알기 위해 균 배양 검사도 할 것입니다.

I am taking the instrument out.

검사 기구를 빼겠습니다.

Now I am checking your uterus with my hands.

자 이제 당신의 자궁을 손으로 검사하겠습니다.

I am touching your uterus now and it feels normal.

지금 당신의 자궁을 만지고 있는데, 정상인 것 같군요.

Okay. We are done.

예. 다 되었습니다.

You can put your legs down.
다리를 내려 놓으셔도 됩니다.

(9) Male Organ (남성 기관)

I am going to do a rectal examination to check your rectum and prostate gland.
직장과 전립선을 체크하기 위해 직장 검사를 할 것입니다.

This is a bit uncomfortable.
조금 불편할 따름입니다.

Please, take off your pants.
팬티를 벗어주세요.

Turn over and curl yourself into a ball with your buttock right over the edge of the table.
돌아서 엉덩이가 진찰대 끝 위에 오도록 웅크려 주실래요?

What I am going to do is a rectal examination.
지금 하는 것은 직장 검사입니다.

I'd like to do a digital rectal exam with a gloved, lubricated finger to evaluate the tone of the muscle and to detect tenderness or mass.
글러브와 윤활유를 바른 손가락으로 직장에 넣어 근육 톤과 아픈 곳, 혹을 검사할 것입니다.

Now I will insert a gloved finger in your body.
이제 당신의 몸에 글러브 낀 손가락을 집어넣을 것입니다.

Just relax.
편안하게 하세요.

I know it is uncomfortable.
불편한 지는 압니다.

Tell me if there is any tender point.
좋습니다. 아픈 곳이 있으면 말해주세요.

It feels completely normal.
정상이군요.

I am wiping the lubricant off.
윤활제를 지금 닦고 있습니다.

OK, I can't find anything wrong in examining you.
알겠습니다. 당신을 검사해 보니 이상한 곳이 없군요.

Get off the table and stand up.
진찰대에서 내려와서 서 주세요.

You can get dressed now
옷을 이제 입어도 됩니다.

Don't hurry. Take your time.
서두르지 마시고 천천히 하세요.

(10) Extremity (사지)

Do you have any pain?
어디가 아프나요?

Please wiggle your fingers.
Please move your fingers.
Can you wiggle your fingers?
손가락을 움직여 보세요.

Squeeze my hand.
내 손을 쥐어보세요.

Can you feel anything in your hands?
손에 감각을 느낍니까?

Slip off your socks.
양말을 벗어주세요.

Wiggle your toes.
Move you toes.
Can you wiggle your toes?
발가락을 움직여 보세요.

Push down with you toes on my hand like a gas pedal.
차 페달 밟듯이 발가락으로 제 손을 눌러 보세요.

Can you feel anything in your legs?
다리에 감각을 느낍니까?

Can you feel me touching them?
제가 만지는 것을 느끼시나요?

Bend your elbows and knees.
팔꿈치와 무릎을 구부려 보세요.

Pull your arms.
팔을 당겨 보세요.

Bend the legs.
다리를 구부리세요.

Does it hurt when I hit here?
이곳을 두드리면 아픕니까?

Do you have any pain in your back?

허리가 아프지는 않나요?

Roll your sleeve up.

소매를 올려 주세요.

Please take off your shoes and socks.

신발과 양말을 벗어주세요.

Please, raise your big toe.

엄지발가락을 올려보세요.

Tell me if this hurt?

아프면 말해주세요.

Keep your leg straight.

다리를 펴고 계세요.

I'll raise your legs.

당신의 다리를 들겠습니다.

How about your leg?

다리는 어떤가요?

Do you have any tingling sensation in your leg?

다리가 저리지는 않습니까?

Let me know when it hurt.

아플 때 말해주세요.

Do you feel pain in this position?

이 자세에서 아픕니까?

Would you sit up for me?

앉아 주실래요?

Put your hands above your head.

손을 머리 위로 올려 볼래요?

Elevate your arm.

팔을 올려 보세요.

Let your arms go loose.

팔에 힘을 빼세요.

Is there any swelling and redness?

붓거나 발적이 있는 곳은 없나요?

Do you have any pain in your joints?

관절이 어디 아프지는 않나요?

Do you feel pain when you move your joint?

관절을 움직이면 아픈가요?

Walk across the room.

방안을 걸어보세요.

(11) Record of physical examination(이학적 검사 기록)

① General appearance
: well-developed, well-nourished, moderate obese,
mental-alert, no abnormal clinical signs.

② Skin
: texture and temperature-normal, good color, no evidence of
dehydration,
no rash or pigmentation, no abnormal region in skin, hair,
nail.

③ Head
: contour-normal, no mass, no tenderness, no scar.

④ Eyes
: normal vision, no lesion, color of the sclera-not icteric,
  normal eyeball movement, normal light reflex, normal
  fundus.

⑤ Ears
: clear canal, normal ear drum, good hearing.

⑥ Nose & Sinuses
: no deformity, normal mucous membrane, no discharge,
septum-midline, pink mucosa.

⑦ Mouth & Throat
: pink mucosa, no ulcer, normal tonsils, normal voice.

⑧ Neck
: trachea-midline, no lumps, normal thyroid, no
  lymphadenopathy.

⑨ Lymph nodes
: no lymph node enlargement in cervical, axillary, inguinal
  region.

⑩ Breast
: symmetrical, no lumps, no tenderness, no discharge, normal
  nipple.

⑪ Chest and Lung
: symmetrical thorax, resonant to percussion, normal breath

sounds.

⑫ Heart
: normal clear heart sounds, no murmur.

⑬ Abdomen
: soft, no tenderness, no mass, no ascites, no scar, normal
bowel sounds.

⑭ Rectum
: normal perianal region, good sphincter tone, no mass,
prostate-no enlarged.

⑮ Genitalia
: Male - normal circumcized, normal developmental, no lesion,
normal scrotum, normal epididymis and spermatic cord
without tenderness.
Female - normal vulva, urethra position-normal, normal
vagina, no discharge, normal cervix and uterus.

⑯ Musculoskeletal
: muscular development-normal, no abnormality of spine,
symmetrical, normal joint, no deformity, no atrophy, range of
motion-normal. no edema.

⑰ Peripheral Vascular
: pulses-normal in arms and feet bilaterally, no varicose vein.

⑱ Neurological
: motor and sensory-normal, coordination-good, gait and
speech-good, deep tendon reflex-normal.

(12) Review of systems (전체적인 검토)

① General appearance
: has gained about 3kg in the past 1 year.

② Skin
: no rashes or no eruptions, no other change.

③ Head
: no headache, no injury.

④ Eyes
: normal vision, good visual acuity, no other symptoms.

⑤ Ears
: good hearing, no tinnitus, no vertigo, no infections.

⑥ Nose & Sinuses
: no clinical symptoms, no sinus trouble.

⑦ Mouth & Throat
: no canker sore, no bleeding of gum, normal voice.

⑧ Neck
: no lumps, no goiter, no pain.

⑨ Breast
: no lumps, no pain, no discharge.

⑩ Respiratory
: no coughing, no wheezing, no dyspnea, no sputum, no tuberculosis, last chest X-ray 3 years ago.

⑪ Cardiac

: no known heart disease, no hypertension, no palpitation, no chest pain, no EKG.

⑫ Gastrointestinal

: good appetite, no nausea, no vomiting, no pain, no jaundice, no diarrhea, no constipation, no bleeding, bowel movement-once daily,

⑬ Urinary

: no pain, no hematuria, no dysuria, no frequency, no infection history.

⑭ Genito-reproductive

: menarche at 12, no bleeding, regular periods, no history of hernia.

⑮ Musculoskeletal

: no weakness, no joint pain, no deformity, no history of fracture.

⑯ Peripheral Vascular

: no varicose vein, no swelling, no history of phlebitis.

⑰ Lymph nodes

: no lymph node enlargement in cervical, axillary, inguinal region.

⑱ Neurological

: no paint, no seizure, good memory, no history of paralysis, motor and sensory-normal.

⑲ Allergy

: no history of allergy, no asthma, no drug sensitivity.

(13) Dialogue

D : Are there any other things you think I should know about?

내가 알아야할 어떤 다른 것들은 없습니까?

P : I was coughing for 2 weeks.

저는 2주 동안 기침을 했습니다.

D : Do you have high blood pressure or diabetes?

당신은 고혈압이나 당뇨병이 있나요?

P : No, I get tired easily.

아뇨. 피로를 쉽게 느낍니다.

D : I would like to listen to your chest.

당신의 가슴을 검사해 보겠습니다.

   Please, take off your clothes.

옷을 벗어주세요.

P : How far do I have to go?

얼마나 벗어야 하죠?

D : Would you mind taking off your clothes?

옷을 벗기가 두려우세요?

P : Yes.

예.

D : Okay, Would you roll up your shirts?

알겠습니다. 셔츠를 올려 줄래요?

P : OK.
알겠습니다.

D : I'll check you heart.
심장을 검사해 보겠습니다.

Take a deep breath and hold.
숨을 깊게 들이쉬고 멈추세요.

OK. Normal heart sounds.
됐습니다. 정상 심음입니다.

Now I'll check your lungs.
이제 폐를 검사해 보겠습니다.

Breathe in and out slowly.
천천히 숨을 들이쉬고 내쉬세요.

Repeat it.
반복해 주세요.

Breath sounds are clear bilaterally.
호흡소리가 양쪽 모두 깨끗하군요.

6) Laboratory and Diagnostic Test

(1) X-ray, Bone scan 검사

I want to do an X-ray.
I want to check your X-rays.
I recommend an X-ray.
I'd like you to have X-ray examination.

I'd like you to have some X-rays.
X-ray를 찍고 싶군요.

You need an X-ray exam.
We need to take an X-ray.
X-ray 검사가 필요합니다.

We're gonna get some X-rays.
We'll take an X-ray.
X-ray를 찍을 것입니다.

X-ray examination is necessary to you for making a diagnosis.
We'll do an X-ray to confirm the diagnosis.
진단을 위해 X-ray 검사가 필요합니다.

X-ray is needed to further evaluate your problem.
추가 검사를 위해 X-ray가 필요합니다.

We need to take X-rays of your chest.
I'd like you to have your chest X-rayed.
흉부 X-ray 검사가 필요합니다.

I'd like you to have an X-ray of your back.
허리 X-ray 사진을 찍길 바랍니다.

Is there any chance that you may be pregnant?
임신 가능성이 있나요?

I will give you an X-ray slip.
X-ray 검사 용지를 드리겠습니다.

Your X-rays will show us more.
X-ray 검사가 더 정보를 줄 것입니다.

I'd like you to go for an X-ray.
Please go for an X-ray.
X-ray를 찍으세요.

I will explain to you after X-ray is developed.
엑스레이가 현상이 되면 당신에게 설명해 드리겠습니다.

You need a bone scan.
골 주사 검사가 필요합니다.

It's a very simple test.
그것은 아주 간단한 검사입니다.

No special preparation is needed for this procedure.
이 검사를 위해 특별히 준비할 것은 없습니다.

They give you a small injection in your arm and a few hours
  later they scan you with a machine.
당신의 팔에 주사를 논 다음 몇 시간 지나서 기계로 검사를 합니다.

It doesn't hurt.
아프지 않습니다.

It shows an abnormality in your bone.
당신 뼈에 있는 이상을 보여줍니다.

Please register at the front desk and go to the X-ray room.
접수창구에 접수한 후 방사선과로 가세요.

(2) X-ray 촬영

Do you have an X-ray slip?
방사선 처방전을 가지고 계시나요?

Please follow me.
저를 따라 오세요.

Remove your top and put on this gown in the dressing room.
탈의실에서 윗옷을 벗고 가운을 입으세요.

Stand here.
이곳에 서세요.

Take a deep breath and hold your breath.
숨을 깊게 들이쉬고 참으세요.

Don't move.
움직이지 마세요.

OK. You can breath now.
됐습니다. 숨을 쉬세요.

Would you please lie down on the table?
검사대에 올라가 누우실래요?

Take a deep breathe and hold.
숨을 깊게 들이쉬고 참으세요.

Breathe.
숨을 내 쉬세요.

Turn on your right side.
오른쪽으로 도세요.

Turn on your left side.
왼쪽으로 도세요.

All done.
다 끝났습니다.

You can put your clothes back on.
옷을 다시 입으셔도 됩니다.

An upper GI series is an X-ray of the esophagus, stomach, and duodenum.
상부 위장관 촬영은 식도, 위, 십이지장을 보는 **X-ray** 검사입니다.

You should drink a chalky liquid called barium to make these organs and any ulcers show up more clearly on the X-ray.
당신은 검사부위와 궤양을 잘 보기 위해, 바륨이라고 불리는 하얀 용액을 마셔야 합니다.

Please go to the outpatient's waiting place until the X-ray is developed.
X-ray가 나올 때까지 외래 대기실에 가서 기다리세요.

I will send X-ray to your doctor.
X-ray는 의사에게 보내어질 것입니다.

(3) Laboratory Test (검사)

We'll know more after the tests.
검사 후 더 알 수 있을 것 같습니다.

Let me run a couples of tests.
몇 가지 검사를 하겠습니다.

I'm going to get some tests done to see what is causing the symptom.
증상의 원인이 무엇인지 알기 위해 검사를 하겠습니다.

You need blood sampling.
I want to run a blood test.
I'd like to run a blood test.

I want you to have some blood tests.
I am going to get some blood tests done.
We will have to do some laboratory tests on your blood.
혈액 검사가 필요합니다.

Blood sampling is necessary to you for detecting any problem.
Blood test is needed to you for further evaluate your problem.
이상유무를 알기 위해 혈액 검사가 필요합니다.

I'll draw some blood.
피를 좀 뽑겠습니다.

You are gonna have to go through some tests.
당신에게 몇 가지 검사가 행해 질 것입니다.

I would strongly advise you to take these tests.
이 검사들을 꼭 하라고 권유합니다.

Nurse will arrange for the test.
간호사가 검사에 대해 안내해 줄 것입니다.

After paying at the reception desk, go to the blood lab.
접수처에서 계산을 한 다음에 혈액 검사실로 가세요.

Follow the blue line to the laboratory.
파란색을 따라 검사실로 가세요.

Lab is around the corner.
검사실은 모퉁이에 있습니다.

Can you give me a urine sample?
소변 샘플을 받아 줄래요?

Take a mid-stream urine by voiding the beginning of the stream.
소변 첫 부분은 버리고 중간 부분을 받으세요.

The results are gonna be reported till the day after tomorrow.
결과는 모레까지 나올 것입니다.

Come and see me again 3 days later when we've got the results.
결과가 나오는 3일 뒤에 다시 오세요.

We need to admit you to run more tests.
몇 가지 검사를 위해 당신을 입원시켜야 할 것 같습니다.

(4) Blood Sampling (채혈)

Do you have a blood test slip?
혈액검사 처방전이 있으세요?

Please come in and have a seat.
들어와 앉으세요.

Please roll up your sleeve.
소매를 걷어올리세요.

Grip your hand.
Clench your fist.
주먹을 쥐세요.

Hold your squeeze.
그대로 쥐고 계세요.

That's fine.
좋습니다.

You feel a little bit prick.
It's gonna sting a little.
It'll sting a little.
조금 따끔함을 느낄 것입니다.

Just relax.
Take it easy.
편안하게 하세요.

We are done.
끝났습니다.

I'll draw some blood through artery.
동맥을 통해 피를 뽑겠습니다.

It'll hurt a bit.
약간 아플 것입니다.

(5) EKG (심전도)

You need EKG.
EKG 검사가 필요합니다.

EKG is used to reflect underlying heart conditions by measuring
the electrical activity of the heart.
EKG 검사는 심장의 전기적 활동을 검사하여 심장의 상태를 아는 검사입
니다.

Take off your shirt.
셔츠를 벗으세요.

Please, lie back on the bed.
침대에 누우세요.

The test takes about 1 minute and painless.
검사는 1 분 정도 걸리고 아프지 않습니다.

A small amount of gel will be applied to the skin.
약간의 젤이 피부에 발라질 것입니다.

I will attach EKG leads to your chest, both arms and legs.
당신의 가슴과 팔, 다리에 **EKG** 선을 붙이겠습니다.

Don't move.
움직이지 마세요.

All finished.
다 끝났습니다.

(6) Ultrasonogram (초음파)

Ultrasonogram is necessary for you.
초음파 검사가 당신에게 필요합니다.

Ultrasonogram uses high frequency sound waves to see image of the organs.
초음파는 고주파음을 이용하여 장기의 모양을 보기 위한 검사입니다.

Don't eat food exception of water for 8 hours prior to the examination.
검사 8시간 전부터 물 외에는 음식을 드시지 마세요.

Drink 1 liter of water one hour prior to the examination for the purpose of filling the bladder.
방광을 채우기 위해 검사 1시간 전 1리터의 물을 마시세요.

Would you please lie down on the table.
침대에 누우실래요?

Bend your knees.
무릎을 구부려 주세요.

I will apply a gel to the surface of your body.
당신의 몸에 젤을 바르겠습니다.

This won't hurt.
이것은 아프지 않습니다.

OK. Lie on your left side.
됐습니다. 왼쪽으로 돌아누워 주세요.

OK. Lie on your right side.
됐습니다. 오른쪽으로 돌아누워 주세요?

All done.
다 끝났습니다.

Wipe off a gel on your body
몸에 있는 젤을 닦으세요.

(7) Barium enema (바륨 관장)

A barium enema X-ray will show the rectum, colon, and lower part of the small intestine to locate any problems.
바륨을 이용한 **X-ray**는 직장, 대장, 소장 끝 부위의 이상 여부를 보여줍니다.

The night before the test, bowel cleansing procedure is necessary to clear the lower digestive tract.
검사 전 날밤, 하부 소화기관을 깨끗하게 하기 위한 준비가 필요합니다.

You should drink a special liquid.
당신은 특수한 약물을 마셔야합니다.

This liquid flushes out the bowel.
이 액체가 장을 씻어줍니다.

A clean bowel is important, because even a small amount of stool in the colon can hide details and result in an inaccurate exam.

깨끗한 장이 중요한데, 그것은 조그만 대변도 부정확하게 만들기 때문입니다.

Because the colon does not show up well on an X-ray, we fill the organs with a barium enema, a chalky liquid to make the area visible.

대장은 x-ray에 잘 안보이므로 그곳이 잘 보이게 하는 하얀 액체를 넣을 것입니다.

You may feel some abdominal cramping when the barium fills the colon, but usually feel little discomfort after the procedure.

당신은 바륨이 찰 때 복통이 있을 수도 있지만, 검사 후에는 불편함이 없어집니다.

Stools may be a whitish color for a few days after the exam.

대변은 검사 후 며칠 동안 하얀 색일 수 있습니다.

(8) Endoscopy (내시경)

An endoscopy is an exam that uses an endoscope, a thin, lighted tube with a tiny camera on the end.

위 내시경은 끝에 작은 카메라가 달려 있는 내시경입니다.

A small tube will be inserted through your mouth and into the stomach to look for ulcers.

작은 튜브가 궤양을 보기 위해 입을 통해 위로 들어갈 것입니다.

This may be a bit uncomfortable.

이것은 약간 불편할 것입니다.

Endoscope will pass into the mouth and down the throat to the
   stomach and duodenum.
내시경은 입을 통해 위와 십이지장까지 내려갑니다.

You'll feel it when it goes in.
안으로 들어갈 때 느끼실 겁니다.

I will take photos of ulcers or remove a tiny piece of tissue to
   view under a microscope.
저는 궤양 사진을 찍고 현미경 관찰을 위해 작은 조직을 띄어낼 것입니다.

Lie on your left side on the bed.
침대에 올라가 왼쪽으로 누워 주세요.

I will spray a local anesthetic to reduce discomfort and gagging.
불편함이나 구토를 줄이기 위해 국소 마취제를 뿌리겠습니다.

You are lightly sedated during procedure.
검사하는 동안 약간 진정제가 투여될 것입니다.

I will perform an endoscopy.
위 내시경 검사를 시작하겠습니다.

It won't hurt much.
많이 아프지는 않을 것입니다.

Relax.
긴장을 푸세요.

During the endoscopy, small samples of the stomach tissue can
   be obtained for biopsy.
내시경 도중 조직검사를 위해 위의 조직 일부가 떼어내 질 수 있습니다.

We are done.
다 되었습니다.

(9) Colonoscopy (대장내시경)

The night before a colonoscopy, you should have a liquid dinner and takes an enema in the early morning.
대장내시경 검사 전날은 죽만 드시고, 아침에 관장을 하여야 합니다.

A light breakfast and a cleansing enema an hour before the test is necessary.
가벼운 아침 식사와 검사 한 시간 전 관장이 필요합니다.

We will use a long, flexible tube with camera on the end to view the entire colon.
대장 전체를 보기 위해 끝에 카메라가 달린 길고 잘 구부려지는 튜브를 씁니다.

You are lightly sedated before the exam.
검사 전에 약간의 진정제가 투여될 것입니다.

During the exam, you lie on your side and we insert the tube through the anus and rectum into the colon.
검사 중 옆으로 누워있으면 항문과 직장을 통해 대장으로 넣을 것입니다.

First, I will examine the rectum with a gloved, lubricated finger.
먼저 장갑을 끼고 윤활유가 발라진 손가락으로 직장을 검사할 것입니다.

I am gonna check your bowel with colonoscopy.
대장내시경으로 장을 살펴보겠습니다.

The procedure may cause a mild sensation of wanting to move the bowels and abdominal pressure.
이 검사 도중 대변을 보고 싶거나 배에 압력을 느낄 수 있습니다.

Sometimes we will fill the organs with air to get a better view.
때론 더 잘 보기 위해 공기를 주입하기도 합니다.

The air may cause mild cramping.
공기는 약간의 복통을 일으킬 수 있습니다.

If you feel any pain, just let me know.
만약 아프면 저에게 말해 주세요.

If an abnormality is seen, we can use the colonoscope to remove
  a small piece of tissue for biopsy.
만약 이상이 보이면 조직검사를 위해 조직 절편 일부를 떼어냅니다.

You may feel gassy and bloated after the procedure.
당신은 시술 후 가스가 차서 배가 부른 것처럼 느낄 수 있습니다.

(10) CT 촬영

I'd like to recommend CT scan to confirm the diagnosis.
확진을 위해 전산화 단층촬영을 권하고 싶군요.

CT scan provides more detailed pictures of your body.
전산화 단층촬영은 몸의 자세한 사진들을 찍게 해줍니다.

Brain CT scan is significantly useful for detecting the brain
  disease.
뇌 전산화 단층 촬영은 뇌질환을 발견하는데 매우 유용합니다.

CT scans do emit more radiation than normal X-rays do.
전산화 단층촬영은 X-선 촬영보다 방사선이 많이 방출됩니다.

But it is safe.
그러나 안전합니다.

The scan shows any area of brain that are abnormal.
스캔은 뇌의 이상한 곳을 다 보여줍니다.

A special dye is injected into a vein before the scan.

스캔 전에 특별한 약이 정맥 내로 주입됩니다.

The dye helps to show differences in the tissues.

약이 조직에서의 다른 점을 보여줍니다.

Just let me know if you have any discomfort.

불편한 점이 있으면 말해 주세요.

I will let you know about the diagnosis as soon as we get the result.

결과가 나오는 즉시 당신에게 진단을 알려 드리겠습니다.

(11) MRI 촬영

Magnetic Resonance Imaging is a way of looking inside the body without radiation.

자기공명영상 장치는 방사선 피폭없이 몸 안을 검사할 수 있는 방법입니다.

We can confirm the diagnosis by MRI.

MRI로 진단을 확진할 수 있습니다.

The exam uses radiowaves and a magnetic field to create images of the soft tissues inside the body.

몸 안의 조직을 형상화시키기 위해 자기장을 이용합니다.

The complete exam takes 30 - 60 minutes.

검사는 30분에서 60분 걸립니다.

You can eat, drink, and take regularly prescribed medications prior to the exam.

검사 전에 식사나 물, 처방된 약을 먹어도 됩니다.

All metallic object on the body are removed prior to obtaining an MRI scan.

MRI 검사 전 몸에 있는 금속은 제거되어야 합니다.

You will lie within the closed environment inside MRI.

당신은 **MRI** 안의 닫힌 곳에 누울 것입니다.

If you feel claustrophobic sensation, a mild sedative will be given prior to obtaining an MRI scan.

만약 당신이 밀실 공포증을 느낀다면, 약간의 진정제가 투여 될 것입니다.

The technologist will position you comfortably on the table and ask you to remain still during the exam

기사가 당신을 테이블에 편안히 자리잡게 한 후, 검사하는 동안 움직이지 말라고 말할 것입니다.

Just lay in the examination and relax.

단지 검사 도중 누워 편안하게 있으면 됩니다.

There is no pain, vibration, or unusual sensation.

고통이나 진동 같은 이상한 것을 느끼지 않습니다.

Relaxation is important during the procedure.

검사하는 동안 편안하게 하는 것이 중요합니다.

Breathe normally.

숨은 정상적으로 쉬세요.

(12) 조영제 사용

Contrast enhanced scanning should be used for the differential diagnosis.

감별진단을 위해서는 조영제 증강 검사가 필요합니다.

Contrast helps us visualize the condition of the disease.

조영제가 질병의 상태를 더 잘 보여줍니다.

We inject some amount of contrast into your vein.

우리는 당신의 정맥으로 약간의 조영제를 투여할 것입니다.

You may feel nausea or vomiting.

오심과 구토를 느낄 수가 있습니다.

You may experience an uncomfortable sensation.

아마도 불편함을 느낄 수도 있습니다.

But it will fade after several minutes.

하지만 몇 분 후에는 약해집니다.

And a few hours later, we can scan you with a machine a little bit like an X-ray machine.

그리고 몇 시간 뒤 우리는 엑스레이 기계와 비슷한 것으로 당신을 검사할 것입니다.

Do you have any allergies?

알러지가 있었던 적이 있습니까?

If you agree to this test, please sign your name in this consent form.

만약 이 검사에 동의한다면 동의서에 사인을 해주세요.

(13) Biopsy (조직검사)

You may have a form of cancer.

암의 일종인 것 같군요.

We need more tests to determine the type of cancer.

암의 형태를 알기 위해 검사가 더 필요합니다.

You need biopsy.
조직 검사가 필요합니다.

It's hard to know before we get the biopsy result.
조직 검사 결과를 보기 전까지는 알 수 없습니다.

I'll give you a local anesthetic.
국소 마취주사를 놓겠습니다.

We're gonna put a fine needle.
작은 바늘을 넣겠습니다.

That will hurt a little.
그것은 약간 아플 것입니다.

Relax.
긴장을 푸세요.

You won't be in severe pain.
많이 아프지는 않을 것입니다.

You'll feel it when it goes in.
들어갈 때 느낄 것입니다.

We will take a piece of the tumor out of your organ.
당신의 조직에서 암의 일부를 떼어낼 것입니다.

It'll take a couple of minutes.
2-3분 걸릴 것입니다.

(14) Dialogue 1.

D : I'd like you to have some tests done.
몇 가지 검사를 해야 될 것 같군요.

X-rays, MRI and tests on your blood, urine, stool may be necessary for detecting any problems.

X-ray와 MRI, 혈액, 소변, 대변 검사에 이상이 있는 지 검사해야 되겠군요.

P : Is there more than one condition that could be causing my problem?

내 문제를 일으킨 원인이 한 가지 이상인가요?

D : I am not sure.

확실히 잘 모릅니다.

P : How can I get my urine?

어떻게 소변을 받습니까?

D : Take a mid-stream urine by voiding the beginning of the stream.

소변 첫 부분은 버리고 중간 부분을 받으세요.

P : Where is X-ray?

X-ray실이 어디에 있죠?

D : Follow the yellow arrow to the X-ray.

노란 화살표를 따라 X-ray실로 가세요.

A technician will take an X-ray in radiology room.

방사선과 기사가 엑스레이 방에서 찍을 것입니다.

P : How do I prepare for MRI.

MRI를 위해 준비할게 있나요?

D : All metal on the body should be removed.

몸에 있는 금속은 없어야 합니다.

And you lie in big tunnel which takes pictures of the inside
 of you.
그리고 당신의 내부사진을 찍기 위해 큰 터널에 누워야합니다.

(15) Dialogue 2.

D : You need biopsy.
조직검사가 필요합니다.

P : What type of biopsy will I have?
어떤 조직 검사를 받아야 하죠?

D : Fine-needle aspiration.
가는 주사를 이용하는 것입니다.

P : How long will it take?
얼마나 걸리죠?

D : Couple of minutes.
2-3분 걸립니다.

P : Will I be awake?
깨어있나요?

D : Of course.
물론입니다.

P : Will it hurt?
아픈가요?

D : No. You feel just prick.
아니오. 약간 따끔함만 느낍니다.

P : How soon will I know the results?
결과는 언제 알죠?

D : Follow up date will be scheduled for you.
다음 재진 날짜가 예약될 것입니다.

I will tell you about your results at that time.
그때 말씀드리겠습니다.

7) Impression & Treatment

(1) Results (결과)

I didn't find anything wrong on my examination.
I didn't find anything wrong on the exam.
Your examination was fine.
이학적 검사 상 별 이상이 없군요.

I couldn't tell you without more tests.
추가 검사 없이는 말할 수 없군요.

I got your test results.
Your results are back.
I picked up your laboratory results.
I have seen the results of tests.
결과가 나왔습니다.

I didn't find anything wrong with you.
I didn't find anything new wrong.
I found nothing wrong.
별 이상을 발견하지 못했습니다.

All looks fine.
모든 것이 좋은 것 같습니다.

Your tests are okay.
Your tests are normal.
검사는 정상입니다.

There doesn't seem to be anything wrong with you.
당신에게는 특별한 이상이 없는 것 같군요.

I didn't think you are in any worse shape.
당신에게 이상이 있다고는 생각하지 않았습니다.

I don't think it's anything serious.
심각한 것은 아닙니다.

There is no reason to worry.
걱정할 이유가 없군요.

Your X-rays are back.
We have your X-rays.
X-ray가 나왔습니다.

Your film looks normal.
X-ray shows nothing wrong.
X-ray는 정상이군요.

All appear normal.
모든 게 정상입니다.

I have the results of your X-rays and laboratory tests.
당신의 X-ray와 검사 결과를 보았습니다.

Your films and tests were fine.
X-ray와 검사들은 좋았습니다.

Your lungs look fine.
폐는 아주 좋군요.

You have an abnormal density in your X-ray.
X-ray에 이상한 음영이 있군요.

You can see there is a density in your lung.
당신의 폐에 음영이 있는 것이 보이죠?

Something abnormal within the structure of your lung.
당신 폐 조직에 이상한 것이 있습니다.

It would be a lot of things.
그것은 여러 가지일 수 있습니다.

It's premature to make a diagnosis before we have seen the chest CT.
흉부 CT를 보기 전에는 미리 진단을 할 수 없군요.

You'll need a bronchoscopy.
기관지경 검사가 필요합니다.

There is a radiolucent density in the bone.
뼈에 음영이 감소된 부위가 있군요.

X-rays suggest that you may have -.
X-ary는 - 같군요.

It's premature to discuss your condition before we have seen the MRI.
MRI를 보기 전에는 미리 판단할 수 없군요.

The X-ray shows that your bone is broken.
X-ray상에서 뼈가 골절되어 있습니다.

It's not bad.
나쁘진 않군요.

Your blood and urine tests are normal.
혈액과 소변 검사가 정상입니다.

The pregnancy test came back negative.
임신 테스트는 정상이었습니다.

It came back positive.
양성으로 나왔습니다.

We need to talk about your blood test.
혈액 검사에 대해 이야기 할 것이 있습니다.

There is something wrong.
약간 이상이 있군요.

I'm afraid that the result isn't good.
결과가 좋지 않군요.

Hemoglobin is 7, which means that you have less than half the
  normal number of red blood cells.
혈액 검사에서는 헤모글로빈이 7이 나왔는데 그것은 정상 적혈구 수의 절
  반 이하를 의미합니다.

Your blood test shows evidence of anemia.
검사 결과는 빈혈을 의미합니다.

Your white cells are high, which is suggestive of infection.
백혈구가 증가되어 있는데 감염을 보여주는 것입니다.

U/A shows white cells too numerous to count.
소변 검사에서 백혈구 수가 너무 많군요.

U/A shows 2 plus protein.

소변검사에서 단백뇨가 보이는군요.

We need to find out why.

이유를 밝혀야합니다.

We need more tests to rule out other disease.
We'll run some more tests to rule out other disease.
We're gonna run some more tests to rule out other disease.

다른 질병을 감별하기 위해 추가 검사를 하겠습니다.

Your history is suggestive of -.

당신의 병력은 -을 의심하게 합니다.

All laboratory results suggest that you may have -.

모든 검사 결과로 볼 때 당신은 - 인 것 같군요.

You may have -, judging from the laboratory figures.

검사 결과로 볼 때 당신은 - 인 것 같군요.

I think your problem is due to -.
Your problem is due to the fact that -.
The problem you've been getting is due to -.
The problem suggests -.

당신의 문제는 - 때문인 것 같습니다.

There is any possibility that you suffer from - .
There is any chance that you may be - .
You have probably got the - .
You may have -.
You probably have -.
I am afraid you have -.
It looks like you have -.

당신의 병은 -일 가능성이 있습니다.

Your test results suggest the pain may be - related.
당신의 결과에 따르면 그 통증은 -과 연관된 것 같군요.

It's nothing serious.
심각한 것이 아닙니다.

It's treatable.
치료가 가능한 것입니다.

It doesn't look good.
별로 좋지 않군요.

You should regard your condition as very serious.
당신의 상태를 심각하게 생각하서야 합니다.

You need to be admitted for more evaluation.
좀 더 검사를 위해 입원하서야 합니다.

The diagnosis is not confirmed and it may be something else.
진단은 아직 확정이 안 되었고, 다른 것일 수도 있습니다.

We shouldn't jump to any conclusions until we know.
우리가 알기 전에 미리 판단하면 안됩니다.

Nothing is certain.
확실한 것은 없습니다.

Wait a final determination.
마지막 결정을 기다리세요.

Your biopsy was positive for cancer.
조직검사에서 암이 양성으로 나왔습니다.

(2) Medical Treatment (내과적 치료)

There are several forms of treatment.
치료방법은 여러 가지가 있습니다.

There is a lot we can do to help you.
당신을 위해 할 수 있는 방법은 여러 가지입니다.

This symptom is usually temporary.
이 증상은 대개 일시적인 것입니다.

No need to be admitted.
입원은 필요 없을 것 같습니다.

The first thing we need to do is bring your symptom down.
첫 번째 우리가 해야할 일은 당신의 증상을 없애는 것입니다.

Medications will cure you.
약물이 치료를 해줄 것입니다.

It can be treated with medication.
약으로 치료할 수 있습니다.

It will take several days to heal over.
나으려면 몇 일이 걸릴 것 같습니다.

You should take several day's off and rest.
You have to take a rest for a couple of days.
며칠 휴식을 취해야 합니다.

You'll be fine in a couple of days or so.
당신은 며칠 안에 좋아 질 것입니다.

If you don't improve, contact me.

호전이 없으면 저에게 오세요.

I want you to come back if there is any symptoms.

만약 어떤 증상이 있으면 다시 오세요.

Come back tomorrow.

내일 다시 오세요.

Come and see me again the day after tomorrow when we've got
the results.

결과가 나오는 모레 다시 오세요

I want to see you next week, preferably on wednesday.

다음 주 수요일 날 보도록 하죠.

Let's make a follow-up appointment for next wednesday.

추시 날짜를 다음주 수요일로 잡도록 하죠.

I'll arrange for you to come in next week.

다음 주에 오도록 날짜를 잡겠습니다.

Not much improvement yet.

아직 호전이 안되었군요.

I am sorry medication isn't helping much.

약이 크게 도움이 안 되는군요.

I am concern about these symptoms.

이 증상들이 걱정이 되는군요.

It will take time to recover.

회복되려면 시간이 걸릴 것 같군요.

It's really too hard to try to treat your disease as an out patient.
통원치료로 하는 것이 너무 힘들군요.

I am afraid your illness is more serious than we first thought.
병이 처음에 우리가 생각했던 것보다 더 심각합니다.

I have been trying to treat this symptom but it hasn't responded to treatment.
이 증상을 치료하려 했지만 치료에 잘 반응하지 않는군요.

Without proper treatments, this can lead to complications.
적절한 치료를 하지 않으면 심각해 질 수 있습니다.

We need to admit you to run more tests.
몇 가지 검사를 위해 당신을 입원시켜야 할 것 같습니다.

It would be better for you to be admitted.
입원하는 것이 좋을 것입니다.

Hospitalization is needed.
Hospital admission is needed.
Hospitalization is required.
Hospitalization is necessary.
You need hospitalization.
You need to be admitted.
입원이 필요합니다.

I'm sure that we can do best for you in the hospital.
당신이 병원에 있어야만 저희가 최선을 다할 수 있다고 생각합니다.

You really need to stay here.
이곳에 꼭 머물러야 합니다.

We will have to admit you and treat you with some medicines.
우리는 당신을 입원시켜 약으로 치료해야 합니다.

We will admit the patient into the hospital.
우리는 환자를 병원에 입원시킬 것입니다.

We're gonna put you on antibiotics.
항생제를 사용할 것입니다.

It needs to be treated with intravenous antibiotics.
정맥 내 항생제 투여로 치료할 필요가 있습니다.

If you respond to the medication, you will be fine soon.
만약 약이 잘 들으면 곧 좋아질 것입니다.

Early treatment with antibiotics can cure your disease.
항생제 초기 투여가 당신의 병을 치료하게 합니다.

Besides antibiotics, you are given supportive treatment.
항생제 외에도 다른 부수적인 치료가 따릅니다.

I'll give you a prescription for some medicines to relieve the
symptom.
증상을 낫게 해 줄 약을 처방해 드리겠습니다.

You responded well to the medication.
약에 잘 반응하는군요.

We try to avoid operation.
수술을 피하려고 노력하고 있습니다.

The antibiotics are working.
항생제가 잘 듣는군요.

You will be discharged from the hospital in a few days.
며칠 내로 퇴원하게 될 것입니다.

It's very contagious.

그것은 감염성이 높습니다.

We'd like to get you into an isolation room for treatment.

치료를 위해 독방에 입원을 해야합니다.

We have some very serious matters to discuss regarding your
disease.

당신의 병에 대해 상의할 중요한 문제가 있습니다.

There is a bad news.

안 좋은 소식이 있군요.

The bad news is that you have a cancer.

나쁜 소식은 당신이 암을 가지고 있다는 것입니다.

I'm afraid your cancer is advanced.

암이 이미 진행되었군요.

This is not easy.

이것은 쉽지 않습니다.

I need to let you know.

당신이 알 필요가 있습니다.

You have a serious condition which needs immediate evaluation.

즉시 검사가 필요할 정도로 심각한 상태입니다.

We have to decide the best way of treating it.

치료할 최선의 방법을 결정해야 합니다.

There are two ways.

2가지 방법이 있습니다.

Medical and surgical.

약물치료와 수술적 치료.

If you don't want to have operation, I'll give you medicine to make you comfortable.

만약 당신이 수술을 원치 않으면, 증상을 수월하게 하는 약을 드리겠습니다.

We hope that medical treatment will help.

약물치료 방법들이 도움이 되기를 기대합니다.

Statistics show that with treatment the 5 year survival rate is over 80 %.

치료를 받으면 5년 생존율이 80%이상입니다.

Chemotherapy is needed to destroy cancer cells.

항암제 치료가 암세포를 죽이기 위해 필요합니다.

You may need to stay in the hospital while receiving chemotherapy.

항암제 치료를 받는 동안 입원할 필요가 있습니다.

Radiation can help relieve pain by shrinking the tumor.

방사능 조사는 암을 줄어들게 해 통증을 완화시켜 줍니다.

You should come to the hospital regularly for radiation therapy.

당신은 방사선 치료를 위해 규칙적으로 병원에 와야 합니다.

Anti cancer medication will stop the growth of the cancer cells but the side effects are difficulty in eating and hair loss.

항암제는 암 세포의 증식을 멈추게 해주지만 식욕감퇴나 탈모의 부작용이 있습니다.

Combination treatment with chemotherapy and radiation therapy is needed to reduce cancer lesion.

항암제와 방사선 치료 요법이 암 부위를 줄이기 위해 필요합니다.

You should be admitted to ICU.

중환자실에 입원을 해야 합니다.

(3) Surgical Treatment (외과적 치료)

Surgery is necessary for you.
You need an operation.
You need surgery.
Surgery is needed.
You will have to undergo surgery.
Your disease require surgery.
Your condition require surgery.

수술이 필요합니다

I recommend surgery.

수술을 권유합니다.

This operation gonna help you.

이 수술이 당신을 도와 줄 것입니다.

The only way to treat this is by an operation.
There is no other way but an operation.

이 치료방법은 수술 밖에 없습니다.

We can remove it by surgery.

수술로 제거할 수 있습니다.

Surgery is a better option.

수술이 더 좋습니다.

Surgery is the best choice in my professional judgement.
직업적으로 판단하건 데 수술이 가장 좋은 선택입니다.

Surgery is the best choice for treatment.
치료를 위해서는 수술이 최선의 선택입니다.

Most patients get better after operation.
대부분의 환자들이 수술 후 좋아집니다.

I will make a surgery appointment.
제가 수술을 예약해 드리겠습니다.

I'll put you on a surgical schedule.
수술 스케줄을 잡겠습니다.

Your surgery will be done under a general anesthetic.
수술은 전신 마취로 할 것입니다.

If your condition is good, surgery would be considered elective.
상태가 좋으면 수술은 정기수술로 할 수 있습니다.

You will be admitted to the hospital on the day before day as
your surgery.
당신은 수술 전날 입원하게 될 것입니다.

The night before, you should have a liquid supper, and then you
should have nothing to eat or drink after midnight.
수술 전날 저녁은 죽을 드시고, 자정 이후로는 아무 것도 먹거나 마시지 마
십시오.

Several hours may be necessary to give the patient fluids and
antibiotics and to prepare the operation.
환자에게 수액과 항생제를 주고 수술을 준비하기 위해 몇 시간이 필요할 수
있습니다.

We need about 2 day's preparation before operation.

수술 전 2일 간의 준비기간이 필요합니다.

The morning of surgery, you will receive an intravenous catheter usually placed in your arm and antibiotics to help prevent wound infections.

수술 당일 당신의 팔에 정맥혈관 주사를 놓고 감염 예방을 위해 항생제를 투여할 것입니다.

You're gonna have an operation tomorrow.

내일 수술을 받을 것입니다.

It's no big deal.

간단한 것입니다.

A lot of patients have had it done.

많은 사람들이 그 수술을 받았습니다.

There is no risk attached to the operation.

수술의 위험은 없습니다.

The mortality rate of operation is estimated 1 % of operation.

수술 중 사망률은 약 1% 정도입니다.

But we can't give a hundred percent guarantee that it would be okay.

하지만 괜찮을 것이라고 100% 보장하지는 못합니다.

The anesthesiologist uses a general anesthetic technique whereby you are put to sleep and made pain free in operation.

마취의사들이 수술 중 통증이 없고 잠을 재우기 위해 전신마취를 합니다.

Occasionally a spinal anesthetic may be used.

때때로 척추 마취를 하기도 합니다.

Certain risks are present when any operation requires a general
  anesthetic and the abdominal cavity is opened.
전신 마취와 개복수술에는 몇 가지 위험이 따릅니다.

Complications can occur.
합병증이 생길 수 있습니다.

The surgery will leave a scar.
수술은 흉터를 남길 것입니다.

Infection is rare but can occur after operation.
감염이 수술 후 드물게 올 수 있습니다.

Adhesions or hernia is a known complication of any abdominal
  operation.
복부 수술 후 유착이나 탈장이 올 수도 있습니다.

You feel better immediately after an operation.
수술 후 곧 좋아질 것입니다.

I'm afraid your cancer is advanced.
암이 이미 진행되었군요.

Surgery is a risk.
수술은 위험한 것입니다.

Treatment is radical operation.
치료는 광범위 절제술입니다.

Sometimes radiation therapy or chemotherapy is done.
때로는 방사선 치료나 항암제 치료가 필요합니다.

Combination treatment with chemotherapy and radiation therapy is needed to relieve symptoms and to destroy cancer cells that may remain in the area.

항암제와 방사선 치료 요법이 증상을 완화시키고, 남은 부위의 암세포를 죽이기 위해 필요합니다.

The success rate is small.

성공률이 적습니다.

Odds are about fifty-fifty.

확률은 50대 50입니다.

You'll get an operation tomorrow.

내일 수술을 받으실 겁니다.

Try to get some sleep.

잠을 좀 자 두세요.

Everything will be all right.

모든 게 잘 될 것입니다.

Surgery was a success.
Operation was fine.

수술은 성공입니다.

Patient will be in intensive care unit.

환자는 중환자실에 있을 것입니다.

I think the patient will be fine.

환자는 좋아질 것이라고 생각합니다.

Take a deep breath and cough in order to free your lungs of any fluid build up that may occur due to the general anesthesia.

전신마취 때문에 당신의 폐에 액체가 고이지 않도록 숨을 크게 쉬고 기침을 하세요.

Pain medication will be ordered to control most of the discomfort.

진통제가 처방되어 불편한 점이 조절될 것입니다.

Pain control pump can be used.

진통 조절 펌프가 사용될 수 있습니다.

Pain control pump is a device that you control with the push of a button that is connected to your IV.

이것은 당신의 정맥주사와 연결되어 당신이 버튼을 눌러 통증을 조절할 수 있는 것입니다.

The pain medication is delivered in a controlled dose, when the button is pushed.

당신이 버튼을 누를 때, 조절된 용량의 진통제가 투여됩니다.

You are allowed to eat when the stomach and intestines begin to function again.

위와 장의 기능이 돌아오면 그때부터 먹을 수 있습니다.

The first meal is a clear liquid diet.

처음 식사는 깨끗한 죽입니다.

If you tolerate this meal, the next meal usually is a regular diet.

이 음식을 먹고 괜찮으면 정상적인 음식이 나올 것입니다.

Resume your normal physical activities as soon as possible.

가능한 빨리 정상적인 활동을 시작하세요.

Walking is good for you.

걷는 것이 당신에게 좋습니다.

You will be discharged from the hospital within 2 weeks after the operation.

수술 후 2주 이내에 퇴원할 수 있을 것입니다.

You have recovered well and will be discharged tomorrow.
당신은 회복이 잘되어 내일 퇴원하게 될 것입니다.

You are able to be back to your normal activities within three weeks.
3주 이내에 정상 생활로 돌아 갈 수 있을 것입니다.

Immediately after discharge, you are go directly home and limit your activity.
퇴원 후 바로 집으로 가서 활동을 줄이세요.

If given a prescription, have it filled and begin taking medication as labeled.
처방을 받은 약이 있으면, 약을 사서 처방대로 복용하세요.

Don't remove suture and bandage.
봉합사를 제거하거나 붕대를 풀지 마세요.

Watch for redness, swelling, fever, persistent bleeding and increased pain.
발적, 부종, 열, 지속적인 출혈이나 통증이 심해지는 지 지켜보세요.

(4) Conversation (상담)

I can understand your distress.
당신의 고민을 이해합니다.

I know how you feel.
어떻게 느끼는 지 이해합니다.

I want you to talk to me about anything.
저에게 어떤 것이든 말하세요.

You will need to remind yourself
당신의 마음을 먼저 안정시키세요.

Don't let it get you down.
속상해 하지 마세요.

You've had a difficult time with this problem.
이 문제로 당신은 아주 어려운 시기입니다.

Try to talk with your family
당신의 가족에게 말하세요.

They will help you and relieve anxiety about the treatment.
그들이 당신을 돕고 치료에 대한 걱정을 줄여줄 것입니다.

We need to notify the family.
가족들에게 알릴 필요가 있습니다.

Could you bring a family with you when I see you in the next
  clinic.
다음 진료 때 가족을 데려 오실 수 있습니까?

Don't jump to any premature conclusions.
미리 속단하지 마세요.

Don't take it seriously.
심각하게 받아들이지 마세요.

It's not serious. It's minor.
심각한 것이 아닙니다. 단순한 것입니다.

Don't be depressed.
우울해하지 마세요.

Bad thing has happened to you.
당신에게 안 좋은 일입니다.

You must be a pretty strong person to have endured this
  problem.
이 문제를 극복할 수 있는 강한 사람이 되십시오.

How do you think we should handle this problem?
이 문제를 어떻게 다루면 좋겠습니까?

I wish there is something I could do to help.
도움이 될 만한 게 있으면 좋겠군요.

I am not saying that.
그렇게 말하지 않았습니다.

Let me explain that a little more.
좀 더 설명해 드리겠습니다.

Your symptom would be an unusual thing.
당신의 증상은 조금 특이한 것일 수 있습니다.

We don't know anything for sure.
확실한 것은 아직 모릅니다.

Try to look on the bright side.
좋은 쪽으로 생각하세요.

I think you'll be fine.
당신은 좋아질 것이라고 생각합니다.

There is nothing to worry about.
걱정하실 필요 없습니다.

Settle down.
흥분을 가라앉히세요.

You need to calm down.
진정할 필요가 있습니다.

I understand your concern.
당신의 걱정을 이해합니다.

That's not the point.
그것이 지금 중요한 것이 아닙니다.

You have to stay for observation.
관찰을 위해 이곳에 있어야 합니다.

We'll take very good care of you.
우리가 당신을 잘 돌봐드릴 것입니다.

I understand what you're going through.
당신이 당하는 고통을 이해합니다.

I really sympathy with you.
진정 당신을 동정합니다.

Are you afraid to tell me the truth?
진실을 말하기가 두렵나요?

I will keep this confidential.
이것을 비밀로 하겠습니다.

Have you been thinking a lot?
많이 생각해 보셨나요?

Why don't you tell me something about what's bothering you?
당신을 괴롭히는 것에 대해 말해줄래요?

You have nothing to worry about.
걱정할 것이 없습니다.

I am sure you don't need to worry about cancer.
암에 대해서 걱정하실 필요가 없습니다.

There is no need for further evaluation.
더 검사할 필요가 없습니다.

I think you'll be fine.
You're gonna okay.
It's gonna be okay.
You'll be fine.
곧 좋아질 것입니다.

You'd like to make a rest and relaxation plan for several days.
휴식을 취하고 며칠 쉴 계획을 세우세요.

You are always welcome to come and see me.
언제든지 저에게 오셔도 됩니다.

Keep this in mind.
이 말을 명심하세요.

You should keep trying to rest your body.
무리하지 않도록 노력하세요.

Do you have any questions for me?
Is there anything you'd like to ask?
저에게 더 물어 볼 것이 있습니까?

Ask questions if you don't understand any information from me.
이해가 가지 않는 것이 있습니까?

Is there anything else we haven't covered or that you'd like to
 tell me?

우리가 빼 먹은 것이나 저에게 하고 싶은 이야기가 있습니까?

Have you got any counseling?

상담을 한 적이 있나요?

Have you told your family any of these problems?

가족들에게 이 문제들에 대해 말했습니까?

Do your family know you're here?

당신의 가족이 당신이 이 곳에 있는 지 압니까?

We need to know where your family are.

당신의 가족들이 어디에 있는지 알아야합니다.

We need to get your family in here as soon as possible.

가능한 빨리 당신들의 가족이 이곳으로 와야 합니다.

We can't have to do this without the family's consent.

가족들의 동의 없이는 할 수 없습니다.

You know you'd hurt yourself.

당신 스스로 당신을 아프게 할 수 있습니다.

I wanna be sure that you know that.

나는 당신이 그것을 꼭 알기를 바랍니다.

I suggest you cooperate.

당신이 협조해주세요.

Is there anyone I should call?

전화를 해드려야 할 사람이 있나요?

If you give me your phone number, I can call your family so they come.

만약 당신이 전화번호를 가르쳐 주면 가족이 오게끔 전화하겠습니다.

I'm calling to inform you of your father's admission to the hospital.

당신 아버지께서 입원하신 것을 알려주려고 전화했습니다.

Patient is extremely ill.

환자는 매우 아픈 상황입니다.

We can't be sure that the patient will pull through.

환자가 이겨낼지 확실하지 않습니다.

The patient has to have surgery.

환자는 수술을 받아야만 합니다.

We need you to sign some consent papers.

동의서에 당신의 사인이 필요합니다.

We don't encourage this test.

이 검사를 꼭 종용하지는 않습니다.

You have to accept the way things are.

자연적인 일들을 받아들여야 합니다.

We will do everything we can.

우리가 할 수 있는 것은 다 할 것입니다.

Patient is in grave condition.
Patient's condition is grave.

환자는 심각한 상황입니다.

Patient's condition is most likely terminal.

환자의 상태는 마지막 상태에 가깝습니다.

There is nothing more we can do to stop the disease from progressing.
병이 진행되는 것을 멈출 수 있는 방법이 더 이상 없습니다.

With or without treatment, the patient couldn't live long.
치료를 하든 안 하든 환자는 오래 살지 못합니다.

The patient is dying.
환자는 죽어가고 있습니다.

He won't make it to the midnight.
밤까지 살지 못할 것입니다.

No one can tell what will result.
어떤 결과가 올지 말하기 힘듭니다.

(5) Prescription (처방)

I'll give you a prescription.
I'll write a prescription.
처방전을 드리겠습니다.

I'll give you a prescription for some medicines to relieve the symptom.
증상을 낫게 해 줄 약을 처방해 드리겠습니다.

I'll give you a prescription for some tablets to ease the pain.
통증을 줄여 줄 약을 처방해 드리겠습니다.

I will prescribe you some medicine, such as antibiotics and anti-inflammatory drugs.
항생제나 소염제와 같은 약들을 처방해 드리겠습니다.

I will write you a prescription such as muscle relaxant.
근이완제와 같은 약들을 처방해 드리겠습니다.

I'm going to give you antibiotics and anti-inflammatory drugs.
항생제와 소염제를 드리겠습니다.

I'm going to give you an anti-spasmodic drug to take.
진경제를 먹도록 해 드리겠습니다.

I'm going to give you a couple of different medicines.
몇 가지 다른 약들을 주겠습니다.

Here is a prescription slip.
There is your prescriptions.
처방전이 여기 있습니다.

Medication will help you get rid of the symptoms.
약이 증상을 없애는 데 도움을 줄 것입니다.

This medicine will relieve your symptoms.
이 약이 당신의 증상을 좋게 해줄 것입니다.

Your symptoms will wear off after taking the medicine.
당신의 증상은 약을 먹으면 없어질 것입니다.

These medicines should help.
이 약들이 도와줄 것입니다.

Take the prescription at the pharmacy.
처방전을 약국에서 받으세요.

Take the prescription to the pharmacy.
처방전을 약국에 가져가세요.

You can have filled at your local drug store.
동네 약국에서 약을 지을 수 있습니다.

You can get it filled at any drug store.
어느 약국에서든 약을 받을 수 있을 것입니다.

I want you to take the medicine three times a day after meal.
약을 하루에 세 번 식후에 복용하세요.

Take two tablets every 12 hours.
2알을 12시간마다 복용하세요.

I want you to take one, two times per day.
하루에 2번 한 알씩 복용하세요.

You can take it with every meal and at bedtime.
매 식사 때와 잠자기 전에 먹으세요.

You should take that medicines continuously.
그 약들을 계속 복용하여야 합니다.

Take it with meals or with something in your stomach.
음식이나 뭔가를 먹은 후 약을 같이 드세요.

Don't take on an empty stomach because it can irritate your
    stomach.
위를 자극하므로 빈속에는 먹지 마세요.

Take medicine from today.
오늘부터 약을 드세요.

I think 2 weeks medication is enough to you.
2주 정도의 복용이면 충분할 것 같군요.

Let me know if this medicine bothers you.

약을 먹고 속이 좋지 않으면 알려 주세요.

If your symptom becomes worse after taking medicine, come to here.

만약 약을 먹고도 증상이 나빠지면 이곳으로 오세요.

I'll give you a shot.

주사를 놔드리죠.

I am going to give you some medicines.

약을 드리죠.

Don't change the dosage of medication.

약 용량을 바꾸지 마세요.

Don't drink alcohol beverages or smoke while taking pain medication.

진통제를 복용할 경우, 술이나 담배를 금하세요.

If your symptom doesn't feel like it's going away in several days, let me know.

당신의 증상이 며칠 내에 없어지지 않으면 내게 알려 주세요.

(6) IV Injection (정맥 주사)

I'll give you IV injection.

정맥주사를 놓겠습니다.

Grip your hand.
Clench your fist.

주먹을 꼭 쥐세요.

You'll feel a needle.
바늘을 느끼실 것입니다.

Oh! We missed the vein.
이런! 정맥으로 안 들어갔군요.

We have to try this one more time.
다시 한번 해야 될 것 같습니다.

I am afraid we missed again.
또 놓쳤군요.

We will try one more time. I am sorry.
다시 한번 해야되겠습니다. 죄송합니다.

You have very tough veins.
정맥이 좋지 않군요.

It'll hurt a bit.
약간 아플 수 있습니다.

OK. I got it.
오케이. 됐습니다.

Open a hand.
손을 펴세요.

Just relax.
긴장을 푸세요.

Press on this cotton.
이 솜을 누르세요.

If you feel any discomfort, just let me know.
If any of abnormal symptoms occur, call me.

만약 이상한 느낌이 들면 알려주세요.

You could be unsteady or drowsy for a couple of hours after
your injection because of the sedative you may received.

당신이 투여 받을 진정제 때문에 몇 시간동안 불안하거나 어지러울 수 있습
니다.

You have been sustained intravenously for so long that your arm
veins are useless for IV.

너무 오랫동안 주사를 맞아와서 당신 팔의 정맥에 주사를 못 놓겠군요.

I'd like to use your leg veins.

당신의 다리에 있는 정맥을 이용하겠습니다.

You haven't get a vein anywhere.

정맥이 어디에도 없군요.

You are gonna need a central line.

중심 정맥이 필요할 것 같군요.

Something is wrong with the three-way stopcock on the
intravenous line.

정맥주사 라인의 3방향 마개가 잘못되었군요.

We have to change the three-way stopcock.

3방향 마개를 바꾸어야 합니다.

(7) IM Injection (근육 주사)

I will give you an injection in your buttocks.

엉덩이에 주사를 놓겠습니다.

Would you please lie down on the bed?

침대에 올라가 누우실래요?

Could you drop your pants and underwear?

바지와 속옷을 내려 주실래요?

Could you turn on you left side?

왼쪽으로 돌아 누우실래요?

It'll sting a bit.

약간 아플 수 있습니다.

Take a relax.

진정하세요.

OK. We are done.

예. 됐습니다.

If you feel any pain, let me know.

통증이 있으면 제게 말해 주세요.

You can expect some soreness after shot.

주사를 맞고 나서 약간 아플 수 있습니다.

Using ice pack at the injection site for 20 minutes will reduce
  your pain.

20분 정도 주사 맞은 곳에 얼음찜질을 하면 통증이 줄어 들 것입니다.

(8) Transfer (전원)

Your condition is serious.

당신의 상태는 심각합니다.

Check with a nearby general hospital or university hospital.
근처의 종합병원이나 대학병원을 찾아보세요.

You can choose a doctor.
당신은 의사를 선택할 수 있습니다.

You can find out more about any physician by searching internet web site.
인터넷에서 전문의를 찾을 수 있습니다.

I will send you to a specialist.
전문의에게 보내드리겠습니다.

I am going to refer you to a specialist in the university.
대학에 있는 전문의에게 전원 해 드리겠습니다.

It's a complicated operation.
그것은 복잡한 수술입니다.

You have to go to another hospital.
다른 병원으로 가야합니다.

(9) Advice (조언)

The brain and muscle have to be used regularly to remain strong.
뇌와 근육을 강하게 유지시키기 위해서는 규칙적으로 사용되어야 합니다.

Aim for a balance of proper diet and exercise.
균형적인 식사와 운동을 하도록 하세요.

Exercise is very important to maintaining health.
운동은 건강을 유지하는데 아주 중요합니다.

Adequate exercises help you lead a healthy life.
적절한 운동은 당신을 건강한 생활로 이끕니다.

You should try to do a little bit of exercise every day.
당신은 매일 조금씩 운동을 하도록 노력해야 합니다.

Exercise helps to reduce your blood cholesterol level and the risk of heart disease or stroke.
운동은 혈액내의 콜레스테롤 수치를 낮추어 주고, 심장병이나 뇌졸중의 위험을 줄여줍니다.

Poorly-fit young adults are 3 to 6 times more likely to develop diabetes, high blood pressure and other illnesses in middle age that put them at greater risk of heart disease or stroke.
운동이 부족한 젊은 사람은 중년의 나이에 심장병이나 뇌졸중을 일으킬 위험성이 높은 질환이나 당뇨병 고혈압 등이 3-6배 더 많이 발생됩니다.

Increasing fitness decreases the risk of by as much as 50%.
운동을 더 많이 할 경우 위험성이 50% 감소됩니다.

The solution lies in a willingness to make lifestyle changes.
해결책은 삶을 변화시키고자 하는 의지에 있습니다.

Exercise will put you in better shape.
운동은 당신을 좀 더 몸매가 좋게 만들 것입니다.

Consider a physical activity to help you burn those extra calories.
여분의 칼로리를 소모시키는 육체 운동에 대해서 고려해 보세요.

Working out at a fitness center will build up your heart and lung.
휘트니스 센터에서 운동은 당신의 심장과 폐를 튼튼하게 해 줄 것입니다.

Have a positive mind.
긍정적인 생각을 가지세요.

Learn a stress reduction technique.
스트레스를 줄이는 방법을 생각하세요.

Sometimes enjoy slow life and relaxation.
때로는 느린 생활과 여유로움을 즐기세요.

Get a sleep and know how much sleep you need.
당신이 필요한 수면을 알고 취하세요.

Sometimes take a multi-vitamin.
때로는 복합 비타민을 먹으세요.

Start your day with breakfast.
아침 식사로 시작하세요

Drink at least six to eight glasses of water.
하루에 물을 최소한 6내지 8컵 드세요.

Do at least one activity each week that brings pleasure.
일주일에 한 번은 즐거움을 주는 활동을 하세요.

Sometimes enjoy breathing fresh air and taking sunshine in
nature.
가끔씩 자연 속에서 신성한 공기를 마시고 햇볕을 쐬는 것을 즐기세요.

Health in old age is predicted by factors such as a stable
marriage, regular exercise, adaptive ability and continuous
reading.
노년의 건강은 안정된 결혼생활, 규칙적인 운동, 적응 능력, 계속적인 독서
와 같은 요소에 의해 예견되어집니다.

(10) Dialogue 1.

P : Can this operation be done on an inpatient basis or outpatient basis?

이 수술은 통원치료가 가능한가요? 아니면 입원해야 되나요?

D : For your convenience, our hospital offers some surgical procedure on an outpatient basis.

당신의 편의를 위해 어떤 수술들은 통원치료로써 가능합니다.

Day surgery is designed for people who are basically fit and healthy.

당일 수술은 수술에 적합하고 건강한 사람을 위해 마련되었습니다.

P : What is day surgery?

당일 수술이 무엇이죠?

D : It means that you arrived at the hospital on the same day as the operation and go home again that day.

당신이 병원에 도착한 날 수술을 받고, 그 날 집으로 가는 것을 말합니다.

It reduces your time and costs in hospital, eliminating the need for an overnight stay.

당신의 시간과 비용을 줄여주고, 하룻밤 머무를 필요가 없습니다.

P : How long do I stay in hospital?

병원에는 얼마정도 있어야 되죠?

D : The average stay is two to eight hours.

평균 머무는 시간이 2시간에서 8시간입니다.

P : Do I need to fast?

굶어야 하나요?

D : Yes, you should not eat or drink for six hours before your visit.

예, 수술 날 오시기 6시간 전까지는 먹거나 마시면 안됩니다.

This includes water.

물도 포함해서요.

P : May I smoke?

담배 피워도 되나요?

D : Smoking can be hazard before an operation.

흡연은 수술 전에 위험합니다.

So, please don't smoke for at least 24 hours beforehand.

수술 24시간 전까지는 담배를 피우지 마십시오.

P : Can I drive?

운전은 해도 되나요?

D : No. Due to the anesthesia you will receive, driving home would be dangerous.

아뇨, 당신이 받는 마취 때문에 집으로 운전하는 것은 위험합니다.

P : What will happen after surgery?

수술 후에는 어떻게 하죠?

D : After surgery, you will be return to the room where hospital staff will monitor your progress until you are well enough to leave.

수술 후에는 병원 스텝이 당신이 좋아져 집에 갈 수 있을 때까지 모니터링 할 수 있는 곳으로 옮겨집니다.

Before you leave, you will be given medications, and a follow-up appointment will be organized.

집으로 떠나기 전에 약이 주어지고, 다음 진료날짜가 예약될 것입니다.

P : Okay.
　　알겠습니다.

D : I will arrange the date and time of your visit directly with the
　　hospital.
　　제가 당신이 바로 병원으로 올 수 있는 날짜와 시간을 잡아 드리겠습니다.

　　The day before your hospital visit, a member of our hospital
　　staff will telephone you to conform the details.
　　당신이 병원 오기 전날 우리 병원 직원이 당신에게 세부사항을 물어보
　　기 위해 전화를 할 것입니다.

　　If you will not be at home, please contact the hospital the day
　　before your operation.
　　만약 당신이 집에 없을 경우엔, 병원으로 수술 전날 전화를 해주세요.

(11) Dialogue 2.

P : I have done all the necessary tests.
　　필요한 검사를 다 했습니다.

　　What are my test results?
　　검사 결과가 어떻습니까?

D : There doesn't seem to be anything wrong with you.
　　별 이상이 없군요.

　　Don't worry about this.
　　걱정하지 마세요..

P : How about X-ray?
　　X-ray는 어떻던가요?

D : The X-rays look fine.
X-선 검사도 정상으로 보입니다.

P : What do you think is causing my problem?
제 문제가 무엇이라고 생각합니까?

D : Nothing serious.
심각한 것은 없군요.

It's quite a common condition.
정상입니다.

P : Could you please give me something for my bowels?
화장실 갈 수 있게 약 좀 주실래요?

I haven't had a descent movement in 3 days.
3일 동안 변을 보지 못했습니다.

D : OK.
알겠습니다.

(12) Dialogue 3.

D : The medicine doesn't seem to be working.
약이 잘 안 듣는 것 같군요.

P : Yes.
예.

D : I will write you different prescription.
다른 처방전을 써 드리죠.

You can try this.
이 약을 드셔보세요.

P : Okay.
알겠습니다.

D : If you don't feel better in a couple of days, let me know.
만약 2-3일 내로 증상의 호전이 없으면, 나에게 알려주세요.

P : How long will I have to take medicine?
얼마나 오랫동안 이 약을 먹어야 하죠?

D : Try to take medicine to take effect.
효과가 있을 때까지 약을 드세요.

P : OK, I will try it.
좋습니다. 복용해 볼게요.

2 *Emergency Room*
(응급실)

1) CPR (심폐소생술)

N : Dr. Kim. Cardiac arrest.
김 선생님. 심장마비입니다.

I don't get a blood pressure.
혈압측정이 안됩니다.

I can't feel a pulse.
맥박이 없습니다.

Heart monitor shows no rhythm.
심장 모니터에 리듬이 없습니다.

D : No pulse. No respiration.
맥박도 없고, 호흡도 없군요.

He is in arrest.
심장마비이군요.

Call the time. 5 o'clock. p.m.
시간을 보죠. 오후 5시입니다.

Dr. Lee. Start the cardiac compression.
이 선생님. 심장마사지를 시작해 주세요.

Let's tube him.
기관내 삽관을 합시다.

Get a laryngoscope and an endotracheal tube.
후두경과 기관내 튜브를 가져오세요.

Can you hold the head position?
머리 자세 좀 잡아 줄래요?

N : OK.
알겠습니다.

D : Laryngoscope.
후두경.

Give me an endotracheal tube 7.0.
ET 튜브 7번을 주세요.

Dr. Lee. Stop the compression.
이 선생님. 심장마사지를 멈추세요.

OK. Push on his larynx.
좋습니다. 후두를 눌러주세요.

OK. It's in.
됐습니다. 안으로 들어갔군요.

Inflate the cuff.
공기를 넣으세요.

The Ambu bag.
암부백.

Let's bag. Hyperventilate.
공기주입을 빠르게 하세요.

Give him an ampule of epinephrine.
에피네프린 한 앰플 주세요.

Dr. Lee. Restart the massage.
이 선생님 심장마사지를 다시 해주세요.

N : OK.
알겠습니다.

D : Let's shock him.
충격을 줍시다.

Defibrillator. Set it on 200J.
제세기. 200J로 맞추어 주세요.

Away from the bed. Clear.
침대에서 떨어지세요. 클리어.

N : No response.
반응이 없습니다.

D : Give him another ampule of epinephrine.
에피네프린 한 앰플 더 주세요.

Bicarbonate 40.
바이카보네이트 40 주세요.

N : OK.
알겠습니다.

D : Change to 250 J. Stand back. Clear.
250J로 바꾸세요. 물러나세요. 클리어.

Pulse is bounding.
맥박이 뛰는군요.

Give him a hundred mg lidocaine.
리도카인 100mg을 주세요.

I want blood gas and electrolytes.
혈액 가스 검사와 전해질 검사를 해 주세요.

2) Coma (혼수)

D : What have we got?
어떤 환자죠?

N : 45-year-old man. Coma.
45세 남자, 혼수입니다.

D : On my count, one, two, three, move gently.
제 숫자에 따라, 하나, 둘 , 셋, 조심스럽게 옮기세요.

Get him off.
옷을 벗기세요.

N : OK.
알겠습니다.

D : Pupils equal, reactive to light.
동공 크기가 같고 빛에 반응 하군요.

Corneal reflex is normal.
각막 반응은 정상이군요.

N : Blood pressure is 110 over 70.
혈압이 110에 70입니다.

D : Give him a liter of saline first.
식염수 1리터를 먼저 주세요.

Let's get a pulse oximeter right away.
지금 당장 펄스 옥시미터를 측정하세요.

N : OK.
알겠습니다.

D : Can you hear me?
제 소리가 들리나요?

Do you know where you are.
여기가 어디인 지 아시겠어요?

If you can hear me, squeeze my hand.
만약 들리면 제 손을 잡아 보세요.

No response.
반응이 없군요.

N : Pulse oximeter is 90.
산소포화도가 90입니다.

D : Give him the O_2 at 2 liters.
산소 2리터를 주세요.

Get an EKG monitoring.
심전도 모니터링 하세요.

He has not got blood in the ear canal.
귀에서 피는 없군요.

Breath sounds are good.
호흡소리는 좋군요.

Abdomen is not rigid. Soft.

복부가 부드럽군요.

Bowel sounds normal.

장운동도 정상이군요.

Capillary refill is not bad.

모세혈관 반응이 나쁘지는 않군요.

Deep tendon reflexes are present bilaterally.

심부건 반사는 양측에 다 있군요.

Babinski reflex is normal.

바빈스키 반사도 정상이군요.

Get a portable X-ray here.

포터블 X-선을 불러 주세요.

Get chest, abdomen, skull and a cross table c-spine.

흉부, 복부, 두개골, 경추 측면 사진을 찍으세요.

Run a blood sugar, CBC, Chemistry, Electrolytes.

혈당과 CBC, 화학물과 전해질 검사를 해주세요.

Get a toxin screen and a blood alcohol.

독극물 검사와 혈액 알코올 농도도 해주세요.

Let's get a blood gas.

혈액 가스 검사를 합시다.

Start a foley catheter.

도뇨관을 넣어주세요.

N : BP is dropped 90 over 60.

혈압이 90에 60으로 떨어졌습니다.

D : I'll start a central line.
중심정맥을 잡겠습니다.

Start another one liter of saline.
식염수 1리터를 더 주세요.

N : X-rays are here.
사진이 나왔습니다.

Blood gas is back.
혈액 가스 검사가 나왔습니다.

D : There is no abnormal finding.
이상 소견은 없군요.

N : BP is 100 over 60.
혈압이 100에 60입니다.

Pulse oximeter is up 100.
산소포화도가 100까지 올랐습니다.

Labs are back.
피검사도 나왔습니다.

D : OK. Let's check brain CT. Non-contrast.
됐습니다. 조영제 투여 없이 뇌 단층 촬영을 하죠.

Where are the family?
가족들은 어디에 있죠?

N : They are staying out there.
그들은 저곳에서 기다리고 있습니다.

D : OK.
알겠습니다.

Hi. I am Dr. Kim.
안녕하세요. 저는 닥터 김입니다.

P : I am his son.
제가 그의 아들입니다.

Can you tell me what happened?
무슨 일인 지 말씀해줄래요?

D : He was founded in a cross walk in comatose condition.
그는 횡단보도에서 혼수상태로 발견되었습니다.

His condition is not serious.
그의 상태는 심각하지 않습니다.

P : Can I see him?
그를 볼 수 있나요?

D : Maybe you'd better wait outside while I treat him.
그를 치료하는 동안 밖에서 기다리는 게 좋을 것입니다.

P : Will he be all right?
그는 괜찮을까요?

D : We don't know yet.
아직은 모릅니다.

We have to rule out brain injury.
뇌 손상에 대해 알아보아야 합니다.

We have been trying to treat him.
그를 치료하려고 노력하고 있습니다.

P : Does he need surgery?
수술이 필요한가요?

D : I can tell you more when we have brain CT.
뇌 단층촬영 결과가 나온 후 말할 수 있습니다.

If you have a seat outside, and I will be right with you.
당신이 밖에서 기다리고 있으면 곧 당신에게 가도록 하겠습니다.

P : Please, do your best.
최선을 다해주세요.

D : OK. I'll come and talk to you as soon as I can.
되도록 빨리 와서 이야기를 해드리겠습니다.

3) DOA (사망)

N : DOA.
DOA입니다.

D : Vital signs?
활력징후는?

N : Negative. No pulse. No breath.
없습니다. 맥박이나 호흡이 없습니다.

D : Pupils are dilated and fixed.
동공이 열려있고 고정되었습니다.

Hearts sounds, negative.
심장소리가 안 들리는군요.

Get the intubation tray.
삽관시술함을 가져오세요.

Give me cricoid pressure.

윤상 부위를 눌러 주세요.

The Ambu bag.

암부백.

Dr. Lee. Start CPR

이 선생님 CPR을 시작해 주세요.

Has the family been notified?

가족들은 알고 있나요?

N : Dr. Kim. The family is over there, on the couch.

김 선생님. 보호자들이 의자에 앉아 있습니다.

D : OK. Mr. Choi. Relatives of Mr. Choi.

알겠습니다. 최씨 보호자분 계십니까?

P : I am here. I am his daughter.

여기 있습니다. 제가 그의 딸입니다.

D : Hi. I am Dr. Kim.

안녕하세요. 저는 닥터 김입니다.

Your father was brought here by ambulance in full cardiac and respiratory arrest.

당신의 아버지는 심장과 폐가 모두 정지된 상태에서 앰블런스로 이곳 으로 실려 왔습니다.

Your father was DOA. Dead on arrival.

당신의 아버지께서는 도착하셨을 당시 이미 사망하셨습니다.

Do you know that?

그것을 알고 계시지요?

P : Yes.
예.

D : How long has he been down?
얼마나 오랫동안 쓰러져 있으셨죠?

P : 10 minutes.
10분입니다.

D : We are trying to bring him back.
우리는 그를 살리려고 노력하고 있습니다.

Wait here. I'll come back and talk to you.
이곳에서 기다리시면 다시 와서 이야기를 해드리겠습니다

P : Doctor. Please do everything you can.
선생님. 할 수 있는 것들을 다 해주세요.

D : OK.
알겠습니다.

Defibrillator. Charging to 300 J.
제세기 300 주울로 맞추세요.

Everybody off. Clear.
모두 비키세요. 클리어.

He is not responding.
반응이 전혀 없군요.

Let's call it.
이만 끝냅시다.

Time of death. p.m. 8 :00
사망 시간 저녁 8시.

D : We used all of our capabilities.
우리는 가능한 모든 것들을 다했습니다.

We tried to revive him for 20 minutes, but with no success.
우리는 그를 살리려고 20분 동안 노력했지만, 성공하지 못했습니다.

We did all we could.
우리가 할 수 있는 것은 다 했습니다.

We were unable to revive him.
우리는 그를 살리지 못했습니다.

I am sorry to inform you that your father has passed away.
당신의 아버지가 돌아가셨다고 말해서 미안하군요.

P : It's all right.
괜찮습니다.

It was expected.
예상하였습니다.

We appreciate what you've done. Doctor.
선생님. 당신이 한 일에 대해서 감사 드립니다.

Can we see him?
그를 볼 수 있을까요?

D : Sure.
좋습니다.

4) Emergency Operation (응급수술)

N : Auto versus pedestrian accident.
자동차와 보행자 사고입니다.

D : Move him on three. One. Two. Three.
셋에 그를 옮기세요. 하나, 둘, 셋.

OK. Let's get clothes off.
됐습니다. 그의 옷을 벗기세요.

N : He is cyanotic.
창백합니다.

Abdomen is rigid.
배는 경직되었군요.

Blood pressure is 100 over 70.
혈압이 100에 70입니다.

Faint pulse at 120.
맥박이 120으로 약합니다.

D : Put him on a mask, O_2 at 2 liters.
산소 마스크 2리터로 씌워주세요.

Get a pulse oximeter.
펄스 옥시미터를 설치하세요.

Take a deep breath.
숨을 크게 쉬세요.

P : OK.
알겠습니다.

D : This is gonna help you breathe.
이것이 호흡을 도와 줄 것입니다.

We're gonna take care of you.
곧 치료해 드리겠습니다.

Is it tender here?
이곳이 아픈가요?

P : Yes.
예.

D : How hypotensive is he now?
지금은 혈압이 얼마나 낮지요?

N : BP is dropped 90 over 60.
혈압이 90에 60으로 떨어졌습니다.

Pulse oximeter is 96.
산소포화도는 96입니다.

D : Medicut. OK. Sampling Tube. Tape.
메디컷 주세요. 됐습니다. 샘플링 튜브. 붙여주세요.

Let's CBC, Type and Cross-match. EKG.
CBC와 혈액형, 크로스매칭, EKG가 필요합니다.

Draw all preoperative lab here.
여기에서 수술 전 검사를 합시다.

Give him 1000cc Hartmann solution in a rapid drop.
하트만 1000cc 용액을 빠르게 주세요.

Can we get the peritoneal lavage prepared?
복부세척 검사를 준비해 주세요.

N : OK. Hartmann is in.
알겠습니다. 하트만 용액을 주었습니다.

D : I will make a nick in your belly, so I can fill your abdomen
with fluid.
당신의 배에 작은 절개를 내어 용액을 넣겠습니다.

Once it's full, I'll watch as the fluid drains out.
일단 다 차면 용액이 흘러나온 것을 관찰 할 것입니다.

If blood comes out, you have abdominal injuries.
만약 피가 나온다면 당신은 복부에 손상을 입은 것입니다.

P : OK.
알겠습니다.

N : Labs are back.
검사가 나왔습니다.

Hemoglobin is 8.
헤모글로빈이 8입니다.

He has lost a lot of blood.
출혈을 많이 했나 봅니다.

D : Bloody fluid is draining out.
피가 섞인 용액이 나오는군요.

Your last meal?
언제 마지막 식사 하셨죠?

P : Breakfast.
아침입니다.

D : You'll need to have surgery.
수술이 필요할 것 같군요.

P : Is it serious?
심각 한가요?

D : Don't worry.
걱정 마세요.

Everything will be fine.
모든 것이 좋아질 것입니다.

N : BP is fallen. 85 over 50.
혈압이 떨어집니다. 85에 50입니다.

Let's get blood going, wide open.
혈액을 먼저 빠르게 주도록 하죠.

N : OK.
알겠습니다.

Blood bank. This is Nurse Lee in ER.
혈액은행이죠? 응급실의 이 간호사입니다.

I need to know what you have available fresh, whole O blood.
쓸 수 있는 신선한 O형 혈액이 얼마나 있는지 알고 싶습니다.

D : We need X-rays, chest and abdomen.
흉부, 복부 X-ray가 필요합니다.

Let's get X-ray.
X-ray를 찍읍시다.

N : OK.

알겠습니다.

D : Call surgeon.

외과 선생님을 부르세요.

Who is a surgical back up?

누가 외과 당직이죠?

N : Dr. Park.

박 선생님입니다.

D : Tell him to come down now.

그에게 지금 바로 내려오시라고 하세요.

N : Yes.

알겠습니다.

D : Notify the OR.

수술실에 알리세요.

Is there any surgery scheduled?

수술 예약이 있나요?

N : No. None at all.

아뇨. 없습니다.

D : Get a foley catheter started.

도뇨관을 지금 넣어 주세요.

N : OK.

알겠습니다.

D : Start a dopamine drip, 400mg in 250 D5W, 10 drops a
   minute.
　도파민 400mg을 5%DW 250cc에 넣어 분당 10번 떨어뜨리세요.

N : OK.
　알겠습니다.

5) Suture (봉합술)

N : Dr. Kim. You have suture case waiting for you.
　김 선생님. 봉합술이 필요한 환자가 있습니다.

D : I'll be right there.
　곧 가겠습니다.

　Which room?
　어느 방이죠?

N : Room 4.
　4번 방입니다.

　One drunken man with a laceration to the scalp.
　두피에 열상을 입은 술 취한 남자입니다.

D : OK.
　알겠습니다.

　Hi. Let me take a look.
　안녕하세요. 잠깐 볼까요?

　How did you hurt?
　어떻게 다치셨죠?

P : Someone struck me on the head.
누가 내 머리를 때렸어요.

This cut is bleeding.
상처에서 피가 나고 있어요.

D : You've got a deep laceration here, about 5 cm.
5 cm 정도의 열상이 이곳에 있군요.

Scalp has a large blood supply.
두피는 혈액이 많이 가는 곳입니다.

It can bleed a lot, but total blood loss may not be serious.
피가 많이 날 수는 있지만, 전체 출혈량은 심각하지 않을 것입니다.

It's minor.
사소한 것입니다.

P : Do I need stitches?
꿰매야 하나요?

D : Yes. You need some stitches.
예. 몇 바늘 꿰매야 되겠군요.

You'd better take care of that wound.
상처부위를 치료해야겠습니다.

I'm gonna clean it up with saline.
식염수로 좀 씻겠습니다.

P : I feel dizziness.
어지럽군요.

D : Have you vomited?
토하지는 안 했습니까?

P : Yes. Once.

예. 한 번 토했습니다.

D : I want to run some tests first.

먼저 검사를 해야 되겠군요.

We need skull series X-rays and CT.

두부 **X-ray**와 **CT** 촬영이 필요합니다.

Do a head CT, non-contrast.

조영제 없이 두부 컴퓨터 단층 촬영을 하세요.

N : OK.

알겠습니다.

D : I'll give you stitches after developing films.

사진이 나온 다음에 꿰매드리겠습니다.

P : OK.

알겠습니다.

D : Don't worry.

걱정하지 마세요.

There is no abnormal finding in your X-ray and CT films.

X-선이나 **CT** 필름에는 이상이 없습니다.

Just simple cut.

단순한 열상입니다.

Only simple sutures are needed.

단지 단순봉합이 필요할 것 같군요.

There won't be a severe scarring.

심한 흉터는 없을 것입니다.

I will have you fixed up right away.
곧 치료해 드리도록 하겠습니다.

P : Thank you.
고맙습니다.

D : Do you have an allergic to local anesthesia?
국소마취에 알러지가 있습니까?

P : No.
없습니다.

D : Any allergic to drugs? No reactions, rashes, anythings?
약에 대한 알러지나 반응, 홍반 등 아무것도 없나요?

P : No. Of course not.
물론 아닙니다.

D : The actual procedure takes about 5 minutes.
시간은 약 5분 정도 걸립니다.

P : Is the procedure painful?
아픈가요?

D : No. Don't worry. I will give you a local anesthesia.
아뇨. 걱정 마세요. 국소마취를 할 것입니다.

Everything is going to be all right.
모든 것이 잘 될 것입니다.

But you should endure the pain during the local anesthesia.
하지만 국소 마취하는 동안은 통증을 참아야 합니다.

P : OK.
알겠습니다.

D : Lie back.
누우세요.

I'll shave your head.
머리를 깎겠습니다.

Just relax.
긴장을 푸세요.

This isn't going to hurt at all.
이것은 아프지 않습니다.

N : What sutures will you be using, Doctor?
선생님, 무슨 실을 쓰실거죠?

D : Nylon 4-0.
나일론 4번을 주세요.

I will clean and stitch the wound.
상처를 씻은 다음 봉합할 것입니다.

Somebody get a light in here.
누가 이곳에 불 좀 비추어 주세요.

N : OK.
알겠습니다.

D : I'll inject both sides of the wound.
상처 양쪽에 주사를 찌를 것입니다.

You're gonna be numb for about 1 hour.
한 시간 정도 감각이 없을 것입니다.

You'll feel a needle.
바늘이 들어가는 것을 느낄 것입니다.

P : Yes.

알겠습니다.

D : Don't move.

움직이지 마세요.

Take it easy.

편하게 하세요.

Are you comfortable?

괜찮으세요?

P : Yes. I am.

예. 괜찮습니다.

D : OK. We are done.

예. 다 끝났습니다.

P : All done?

다 끝났나요?

D : Yes. All finished.

예. 모든 것이 끝났습니다.

P : Thank you. Doc.

감사합니다, 선생님.

D : You are welcome.

천만에요.

It might get infected.

감염이 될 수도 있습니다.

When was your last tetanus shot?

파상풍 주사를 언제 맞았죠?

P : I don't know.

모르겠는데요.

D : I'll give you a shot of 250 unit tetanus.

당신에게 파상풍 주사 250 unit를 주겠습니다.

And I will give you antibiotics and anti-inflammatory medicines.

그리고 항생제나 소염제를 드리겠습니다

Take that medicine, three times a day.

그 약을 하루에 3번 드십시요.

P : When do I get my stitches out?

언제 실밥을 뽑죠?

D : Sutures can be removed in 10 days.

봉합사는 10일 내에 뺄 수 있을 것입니다.

P : Can I wash?

씻어도 되나요?

D : Yes, But you'd better wash after the stitches are removed.

예, 하지만 실밥을 뽑은 후 씻으면 좋습니다.

P : Thank you.

감사합니다.

D : I will make an appointment for you.

내가 다음 오셔야 할 날짜를 잡아 드리겠습니다.

6) Sprain (염좌)

D : Where is your pain?
　　어디가 아프시죠?

P : My right ankle hurts.
　　오른쪽 발목이 아파요.

D : How did you hurt?
　　어떻게 다쳤죠?

P : I tripped over a rock.
　　돌에 걸려 넘어졌어요.

D : Let me take a look.
　　Will you roll up your pants?
　　잠깐 볼까요?
　　바지를 올려 주실래요?

P : OK.
　　알았습니다.

D : Do you have intense ankle pain when you put weight on it.
　　체중을 실으면 발목이 아프던가요?

P : Yes.
　　예.

D : Are you unable to walk on the foot?
　　걸을 수 없나요?

P : Yes. It really hurts when I walk.
　　예. 걸으면 너무 아픕니다.

D : Do you feel any heating sensation?
열감 같은 것을 느끼시나요?

P : Yes.
그렇습니다.

D : Did you have any treatment?
어떤 치료를 받았었나요?

P : Acupunture didn't help.
침은 도움이 되질 않더군요.

D : Your injured ankle swelled up.
다친 발목이 부었군요.

P : That's why I gave up and came to you.
그래서 포기하고 이곳으로 온 이유입니다.

D : We are gonna check X-ray of your ankle.
발목 사진을 찍겠습니다.

We will check if there are any broken of bone.
뼈에 골절이 있는 지 검사할 것입니다.

A technician will take X-ray in X-ray room.
방사선과 기사가 X-ray 방에서 사진을 찍을 것입니다.

I will return after X-ray is developed.
엑스레이가 현상이 되면 다시 오겠습니다.

P : OK.
알겠습니다.

D : I have the results of your X-rays.
당신의 엑스레이 결과를 보았습니다.

There doesn't seem to be anything wrong with you.
이상이 없는 것 같습니다.

I see no evidence of fracture or joint dislocation.
골절이나 관절탈구 소견은 없습니다.

Your ankle pain is from damage to the ankle ligament.
당신의 발목관절 통증은 발목인대 손상으로 오고 있습니다.

P : What is a sprain?
염좌가 뭐죠?

D : A sprain is a stretched or torn ligament.
염좌란 인대가 늘어났거나 찢어진 것을 말합니다.

P : How can ankle sprain be treated?
발목 염좌는 어떻게 치료하지요?

D : You should take several days off and rest.
당신은 며칠 휴가를 내어 쉬어야 합니다.

P : Should I use heat to ease pain?
통증을 줄이기 위해 뜨거운 찜질이 좋습니까?

D : No. Use ice and anti-inflammatory medicine.
아닙니다. 얼음이나 소염제를 이용하세요.

P : What is the best way to use ice?
얼음을 어떻게 사용해야 가장 좋죠?

D : Keep ice pack wrapping with towel directly on the lesion, 20
to 30 minutes, several times a day for 3 days.
얼음찜질을 수건에 감싸서 다친 곳에 대고 한 번에 20분 또는 30분 씩,
하루에 예닐곱 번, 3일 간 해 주세요.

Using ice packs can decrease the swelling and pain.
얼음찜질은 통증과 부종을 줄여 줄 것입니다.

I will wrap your ankle with elastic bandage to avoid swelling.
당신의 발목을 부종을 막기 위해 탄력 붕대를 감아드리겠습니다.

Use crutches or a cane until it is no longer painful to put weight on the ankle when you stand.
당신이 서서 체중을 실어도 아프지 않을 때까지 목발이나 지팡이를 사용하세요.

P : OK. Thank you sir. I'll try.
알겠습니다. 감사합니다 선생님. 노력해 볼께요.

D : Try to keep your ankle elevated for about 2 to 3 hours a day if possible.
가능한 하루에 발목을 2, 3시간 정도 높일 수 있도록 하십시오.

P : How long should I expect it to take before I am fully recovered?
완전히 회복될 때까지 얼마나 치료해야 되죠?

D : It will take 2 to 4 weeks.
2주에서 4주정도 걸릴 것입니다.

P : How soon can I exercise or play sports?
언제 운동이나 스포츠를 할 수 있지요?

D : You will probably be able to return to your sport in a couple of months.
당신은 아마도 2-3개월 내에 운동을 할 수 있을 것입니다.

P : How can I prevent reinjury?

다시 손상당하는 것을 어떻게 막죠?

D : Special brace will help prevent reinjury.

특별한 보조기가 재손상을 막는데 도와줄 것입니다.

But relaxation should be the first consideration.

휴식을 먼저 고려해야만 합니다.

P : I agree with you on that point.

그 말에는 동감입니다.

D : I will prescribe you some medicine such as muscle relaxant.

나는 당신에게 근이완제와 같은 약을 처방해 주겠습니다.

If your pain is worse, physical therapy will be necessary.

만약 통증이 있으면 물리치료가 필요할 것입니다.

P : OK.

알겠습니다.

D : I will arrange to see you again 2 weeks later.

당신이 2 주 뒤 볼 수 있도록 예약하겠습니다.

7) Fracture (골절)

N : Dr. Kim

김 선생님

D : What is it?

무슨 일이죠?

N : You've got patients to see.
볼 환자가 있습니다.

D : Can't the intern take it?
인턴 선생님이 볼 수 없나요?

N : Two patients came in at once.
두 명의 환자가 한꺼번에 왔어요.

D : OK. I 'll be right there.
알겠습니다. 곧 가죠.

I'll take the traffic accident patient.
제가 교통사고 환자를 보죠.

Dr. Lee. You take the child.
이 선생님이 어린아이를 보세요.

Do we have a room?
빈방이 있나요?

N : Room 2 is free.
2번 방이 비었습니다.

D : OK. Take her to trauma room 2.
알겠습니다. 그녀를 2번 방으로 옮겨주세요.

How are you doing?
안녕하세요

Do you have pain?
어디가 아프시죠?

Can you point to the pain.
아픈 곳을 가리킬 수 있습니까?

P : My right leg.

제 오른쪽 다리입니다.

D : How did you hurt?

어떻게 다쳤습니까?

Were you in a car accident?

자동차 사고입니까?

P : Yes, I can't stand pain.

예. 통증을 참을 수가 없어요.

D : OK, I would like to examine you.

알겠습니다. 검사를 좀 하겠습니다.

We have to remove your clothes.

옷을 제거해야 되겠군요.

Sorry about the suit.

바지를 잘라 죄송합니다.

You have open wounds.

개방성 상처를 입었군요.

It's probably broken.

아마도 골절 인 것 같군요.

Can you feel anything in your leg?

다리에 감각을 느낍니까?

P : Yes.

예.

D : Do you feel any pain here?

여기가 아픈가요?

P : Yes.
예.

D : How about here?
이곳은 어떤가요?

P : Yes.
아픕니다.

D : Push down with you toes on my hand like a gas pedal.
차 페달 밟듯이 발가락으로 제 손을 눌러 보세요.

OK. Wiggle your toes.
됐습니다. 발가락을 움직여 보세요.

We are gonna get you some X-rays and see what's going on.
X-선 검사로 어떤 지 봐야 되겠습니다.

Leg X-rays are necessary.
다리 X-선 검사가 필요합니다.

We will know more when we have the X-rays.
X-ray가 나오면 더 잘 알 수 있을 것입니다.

They'll take you to X-ray.
그들이 당신을 방사선과로 데려갈 것입니다.

P : OK.
알겠습니다.

D : I have your result.
결과가 나왔습니다.

I am afraid you have a fracture.
이런 골절이 되었군요.

The X-ray shows that your tibia is broken.
엑스레이에서 경골이 골절되어 있습니다.

P : Oh my god.
이런.

D : Don't worry.
걱정하지 마세요.

Everything gonna be fine.
모든 것이 잘 될 것입니다.

We will have to admit you after dressing.
드레싱 후 입원을 시켜야 되겠습니다.

We are gonna get you up.
당신을 곧 설 수 있게 만들어 드리겠습니다.

P : Will I need to wear a cast?
석고 고정이 필요한가요?

D : The fracture should be immobilized with a splint.
골절부위는 부목으로 고정시켜주어야 합니다.

P : Do I need surgery?
수술이 필요합니까?

D : May be Yes.
아마도 그럴 것입니다.

Orthopaedic surgeon will make a decision for treatment method.
정형외과 의사가 치료 방법을 결정할 것입니다.

P : How long should I wear a cast?
얼마나 오랫동안 석고를 해야하죠?

D : About 3 or 4 months.
약 3 내지 4개월입니다.

P : When can I return to work?
언제쯤 일을 다시 할 수 있죠?

D : It depends on your condition.
당신의 상태에 따라 다릅니다.

I'll give you injection for the pain.
통증을 줄여줄 주사를 놔주겠습니다.

P : OK.
알겠습니다.

D : Give her 1 ampule of morphine right.
이 사람에게 몰핀 한 앰플을 놔주세요.

Notify the orthopaedics we have a tibia fracture.
경골골절 환자가 있다고 정형외과의사에게 알려주세요.

8) Angina Pectoris (협심증)

P : Doc. Is it all right to see you for a minute?
선생님. 잠깐 뵈어도 될까요?

D : No problem.
예 그러시죠.

P : Am I going to be all right?
제가 좋아질까요?

D : How are you feeling now?
지금은 어떻습니까?

P : I am feeling better.
좀 좋아졌습니다.

D : You are a little better than when you came to the ER.
응급실로 왔을 때보다는 더 좋아졌군요.

P : I think so.
저도 그렇게 생각합니다.

I collapsed in the waiting room.
저는 대기실에서 쓰러졌었어요.

Am I having a heart attack?
제가 심장 발작이었나요?

D : Yes. But EKG seems all right now.
예. 하지만 지금 심전도는 정상인 것 같군요.

P : My heart is beating a little bit fast.
심장이 약간 빠르게 뜁니다.

D : Your condition is stable, but you are not out of danger yet.
당신의 상태는 안정되었지만 아직 위험을 벗어난 것은 아닙니다.

You have to stay for observation.
관찰을 위해 이곳에 있어야 합니다.

P : I have mild chest discomfort.
가슴이 약간 거북합니다.

How is my heart doing?

제 심장이 어떻죠?

Am I going to get well?

제가 잘 회복되어가고 있나요?

D : Yes.

예.

P : Could you explain what's going on with me?

지금 제가 어떤 지 말해 줄래요.

This is not angina, is it?

이것은 협심증이 아니죠? 그렇죠?

D : Yes. This is angina.

아뇨. 이것은 협심증입니다.

P : Oh, that can be bad.

오, 나쁜 것이겠군요.

I could have a heart attack again.

다시 심장 발작이 올 수도 있겠군요.

D : Yes, you could and that is what we would like to avoid.

그럴 수도 있습니다. 하지만 그것을 피하는 것이 우리들의 목적이죠.

Don't worry.

걱정하지 마세요.

Everything will be fine.

모든 것이 좋아질 것입니다.

P : I have been here for hours now.
지금까지 몇 시간이나 이곳에 있었습니다.

Can I go to home?
집에 갈 수 있나요?

D : Not until the attending cardiologist gives the okay.
심장 전문의가 허락할 때까지는 안됩니다.

We need to keep you here for a while and run some tests.
잠시 이곳에 있으며 몇 가지 검사가 필요합니다.

We called cardiology.
심장 전문의를 불렀습니다.

We need to get a consult.
전문의의 진찰이 필요합니다.

9) Gastric lavage (위 세척)

D : What did you take?
무엇을 먹었죠?

Can you hear me?
제 말이 들리나요?

How much did you take?
얼마나 먹었죠?

When did you take it?
언제 먹었어요?

Please tell me.
말해주세요.

N : Vitals are normal.
활력징후는 정상입니다.

D : Are you her mother?
그녀의 어머니 되나요?

P : Yes.
예.

D : We have to pump her stomach.
그녀의 위를 세척해야 합니다.

Did you see any pill bottle?
약병을 보았나요?

P : No.
아닙니다.

D : OK. We're gonna clean out her stomach.
알겠습니다. 그녀의 위를 세척하겠습니다.

Set up for a gastric lavage.
위세척 준비를 해주세요.

Ewald tube, saline 3 liters, charcoal.
튜브와 식염수 3리터, 숯을 주세요.

Roll on your side.
옆으로 누우세요.

Can you hear me?
제 말 들리세요?

We're gonna put this tube into your stomach.
이 튜브를 당신의 위에 넣을 것입니다.

We're gonna clean it up with saline.
식염수로 씻을 것입니다.

It's not pleasant.
불편할 것입니다.

Just keep breathing.
숨을 계속 쉬세요.

We have washed all the medicine out.
약을 다 씻어 냈습니다.

We're putting charcoal in her stomach to absorb what's left.
남은 것들을 흡수시키기 위해 챠콜을 넣을 것입니다.

10) Hemothorax (혈흉)

P : I can't breathe too well.
숨을 잘 쉴 수가 없습니다.

D : Take it easy.
진정하세요.

You're gonna be okay.
곧 좋아질 것입니다.

N : He is hyperventilating, shortness of breath.
숨을 가쁘게 쉬는군요.

D : No breath sounds on the right side.
오른쪽에 호흡음이 없군요.

Give him the O_2 at 2 liters.
산소 2리터를 주세요.

Start one liter of saline IV.
식염수 1리터를 IV 로 주세요.

Let's get an arterial blood gas.
동맥 혈액 가스 검사를 합시다.

I wanna chest X-ray.
흉부 사진을 찍어주세요.

Let's send him to radiology.
방사선과로 보내주세요.

N : X-rays are back.
필름이 나왔습니다.

D : You have got a hemothorax.
혈흉이 있군요.

We have to drain the blood through chest tube.
흉부 튜브를 통해 피를 바깥으로 빼주어야 합니다.

Set up a chest tube tray.
흉관삽관 준비를 해주세요.

P : Why don't you put me to sleep?
왜 잠을 재워주지 않죠?

D : Putting you to sleep is not as easy as you think.
잠재우는 것이 당신이 생각하는 것만큼 쉽지 않습니다.

Anesthesia always caries a risk.
마취는 항상 위험이 따릅니다.

There is no risk in this procedure.
이것은 위험이 없는 것입니다.

Don't worry. Everything will be all right.
걱정마세요. 모든 것이 잘 될 것입니다.

P : OK.
알겠습니다.

D : Number 32 french tube. Curved kelly.
32번 튜브와 커브드 캘리 주세요.

I'm in. It's draining.
안으로 들어갔군요. 나오는군요.

Do you feel much better?
좀 더 나은가요?

11) Asthma (천식)

N : Asthma attack.
천식 발작입니다.

D : He is cyanotic.
창백하군요.

Let's get a pulse oximeter.
펄스 옥시미터를 설치해 주세요.

Let's start the O$_2$ at 2 liters.
O$_2$ 2리터를 주세요.

Set up a nebulizer.
분무기 준비해 주세요.

N : OK.
알겠습니다.

D : What's the pulse oximeter?
펄스 옥시미터가 얼마죠?

N : 85.
85입니다.

D : Turn up the O$_2$, 4 liters.
산소를 4 리터로 올리세요.

I need you to take a deep breath on nebulizer.
분무기에 대고 깊게 숨을 들이키세요.

This gonna help you breathe.
이것이 숨을 쉬게끔 도와 줄 것입니다.

How is his pressure?
혈압이 얼마죠?

N : BP is 130 over 90.
혈압은 130에 90입니다.

D : Put him on a heart monitor and let's check a rhythm.
심장 모니터를 연결해 리듬을 체크합시다.

12) Pulled elbow (주관절 아탈구)

D : I'm sorry you had to wait so long.
오래 기다리게 해서 죄송합니다.

P : My son doesn't use his arm.
아들이 손을 쓰지 않습니다.

D : Has it happened before?
전에도 이런 적이 있나요?

P : No.
없습니다.

N : Here are the X-rays.
여기 **X-ray**가 있습니다.

D : X-ray shows nothing wrong.
X-선 검사는 이상이 없습니다.

One of the ligaments in elbow slipped out of place.
팔꿈치에 있는 인대 하나가 비끌린 것입니다.

I'm gonna fix it.
바로 치료해 드리겠습니다.

It'll only hurt for a second.
순간만 아플 뿐입니다.

OK. We are done.
됐습니다.

I'll give your child an arm sling.
팔걸이를 아이에게 주겠습니다.

Keep it for a couple of days.
며칠 동안 채우세요.

P : Will he be all right?
괜찮아질까요?

D : Come back to me if your child still has pain after 24 hours.
24시간이 지나도 아파하면 저에게 다시 오세요.

Don't pull your child by the hand.
아이 손을 잡아당기지 마세요.

13) Cerebral contusion (뇌좌상)

P : High speed collision.
빠른 속도에서 부딪혔습니다.

He was thrown from the vehicle.
그는 차 밖으로 나뒹굴었어요.

How is he?
그가 어떤가요?

D : He has a severe cerebral contusion and some brain swelling.
그는 심한 뇌좌상을 가지고 있고, 뇌가 부어있습니다.

P : Is he gonna be okay?
그가 좋아질까요?

D : We don't know yet.
아직 모릅니다.

P : He was in perfect health.
그는 아주 건강했습니다.

D : We have to wait and see how much he wakes up.
그가 얼마나 깨어날지 기다려야 합니다.

It's premature to discuss his condition before we have seen
follow up CT.
추시된 CT를 보기 전에는 미리 판단할 수 없군요.

We did everything we could.
우리가 할 수 있는 것은 다했습니다.

We'll just keep our eye on him.
우리는 단지 그를 지켜 볼 뿐입니다.

And we have to hold him here until there is a bed in the ICU.
그리고 중환자실에 침대가 날 때까지 이곳에서 기다려야 합니다.

P : OK.
알겠습니다.

D : How much IV fluid has he had over the last 12 hours?
12시간 동안 얼마나 많은 수액이 들어갔지요?

N : It's been about 1.2 liters of saline.
거의 1.2리터 식염수가 들어갔습니다.

D : What are his input's and output's exactly?
들어가고 나간 게 정확히 얼마나 되죠?

N : It's all here on the input-output sheet.
이 기록지에 있습니다.

1200cc's in, 500cc's out.
1200cc가 들어가고 500cc가 나왔습니다.

14) 응급 전화상담

(1) Situation (상황)

What's your emergency?
어떤 응급상황입니까?

Is the patient breathing?
환자가 숨을 쉬나요?

Does the patient have a pulse?
맥이 뛰나요?

Please check the patient's pulse on the side of the neck.
목옆에서 맥박을 체크해보세요.

Calm down.
진정하세요.

Please tell me your address.
주소를 말해주세요.

Call 119 for help.
119에 도움을 청하세요.

We are gonna send ambulance.
앰블런스를 보내드리겠습니다.

Can you tell me your phone number?
전화번호를 말해줄래요?

(2) Shock (쇼크)

Keep him warm and elevate the feet
환자를 따뜻하게 해주고, 다리를 올려주세요.

Open his airway by tilting the head back and moving the chin
  forward.
환자의 목을 젖히고 턱을 앞으로 내밀어 기도를 확보하세요.

A person who has a pulse but isn't breathing needs rescue
  breathing.
맥박은 뛰는데 호흡이 없으면 호흡을 도와주는 것이 필요합니다.

Pinch his nose closed and place your mouth over his mouth.
Slowly breathe two full breaths and repeat every 5 seconds until
  119 arrives.
환자의 코를 막고 입과 입을 통해 큰 숨을 두 번 불어넣고, 119가 도착할 때
  까지 5초 간격으로 해 주세요.

(3) Bleeding (출혈)

Apply direct pressure to the wound for several minutes.
상처 부위를 수분간 눌러 주세요.

Tie the wound with any bandage.
어떤 붕대로 묶어주세요.

Get to the nearest hospital as fast as you can.
될 수 있는 한 빨리 가장 가까운 병원으로 가세요.

(4) Choking (질식)

Stand behind your child and wrap your arms around child's waist.
어린이 뒤에 서서 당신 팔로 어린이의 허리를 감으세요.

After making the tight fist with two hands, press your fist into her abdomen with quick inward and upward thrusts.
두 손으로 주먹을 만들어 복부에 대고, 안쪽 위로 미세요.

(5) Anaphylaxis (과민반응)

Allergic reaction to food or insect bite can lead to breathing difficulty.
음식이나 곤충에 물린 후 과민반응은 호흡장애를 일으킬 수 있습니다.

Anaphylaxis is a life threatening emergency.
과민반응은 생명이 위험한 응급상황입니다.

Take an antihistamine medicine.
항히스타민제를 복용하세요.

Call 119 for help.
119에 도움을 요청하세요.

(6) Burn (화상)

Cool the burn area right away with cool water.
찬 물로 화상 부위를 즉시 차갑게 하세요.

Don't apply ice.
얼음을 대지 마세요.

Don't use oil.

기름을 바르지 마세요.

Keep the area uncovered and elevated.

감지말고 높이 올려주세요.

If it's necessary to bandage the affected area, use a single layer of loose gauze that does not stick to the skin.

만약 붕대로 감아야 한다면, 피부에 붙지 않게 거즈 한 장만 사용하세요.

Don't break any blister that may form.

물집이 생기면 트지 마세요.

(7) Heat stroke (열사병)

Drink lots of liquids to replace the fluids lost through sweating.

땀을 흘려 잃은 수분을 보충하기 위해 많은 양의 물을 먹이세요.

Don't drink caffeinated liquids or alcohol.

카페인이 든 물이나 알코올은 먹지 마세요.

Cool off by opening windows, using fans.

창문을 열거나 선풍기로 시원하게 하세요.

Wear protective clothing such as light, loose-fitting clothes that will shield body from the direct sun.

햇빛으로부터 보호해 줄 가볍고 느슨한 옷을 입으세요.

15) Report (보고) - Case

Case 1.

A patient with a nearly severed leg resulting from a car accident was being transferred in from local hospital.

자동차 사고로 다리에 심한 부상을 입은 환자가 로컬 병원에서 전원 되어 왔습니다.

She was thirty-five years old, was speaking normally, and looked quite pale.

그녀는 35세인데, 말을 정상적으로 하였고, 얼굴은 창백했습니다.

Her right leg was splinted and her right hand was bandaged.

그녀의 다리는 부목 고정이 되어 있었고, 우측 손에 붕대가 감겨져 있었습니다.

Right hand needed some stitches.

우측 손은 봉합술이 필요했습니다.

The right leg above the injury was severely swollen and it looked deformed.

손상을 받은 우측 다리는 심하게 부어있었고, 변형되어 있는 것처럼 보였습니다.

The color of the leg was mild reddish and there were several bullaes.

다리 색깔은 약간 붉은 색이었고, 물집이 몇 군데 생겨있었습니다.

I checked pulses and found it on the foot dorsum.

맥박을 재어보니 발등에서 느껴졌습니다.

He wiggled her toes and felt normal sensation.

그녀는 발가락을 움직였고 정상 감각이었습니다.

X-ray showed her tibia was broken.

X-ray에서 그녀의 경골이 골절되어 있었습니다.

We immobilized with a long leg splint after manipulative reduction.

도수 정복술후 장하지 석고고정을 시행하였습니다.

Case 2.

An young woman came to the emergency department with a complain of dizziness.

젊은 여자가 어지러움을 주소로 응급실로 내원하였습니다.

She reported no other medical problems.

특별한 의학적인 문제는 없다고 말했습니다.

She missed recent her periods.

그녀는 최근에 생리가 없었습니다.

I worried about pregnancy or other disease.

저는 임신과 다른 질병에 대해 걱정하였습니다.

I did a physical examination and all this was normal.

이학적 검사를 하였는데 모든 것이 정상이었습니다.

She had a temperature of 37 degrees.

그녀의 체온은 37도였습니다.

A chest X-ray and electrocardiogram were normal.

흉부 X-ray 사진과 심전도는 정상이었습니다.

I sent off a serum pregnancy test and checked complete blood cell count.

임신반응 검사를 시행하고 CBC를 검사했습니다.

The pregnancy test came back negative.

임신 테스트는 정상이었습니다.

Laboratory studies showed that red, white cells and platelet count were extremely low, which is suggestive of aplastic anemia.

혈액 검사에서 적혈구 백혈구, 혈소판이 아주 낮아 재생불량성 빈혈 가능성이 있습니다.

The patient has not been hospitalized until the present admission.

환자는 이번 입원말고는 병원에 입원한 적은 없습니다.

I admitted her to hematology for further evaluation.

추가 검사를 위해 그녀를 혈액 내과에 입원시켰습니다.

Case 3.

Patient was experiencing pain in the left lower extremity.

환자가 좌측하지의 통증을 호소하였습니다.

Patient's calf was found to be tender and 5 centimeters larger than the unaffected side.

환자의 다리는 통증이 있고 정상 측보다 5cm 더 커져있었습니다.

Recent history showed that he had a short leg cast for 2 months due to ankle fracture.

최근 병력은 족관절 골절로 3달간 단하지 석고고정을 했었습니다.

The patient was treated by a local doctor.

환자는 개인병원 의사에게 치료를 받았습니다.

Differential diagnosis includes deep vein thrombosis and cellulitis.

감별한 진단은 심부 정맥 혈전증과 봉와직염입니다.

We consulted him to vascular surgery.

혈관외과에 진료를 의뢰하였습니다.

Case 4.

50-year-old drunken man was brought to the ER for shortness of breath.

50세 술에 취한 남자가 호흡곤란으로 응급실로 왔습니다.

His vitals were stable.

그의 활력 징후는 안정적이었습니다.

But he could barely answer questions.

하지만 그는 질문에 거의 대답을 하지 못했습니다.

He had a history of alcoholism.

그는 알코올리즘 병력이 있습니다.

Physical examination showed no wound.

이학적 검사에서 상처는 없었습니다.

Breath sounds were wheezing.

호흡음은 색색거렸습니다.

Reviewing his chest X-ray, we noticed a round density in the right chest.

흉부 X-ray에서 둥근 음영을 발견하였습니다.

I called pnematology.

호흡기내과를 불렀습니다.

Case 5.

12-year-old boy was brought in with a head injury sustained in a car accident.

12세 소년이 교통사고로 머리에 손상을 입고 왔습니다.

After repeated seizure, he was unconscious.

그는 몇 번의 경련 후 의식을 잃었습니다.

On physical examination it is discovered that his scalp had deep laceration.

이학적 검사상 그의 두피가 깊게 찢어져 있었습니다.

I did a neurological examination, testing his pupils and then his reflexes.

그의 동공과 신경반응 검사를 시행했습니다.

No abnormal signs.

이상 징후는 없었습니다.

Skull radiographs revealed a fracture of skull.

X-ray에서 두개골 골절이 보였습니다.

We did a brain CT to make confirmation of brain injury.

뇌손상을 확인하기 위해 뇌 CT 촬영을 하였습니다.

CT showed an acute epidural hematoma.

CT에서 급성 경막외 출혈이 보였습니다.

Neurosurgery had performed emergency operation.

신경외과에서 응급수술을 시행하였습니다.

Case 6.

19-year-old boy came to ER.
19세 소년이 응급실로 왔습니다.

Symptoms showed 2 days history of nausea, vomiting and abdominal pain.
증상은 2일간의 오심, 구토와 복통이었습니다.

The pain occurred in the night, and awaken from his sleep.
통증은 밤에 와서 잠을 자주 깨곤 했습니다.

The duration of the pain was said to be variable.
통증 기간은 다양했다고 합니다.

There is no history of hematoemesis or melena.
피를 토하거나 혈변을 눈 적은 없었습니다.

I gave him an antacid and drugs that block acid production.
제산제와 위산억제제를 처방했습니다.

Case 7.

27-year-old young male patient was brought to ER.
27세 남자가 응급실로 데려와졌습니다.

He experienced sudden pain in right lower quadrant abdomen.
그는 우측 하복부에 갑자스러운 통증을 호소하였습니다.

He vomited two times.
그는 2차례 토했습니다.

A diagnosis of acute appendicitis was made.
급성 충수염으로 진단되었습니다.

Emergency surgery was performed immediately.

응급수술이 바로 시행되었습니다.

Case 8.

The ambulance transported 76-year-old woman to our ER.

앰블런스가 76세 할머니를 응급실로 데려왔습니다.

She suffered a full cardiac arrest at home.

그녀는 집에서 심장마비가 있었습니다.

Her heart monitor showed no rhythm.

EKG에서는 심박동이 없었습니다.

We did the CPR for 20 minutes.

우리는 20분간 심폐소생술을 시행하였습니다.

We were unable to resuscitate her.

그녀를 되살릴 수 없었습니다.

We pronounced her dead and told her family of her death.

우리는 사망을 확인하고 그녀의 가족들에게 그녀의 죽음을 말했습니다.

3 *Internal Medicine*
(내과)

1) Common Cold, Flu (감기, 독감)

(1) 기본적인 질문

Do you have a fever or chill?
열이나 오한은 없으세요?

Do you have a headache or general aches?
두통이나 몸이 아프지는 않나요?

Do you have a sore throat?
목이 아프세요?

Do you have a cough, sneezing or runny nose?
기침이나 콧물이 나오지는 않으세요?

How long have you had cough?
기침이 얼마나 되었지요?

When did your cough begin?
언제 기침이 시작되었죠?

When do you get cough?
언제 기침을 하지요?

Do you cough up phlegm?
Have you been coughing anything up?
가래가 나오나요?

Does your cough produce yellow or red mucus?
기침에서 노랗거나 붉은 가래가 나오지는 않던가요?

Are you coughing up blood?
기침에 피가 나오지는 않던가요?

Have you ever coughed up blood or bloody sputum?
피가 섞인 가래를 뱉은 적이 있나요?

Do you have any difficulty with your breathing?
숨을 쉬는데 불편하지는 않나요?

Could you have been exposed to tuberculosis?
결핵에 노출된 적은 없나요?

Does anyone else in your family have this cough?
당신 가족 중에 이런 기침을 하는 사람이 있습니까?

(2) 기본적인 설명

You may have got the flu.
You have probably got the flu.
독감에 걸리신 것 같군요.

The first signs of a cold or the flu may appear about one to four
days after the virus has entered the body.
감기나 독감의 첫 증상은 바이러스가 몸에 들어온 지 하루 내지 4일째 나타
납니다.

The flu usually lasts about one week.

독감은 보통 일주일 정도 지속됩니다.

Most people start to feel better after a few days.

대부분의 사람들은 며칠 지나면 좋아지기 시작합니다.

Get adequate rest and plenty of sleep.

충분한 휴식을 취하고 잠을 많이 자세요.

Drink plenty of fluids.

물을 많이 마시세요.

Get plenty of vitamin C and healthy food.

비타민 C와 몸에 좋은 음식을 드세요.

Take a hot shower and use a humidifier.

따뜻한 목욕을 하고 가습기를 사용하세요.

Humidifier will make it easier for you to breathe and relieve cough.

가습기는 숨쉬기 편하게 해주고, 기침을 줄여 줄 것입니다.

Gargling may help relieve your sore throat.

가글링은 편도선이 아픈 것을 줄여 줄 것입니다.

You can try some immune boosting herbal such as Ginseng, Ginger tea, Royal jelly.

당신은 면역력을 높여주는 인삼이나, 생강 차, 로열젤리와 같은 식품 등을 먹어도 좋습니다.

I will prescribe the medicine that may shorten the symptoms of the flu.

독감 증상들을 줄여 줄 약을 처방해 드리겠습니다.

Antibiotics are no help against the flu.

항생제는 독감에 별 도움이 안됩니다.

I will prescribe some medicine to help you stop coughing and sneezing.

기침과 콧물이 멈추도록 약을 처방해 드리겠습니다.

Prevent the flu with a flu shot in November each year.

매년 11월에 독감 예방 주사를 맞아 독감을 예방하세요.

People over 65 and others suffering from illnesses such as respiratory diseases and diabetes are urged to take vaccine shots.

65세가 넘은 노인, 또는 호흡기 질환이나 당뇨병을 앓고있는 사람들은 백신 주사를 맞는 것이 좋습니다.

A yearly flu shot is recommended for you.

당신은 매 년 독감 예방 주사를 맞아야 합니다.

It will take up to four weeks for the vaccine to become effective.

백신이 효과가 있으려면 길게는 4주정도 걸립니다.

Some of the complications caused by flu include bacterial pneumonia, dehydration, and worsening of chronic medical conditions.

독감의 합병증으로 세균성 폐렴이나 탈수증, 또는 만성적인 질환이 악화될 수 있습니다.

(3) Dialogue

D : What is your main complaint?

　　주 증상이 무엇이지요?

P : I have a mild fever and a runny nose.
열이 나며 콧물이 납니다.

D : Do you have a chills?
오한도 느끼나요?

P : Sometimes I feel.
가끔씩 느낍니다.

D : Do you have a cough?
기침이 나오십니까?

P : I have been coughing for 3 days.
3일 동안 기침을 했습니다.

D : Do you cough up phlegm?
가래가 나오나요?

P : Yes, my phlegm is yellowish color.
가래가 있는데 노랗습니다.

D : You may have the flu.
독감에 걸린 것 같군요.

Flu outbreak spreads across this country.
독감이 발생되어 이 나라 전역에 퍼졌습니다.

Emergency rooms have been filled with sick patients.
응급실은 아픈 환자들로 만원을 이루었습니다.

P : I have neck pain and it's painful when I swallow.
목이 아프고 삼킬 때는 아파요.

D : OK, I'll check your throat.
알겠습니다. 당신의 목을 검사해보겠습니다.

Let me take a look at your throat.

목안을 보여 주세요.

Please say ah- and stick out your tongue.

아- 하면서 혀를 내밀어 주세요.

I can see white patches on the edematous tonsils.

부은 편도선에 하얀색 반점이 있군요.

P : How long will it last?

얼마나 증상이 가죠?

D : The symptom usually lasts about several days.

증상은 보통 며칠 정도 지속됩니다.

I want you take these medicines.

이 약을 드시기 바랍니다.

Lots of fluid.

물을 많이 드세요.

Rest and follow up next.

쉬고 다음에 오세요.

2) Hypertension (고혈압)

(1) 기본적인 질문

Do you feel dizzy?
Do you ever become dizzy?

어지러움을 느낀 적이 있습니까?

Do you ever have palpitations?

Do you have episodes of palpitations?
가슴이 두근거린 적은 없나요?

Do you have any chest discomfort or chest pain?
가슴이 아프거나 답답하지는 않나요?

Do you have shortness of breath?
숨이 차지는 않습니까?

Have you ever fainted?
Do you ever feel fainting?
졸도한 적은 있나요?

Do you suffer from headache?
두통이 있나요?

Do you know the fact that you have hypertension?
당신이 고혈압을 가지고 있다는 사실을 알고 있나요?

When did you know that?
언제 그것을 알았죠?

Do you have a history of hypertension in your family?
가족 중에 고혈압이 있었던 적이 있나요?

Do you check your blood pressure regularly?
당신의 혈압을 규칙적으로 측정하고 있습니까?

(2) 기본적인 설명

Your blood pressure is 150 over 90.
당신의 혈압은 150에 90이군요.

A normal blood pressure is less than 130 over 85.

정상혈압은 130에 85이하입니다.

That is a high blood pressure.

고혈압입니다.

High blood pressure is when your blood pressure is 140 over 90 or higher.

고혈압은 혈압이 140에 90 이상일 때를 말합니다.

It could be a hypertension, but it's not typical.

고혈압일 수 있지만 전형적인 증상은 아닙니다.

High blood pressure damages blood vessels.

고혈압은 혈관을 손상시킵니다.

This raises your risk of stroke and heart attack.

고혈압은 뇌졸중과 심장질환의 위험을 높여줍니다.

Treatment for hypertension ranges from conservative lifestyle changes to aggressive medication.

혈압의 치료는 생활습관을 변화하는 것부터 적극적인 약물치료까지 있습니다.

Treatment begins with changes you can make in your life style to help lower your blood pressure, such as regular exercise and low salt diet.

치료는 먼저 자신의 생활 습관을 규칙적인 운동이나 저염식과 같은 혈압을 낮추는 습관으로 변화시켜야 합니다.

Exercise regularly.

규칙적으로 운동을 하세요.

Lose weight if you're overweight.
과체중이면 체중을 줄이세요.

Quit smoking and avoid alcohol.
담배를 끊고 술을 마시지 마세요.

Reduce personal stress and anger.
개인적인 스트레스와 화를 줄이세요.

Stress causes blood pressure to rise.
스트레스는 혈압을 올려줍니다.

Eat a diet low in salt and high in fiber.
저염식과 고섬유질 음식을 드세요.

Excess cholesterol causes the formation of fatty deposits along
artery walls.
과도한 콜레스테롤은 동맥에 지방을 침착 시킵니다.

Exercise controls cholesterol levels and obesity and also helps
lower blood pressure.
운동은 콜레스테롤 수치와 비만을 조절해 주고, 혈압을 낮추어 줍니다.

Diet low in total and saturated fat and rich in fruits, vegetables,
and low-fat dairy foods can significantly lower blood pressure.
지방이 적은 과일이나 야채, 우유 제품들은 의미있게 혈압을 낮추어줍니다.

If these changes don't work, you may also need to take
medicine.
만약 이렇게 습관을 변해도 효과가 없으면 약을 드셔야합니다.

If lifestyle modifications have no effect, antihypertensive drugs
may be added to the treatment plan.
만약 생활습관을 변화시켜도 효과가 없으면, 고혈압 약을 드셔야 합니다.

High blood pressure makes the heart work and pump harder.
고혈압은 심장의 일과 펌핑을 어렵게 만듭니다.

Keep a log and have your pressure checked on a regular basis.
혈압을 정기적으로 체크하고 기록하세요.

You should try to have more control over your blood pressure.
혈압을 조절하려고 더 노력해야 합니다.

(3) Dialogue

D : How have you been feeling?
　지금은 어떠십니까?

P : I am feeling under the weather.
　몸이 좋질 않아요.

D : What seems to be the trouble?
　무슨 문제 있으세요?

P : I feel fatigue and palpitation.
　피곤함과 두근거림을 느낍니다.

　I'd like to get my blood pressure checked.
　혈압을 재고 싶습니다.

D : OK. I'll check your blood pressure.
　알겠습니다. 당신의 혈압을 체크해 보겠습니다.

　Will you roll up your sleeve?
　소매를 올려 주실래요?

P : OK.
　알겠습니다.

D : It is 140 over 90.
   That is high for you.
   90에 140이네요.
   당신의 혈압은 높군요.

P : What is normal?
   어떤 게 정상이죠?

D : It should be more like 120 over 80.
   혈압은 120에서 80이 정상이에요.

   Has that been found before?
   전에도 혈압이 높았던 적이 있나요?

P : No. Is hypertension hereditary?
   아뇨. 혈압이 유전되나요?

D : Sometimes it is inherited.
   가끔씩 그것은 유전이 됩니다.

P : My mother has high blood pressure.
   어머니께서 고혈압이 있으세요.

D : Reduce your stress and eat a diet low in salt.
   스트레스를 줄이고 소금이 적은 음식을 드세요.

3) Diabetes (당뇨병)

(1) 기본적인 질문

Do you have diabetes?
당뇨병이 있나요?

Are you checking your blood sugar?
혈당을 체크하고 있습니까?

Do you have regular check-up for blood sugar?
혈당을 규칙적으로 측정하고 있나요?

What are your sugars in the morning?
아침에 혈당이 얼마였죠?

When did you get it?
언제 당뇨병에 걸렸죠?

Are you taking any tablet or insulin?
약을 먹거나 인슐린을 맞고있나요?

Do you take insulin?
인슐린을 맞고 있나요?

Have you been adjusting your insulin?
인슐린을 조절하고 있나요?

Have you been adjusting insulin when it goes high?
혈당이 높으면 인슐린을 조절하나요?

Are you taking your pills for your sugar?
혈당 조절을 위해 약을 복용하고 있나요?

Do you do anything when you have low sugars?
혈당이 낮을 때 어떻게 조치하시죠?

Do you have any tingling of the hands or feet?
손이나 발이 저리시지는 않습니까?

Do you have a history of diabetes in the family?
가족 중에 당뇨병이 있었던 적이 있나요?

Have you been drinking excessive fluids?

물을 많이 마시나요?

Are you trying to lose some weight?

체중을 줄이려고 노력하고 있나요?

(2) 기본적인 설명

I'm going to get some blood tests done to see what is causing the symptom.

증상의 원인이 무엇인지 알기 위해 혈액 검사를 하겠습니다.

Your sugars were high.

혈당이 높군요.

You may have diabetes, a metabolic condition in which your body lacks insulin and can't use sugar.

당신은 아마도 인슐린이 부족하고 당분을 조절하지 못하는 당뇨병인 것 같습니다.

Early symptoms of diabetes include extreme hunger, thurst, frequent urination, weight loss and unusual tiredness.

당뇨병 초기 증상은 심하게 배고프거나, 목마름, 소변을 자주 보는 것, 체중 감소, 이상한 피로감등입니다.

Diabetes tends to run in families.

당뇨병은 유전되는 경향이 있습니다.

Diabetes is a disease that occurs when your body doesn't make enough of a hormone, called insulin, or if your body doesn't use insulin the right way.

당뇨병은 당신의 몸에서 인슐린을 충분히 만들지 못하거나 인슐린을 정상적으로 사용하지 못해 생기는 병입니다.

Diabetes is a chronic disease characterized by having too much glucose in the blood because the body is not producing insulin or not using insulin properly.

당뇨병은 인슐린이 만들어지지 않거나 인슐린을 적절히 이용하지 못해 혈액 내에 포도당이 너무 많아지게 되는 만성질환입니다.

All over the world, people's lifestyles are changing and populations are aging.

전 세계적으로 사람들의 생활습관이 바뀌고 있으며 고령화되고 있습니다.

The number of diabetes cases could double in the next 30 years because of increasingly unhealthy diets and less exercise.

좋지 않은 음식과 운동부족으로 30년 안에 당뇨병이 2배 증가할 수 있습니다.

Some 90% of the world's estimated 170 million people with the disease have type 2 diabetes, which is associated with obesity and lack of exercise.

전 세계 1억 7천 만 명으로 추정되는 당뇨병환자의 90%가 비만이나 운동부족으로 인하여 생기는 2형 타입입니다.

At least one death in every 20 worldwide is due to diabetes.

최소한 세계적으로 20명중 1명이 당뇨병으로 죽고 있습니다.

If left untreated, it may result in blindness, heart attacks, strokes, kidney failures.

만약 치료를 하지 않으면, 시력을 잃거나 심장병, 뇌졸중, 신장병 등이 올 수 있습니다.

High blood sugar levels can damage the nerves and blood vessels in your body.

고혈당이 당신의 신경과 혈관에 손상을 줄 수 있습니다.

The goal of diabetes treatment is to keep your blood sugar level
as close to normal as possible.
당뇨병 치료의 목적은 혈당을 정상치에 가깝게 유지하는 것입니다.

Control of blood sugar is the mainstay of diabetic therapy.
혈당 조절이 당뇨병치료의 기본이죠.

Controlling blood sugar will help reduce the risk of
complications.
혈당 조절은 합병증을 줄여줍니다.

Keep your blood sugar level as close to normal as possible.
가능한 정상에 가깝게 혈당을 유지하세요.

Insulin is used to reduce the amount of sugar in your blood.
인슐린이 당신의 혈당을 줄여줄 것입니다.

I have seen the results of tests.
검사 결과를 보았습니다.

Look at your sugar today.
오늘의 혈당을 보세요.

We are going to have to increase your insulin to cover these high
sugars.
높은 혈당을 치료하기 위해 인슐린 양을 늘려야겠습니다.

You need to take a hypoglycemic medication.
혈당강하제를 복용할 필요가 있습니다.

You need to monitor your blood glucose regularly.
규칙적으로 혈당을 측정해야 합니다.

Use a home glucose testing kit.
집에서 쓰는 혈당 측정기 세트를 이용하세요.

You prick your finger with a lancet and place a drop of blood on a glucose meter.

손가락을 란셋으로 찔러 피 한 방울을 혈당 측정기에 올리세요.

The first step is to have a healthy diet and to excercise.

첫 번째 할 일이 건강식과 운동을 하는 것입니다.

These are the single most important things you can do.

이것들이 당신이 할 수 있는 가장 중요한 것들입니다.

You have to design a meal plan.

당신은 음식 계획을 세워야합니다.

Eat a variety healthy food and avoid foods that are high in fat and sugar.

건강에 좋은 음식을 먹고 지방이나 당분이 많은 음식은 피하세요.

You have to avoid any food containing too much cholesterol or fat.

당신은 콜레스테롤이나 지방이 많은 음식은 피하여야 합니다.

Healthy diabetes meal consists of 55% of calories from carbohydrates, 15% from protein and less than 30% from fat.

건강식은 탄수화물에서 55%, 단백질에서 15%, 지방에서 30% 이하의 칼로리를 섭취하는 것입니다.

You have to try to change your eating.

당신은 먹는 것을 변화시켜야 합니다.

Avoid butter, oils, fatty meats, fried foods.

버터나 기름, 지방이 많은 고기나 튀긴 음식을 피하세요.

Diet and exercise are of paramount importance.

다이어트와 운동이 아주 중요합니다.

Exercise regularly and quit smoking.
운동을 규칙적으로 하고 담배를 끊으세요.

Keep your feet healthy.
발을 건강하게 관리하세요.

Don't smoke and never drink alcohol.
담배를 피지말고 술을 마시지 마세요.

Have your eyes tested every year.
눈 검사를 매년 받으세요.

It smells like fruit.
과일향처럼 나는군요.

We have to run some tests.
몇 가지 검사를 해야합니다.

The patient has ketoacidosis.
환자는 케톤산 혈증을 가지고 있습니다.

It looks like diabetic coma.
당뇨병성 혼수인 것 같습니다.

Diabetic ketoacidosis is a state of insulin deficiency
  characterized by hyperglycemia with acidosis.
당뇨병성 케톤산 혈증은 산성과 함께 고혈당이 오는 상태입니다.

Treatment of ketoacidosis should aim at correcting dehydration,
  reversing the acidosis, reducing plasma glucose concentration
  to normal and replenishing electrolytes.
케톤산 혈증의 치료의 목표는 탈수를 교정하고 산증을 회복시키고 혈당을
  정상으로 만들고 전해질을 보충하는데 있습니다.

We'll give the patient saline and insulin first.
우리는 먼저 환자에게 식염수와 인슐린을 먼저 줄 것입니다.

We'll give him saline solution rapidly depending on the patient's
  vital signs.
환자의 활력 징후에 따라 식염수를 빠르게 줄 것입니다.

We'll check glucose and electrolytes every 2 hours.
우리는 혈당과 전해질들을 2시간 간격으로 체크할 것입니다.

Intubation should be considered for coma.
혼수상태인 경우 기관내 삽관이 고려되어야 합니다.

We'll insert nasogastric tube into stomach to prevent aspiration.
질식을 예방하기 위해 위에 튜브를 넣을 것입니다.

(3) Dialogue 1.

D : What can I do for you?
  어디가 불편하시죠?

P : I've been having a lot of pain.
  너무 많은 곳이 아픕니다.

D : Where exactly is it located? Show me where.
  정확히 어디가 아프시죠? 그곳을 가르쳐주세요.

P : I have pain all over my body.
  온 몸이 아픕니다.

D : OK. If you had to point to one place where it is worst, where
      would it be?
  알겠습니다. 만약 가장 아픈 곳을 한 곳 지정하라면 어디가 가장 아픕
      니까?

P : My feet and legs.
발과 다리가 아파요.

D : How long do your symptom last?
증상은 얼마나 지속되죠?

P : I get them all the time.
항상 가지고 있어요.

It never leaves, but sometimes it does seem worse.
통증이 절대 없어지지 않고, 가끔씩은 더 아픕니다.

D : Does anything special make it worse?
이것을 악화시킨 계기가 있습니까?

P : No. but I am diabetic.
아닙니다. 하지만 전 당뇨병 환자입니다.

D : When did you get it?
언제 당뇨병에 걸렸죠?

P : That was about 4 years ago.
4년 전입니다.

D : Who is your diabetes Doctor?
당뇨병을 관리해 주는 의사가 있나요?

P : Internist Dr. Kim has been treating me.
내과의사인 닥터 김이 계속 치료를 해 주고 있어요.

D : Do you have regular check-up for blood sugar?
혈당을 규칙적으로 측정하고 있나요?

P : Yes. I think it came on when I came back from my vacation.
예. 저는 이 증상이 제가 휴가를 갔다 온 다음부터 왔다고 생각합니다.

D : Do you take insulin?
　인슐린을 맞고 있나요?

P : I usually take 12 units.
　항상 인슐린 12 유닛을 맞고 있습니다.

D : Diabetic neuropathy most often affects the feet and legs.
　당뇨병성 신경염은 다리와 발을 자주 침범합니다.

　This can cause diminished sensation and changed feeling in
　the feet.
　이것은 다리의 감각을 감소시키고 느낌을 변화시키기도 합니다.

P : Can diabetes be treated?
　당뇨병은 치료가 되는 건가요?

D : Diabetes can't be cured, but it can be controlled.
　당뇨병은 치료가 되지는 않습니다. 하지만 조절은 됩니다.

　Did pain-killers help you?
　진통제들이 도움이 되던가요?

P : Sometimes Tylenol can help.
　가끔씩 타이레놀이 도움이 됩니다.

D : I just need you to go to the lab for a blood test to see how
　well your sugar has been controlled for the last 3 months.
　당신의 혈당이 최근 3개월 간 얼마나 잘 조절되고 있는지 검사실에 가서
　혈액 검사를 해 보아야 될 것 같군요.

P : OK.
　알겠습니다.

D : Your level of glycosylated hemoglobin should be a level less than eight.

당신의 혈당 혈색소 치는 8 이하여야 합니다.

(4) Dialogue 2.

D : You should try to do at least a little bit of exercise every day.

당신은 매일 조금씩 운동을 해야 할 것 같군요.

P : How can exercise help my diabetes?

운동이 어떻게 당뇨병에 도움을 주지요?

D : Exercise can help control your weight and lower your blood sugar level.

운동은 당신의 몸무게를 조절해 주고 혈당도 줄여줍니다.

It also lowers your risk of heart disease and help you feel better about yourself.

그리고 심장병 위험을 줄여주고 당신의 기분을 좀 더 좋게 만들어 줄 것입니다.

P : What kind of exercise should I do?

어떤 운동을 해야 하지요?

D : I recommend aerobic excercise, which makes you breathe more deeply and make your heart work harder.

유산소 운동은 호흡을 더 깊게 할 수 있게 해주고, 심장 운동을 더 튼튼하게 해주어 권유합니다.

Examples of aerobic exercise include walking, jogging, bicycling or dance.

유산소 운동은 예로써 걷기, 조깅, 자전거 타기, 춤 등입니다.

P : Are there any risks to exercising for people with diabetes?
운동하는 당뇨병 환자들에게 위험도 있나요?

D : Yes. Exercise change the way of your body reacts to insulin.
예. 운동은 당신의 몸이 인슐린에 반응하는 것을 변화시켜 줍니다.

Regular exercise makes your body more sensitive to insulin, and your blood sugar level get to low after exercising.
규칙적인 운동은 당신의 몸을 인슐린에 잘 반응하게 만들어주고, 운동 후 혈당이 떨어지게 만듭니다.

You may need to check your blood sugar level before and after excercise.
당신은 운동 전후로 혈당을 체크하는 것이 좋습니다.

P : How will I know if my blood sugar is too low while I'm exercising?
혈당이 떨어지는 것을 어떻게 알죠?

D : You may feel a change in your heartbeat, suddenly sweat more and dizzy.
당신은 심장 박동이 변화가 오고 갑자기 땀을 많이 흘리고 어지러울 것입니다.

When you feel this way, you should stop exercising and eat candy or chocolate.
이런 증상이 있으면 즉시 운동을 중단하고 캔디나 초콜릿을 먹으세요.

P : Okay, I will try to excercise regularly.
알겠습니다. 운동을 규칙적으로 하도록 노력하겠습니다.

By the way, scar was formed in my injection sites.
그런데 주사 맞는 자리에 흉터가 났어요.

D : To minimize scar forming, rotate injection sites when taking
insulin.

흉터를 줄이려면 인슐린을 놓을 때 자리를 돌려가며 놓으세요.

P : How can I trim my toenails?

발톱은 어떻게 손질하죠?

D : Don't trim toenails too short.

너무 짧게 깍지 마세요.

4) Heart (심장)

(1) 기본적인 질문

Do you get pain in your chest?

가슴이 아픕니까?

Do you ever get chest pain?
Do you ever feel chest discomfort?

가슴 통증이 있었던 적이 있습니까?

Do you have a history of cardiac trouble?
Have you ever had heart problems?
Have you ever had a heart attack?

심장에 문제가 있었던 적이 있었나요?

Do you have chest pain or any chest discomfort?
Do you have pressure in your chest?
Do you ever feel tightness in chest?
Do you feel any discomfort in chest?

가슴이 아프거나 답답하지는 않나요?

Have you ever felt your heart fluttering very quickly?

심장이 빨리 두근거린 적이 없나요?

Does the pain move around?
Does the pain spread anywhere?
Does the pain go anywhere else?

통증이 주위로 퍼져가나요?

Do you feel any discomfort in other area?

다른 곳에 불편감은 없나요?

Do you have any episode of pressure under the chest by cold air, activity?

찬 공기나 운동 후 가슴 아래에 통증이 있었던 적이 있나요?

Tell me about your chest pain and how it began?

저에게 가슴 통증과 그것이 어떻게 시작되었는지 말씀해 주실래요?

Does the chest pain appear to be brought on by anything in particular?

가슴 통증이 일어난 특별한 이유가 있나요?

Does the pain occur more commonly when you are exercising?

운동할 때 통증이 더 잘 일어나던가요?

How do you feel your pain?

통증의 느낌이 어떻던가요?

Could you describe your pain?
Can I get you to describe the character of the pain?

통증이 어떤지 설명해 주실래요?

Could you remind me what else you notice when you get pain?

통증이 있을 때 주의할 만한 일이 있었나요?

What about your breathing when you have the pain?
통증이 있을 때 숨쉬는 것은 어떠했나요?

Do you ever have palpitations?
Do you have episodes of palpitations.
가슴이 두근거린 적은 없나요?

Do you have shortness of breath?
Are you troubled by shortness of breath?
숨이 차지는 않습니까?

Have you ever fainted?
Do you ever feel fainting?
졸도한 적은 있나요?

Have you ever had rheumatic fever?
류마티스열을 앓은 적은 없습니까?

Did you ever had an electrocardiogram?
심전도 검사를 받은 적이 있습니까?

Have you recently had an echocardiogram?
최근에 심장 초음파 검사를 하셨나요?

(2) Angina Pectoris (협심증)

I suspect this may be a heart problem.
심장에서 오는 문제인 것 같이 의심되는군요.

Your pain may be from a heart disease called angina.
당신의 통증은 협심증이라는 심장질환 같습니다.

Electrocardiograms seems to be normal in the first few hours after onset.
증상이 발생한 후 몇 시간은 심전도가 비교적 정상인 것 같습니다.

I think your problem is due to angina pectoris.
당신의 증상이 협심증으로 생각되는군요.

Your chest pain is coming from poor blood supply to the heart.
당신의 가슴 통증은 심장으로 혈액공급이 잘 안되어 생긴 것입니다.

It occurs when part of the heart does not receive enough oxygen due to disease in the coronary arteries that supply blood to the heart.
그것은 심장으로 혈액을 보내주는 관상동맥에 병이 생겨 심장이 충분한 산소를 받지 못할 때 생깁니다.

Typical angina pectoris is induced by exercise and emotional stress.
전형적인 협심증은 운동이나 스트레스와 같은 감정 때문에 옵니다.

I'll give you nitroglycerin sublingually.
당신에게 니트로 글리세린을 혀 밑에 주겠습니다.

I want you have a 12-lead EKG, Chest X-ray, CBC, Chemistry, Cardiac enzymes.
심전도, 흉부 사진과 혈액 검사들을 하겠습니다.

I want to rule out myocardial infarction.
심근 경색증 여부를 검사해야겠습니다.

I need to do some further testing.
조금 더 검사가 필요합니다.

Some tests are necessary to you for detecting any problem.
이상 유무를 알기 위해 몇 가지 검사가 필요 할 것 같군요.

Diagnosis can be established through a stress test, that is EKG
  monitoring in combination with excercise.
진단은 운동을 하며 심전도를 보는 스트레스 검사로 할 수 있습니다.

Angina must be treated under doctor's care.
협심증은 반드시 의사들에게 치료를 받아야합니다.

Don't smoke and drink moderately.
담배를 피우지 마시고 술은 적당히 드세요.

Eat a balanced, very low sodium diet.
균형식과 저염식을 드세요.

Lose weight if necessary.
필요하면 체중을 줄이세요.

Control your blood pressure and cholesterol.
혈압과 콜레스테롤을 조절하세요.

Exercise and relax yourself.
운동을 하시고 항상 자신을 편안하게 하세요.

Manage your anger.
화를 조절하세요.

Have your blood pressure monitored regularly.
혈압을 규칙적으로 체크하세요.

A healthy lifestyle will improve your heart's condition.
건강한 생활이 심장의 상태를 좋게 만들 것입니다.

You may need medication, especially if you have chest pain or if you have blood pressure or high blood cholesterol that was not lowered enough with lifestyle changes.

만약 생활 습관을 바꾸더라도 가슴에 통증이 있거나, 혈압이 떨어지지 않거나, 콜레스테롤이 높으면, 약을 드셔야 합니다.

Aspirin helps prevent heart attacks when taken regularly in a low dose.

적은 용량의 아스피린은 심장 발작의 위험을 예방해 줍니다.

Angina decreases with rest or removing emotional stress and also relieved by coronary vasodilator drugs such as nitroglycerin.

협심증은 쉬거나 스트레스를 없애면 증상이 줄어들고, 니트로 글리세린과 같은 혈관 확장제로 좋아질 수 있습니다.

I will prescribe you.

처방을 해 드리겠습니다.

(3) Myocardial Infarction (심근 경색증)

We need to get an echo of your heart.
We need to do echocardiogarm.
You need to have echocardiogram.

심장초음파 검사가 필요합니다.

Most heart attacks start slowly, with mild pain or discomfort.

대부분의 심장 발작은 천천히 가벼운 통증으로 시작됩니다.

We have some serious matters to discuss regarding your heart.

당신의 심장에 대해 상의할 중요한 문제가 있습니다.

I am afraid heart problem is more serious than we first thought.

심장병이 처음에 우리가 생각했던 것보다 더 심각합니다.

Cardiac arrest strikes immediately and without warning.
심장마비는 갑자기 발생됩니다.

Now the electrocardiogram demonstrates severe condition.
지금 심전도는 나쁜 상태를 보이고 있습니다.

You suffer from acute myocardial infarction.
당신은 급성 심근 경색증을 앓고 있습니다.

Acute myocardial infarction is more dangerous than angina
  pectoris.
급성 심근 경색증은 협심증보다 더 심각합니다.

It is usually caused by coronary artery atherosclerosis.
그것은 관상동맥의 동맥경화증 때문에 옵니다.

I can't let this go on any longer.
더 놔두면 안될 것 같아요.

Without proper treatments, this can lead to complications.
적절한 치료를 하지 않으면 심각해 질 수 있습니다.

Pain of myocardial infarction is not alleviated by rest or by
  nitroglycerin.
심근 경색증은 쉬거나 니트로 글리세린을 투여해도 통증이 줄어들지 않습
  니다.

Chest pain will be treated with opiates, such as intravenous
  morphine.
흉통은 몰핀과 같은 마약을 정맥 내로 투여하여 치료할 것입니다.

Also oxygen will be administered by face mask.
산소 역시 안면 마스크를 통해 투여될 것입니다.

Control of pain will reduce oxygen consumption.
통증을 줄이면 산소 소모량이 줄어들 것입니다.

You should be admitted to a coronary care unit.
당신은 심장질환 중환자실에 입원해야만 합니다.

Complete bed rest is recommended.
절대적인 침상안정이 필요합니다.

You may need a coronary angioplasty to improve blood flow.
혈액흐름을 증가시키기 위해 혈관성형술이 필요합니다.

A fine tube is threaded through an artery to the narrowed heart vessel, where a tiny balloon at its tip is inflated to improve blood flow.
작은 튜브가 좁아진 혈관을 통해 들어가 혈액 흐름을 좋게 하기 위해 끝을 부풀릴 것입니다.

Coronary artery bypass graft surgery is needed.
관상동맥 우회 이식술이 필요합니다.

Bypass graft surgery is done when the blockages in an artery can't be reached by angioplasty or are too long or hard for angioplasty.
혈관 이식술은 혈관성형술로 닿지 않는 곳이나, 너무 긴 곳, 하기 어려운 곳일 때 행해집니다.

(4) Dialogue 1.

D : Show me where it hurts.
어디가 아프시죠?

P : I feel discomfort in the center of the chest that lasts more than a few minutes, or that goes away and comes back.
가슴 중간이 몇 분간 아팠다가 나았다가 다시 아프곤 합니다.

D : Have you ever had heart problems?
심장에 문제가 있었던 적이 있었나요?

P : No.
없습니다.

D : Could you describe your pain?
통증이 어떤지 설명해 주실래요?

P : I feel like uncomfortable pressure and fullness or pain.
어떤 압박감과 심한 통증을 느낍니다.

It's like somebody is squeezing my chest.
그것은 마치 누가 내 가슴을 쥐어짜는 것 같습니다.

It commonly starts below the breastbone and on the left side of the body.
그 증상은 자주 가슴뼈 아래와 몸 왼쪽에서 시작됩니다.

Sometimes it spreads to the neck and left shoulder.
가끔씩 그 것은 목과 왼쪽 어깨 쪽으로 뻗어 갑니다.

D : What brought your pain?
무엇을 하다가 통증을 느끼게 되셨죠?

P : It started in the running.
달리기 도중 시작되었습니다.

D : You don't smoke?
담배는 피우지 안으십니까?

P : I stopped smoking five months ago.
5개월 전에 담배를 끊었습니다.

D : Your pain may be from a heart disease called angina.
당신의 통증은 협심증이라는 심장질환 같습니다.

P : Do you mean a heart disease?
심장질환 말인가요?

D : Yes. But I can't be absolutely sure.
예. 하지만 확신할 수는 없습니다.

I'd like you to have some tests done.
몇 가지 검사를 해야 될 것 같군요.

P : Oh my god!
오 이런!

D : Don't worry. You are gonna be fine.
걱정하지 마세요. 좋아지실 것입니다.

(5) Dialogue 2.

D : You are cyanotic.
당신은 창백하군요.

Breathe through Oxygen mask.
산소 마스크를 통해 숨을 쉬세요.

Can you describe your symptoms?
증상이 어떤 지 말씀해 주실래요?

P : It's like pressure.
압박감 같은 것이에요.

I had a sudden onset of severe chest pain and respiratory distress.

갑자기 가슴이 아프고 숨쉬기가 힘들었습니다.

D : How long have you been in pain?

통증이 있은 지 얼마나 됐죠?

P : Two hours. Is it a heart attack?

2시간 되었습니다. 심장발작이죠?

D : I am not sure.

확실하지는 않습니다.

Is there anything else about your current health that you would like to tell me about?

당신의 현재 건강상태에 대해 나에게 말하고 싶은 것이 있나요?

P : I have been having angina. off and on.

협심증이 있었어요. 있다 없다 했습니다.

D : We will check EKG and some blood test.

심전도와 혈액검사를 검사할 것입니다.

P : How much longer am I gonna have to be here?

얼마나 오랫동안 여기에 있어야 되죠?

D : A couple of more hours.

몇 시간 정도입니다.

Nurse will keep an eye on you while we wait the results.

결과가 나올 때까지 간호사가 돌봐드릴 것입니다.

P : OK.

알겠습니다.

D : I think that your trouble is more than angina.
제 생각엔 당신의 문제는 협심증 이상일 것 같군요.

Acute myocardial infarction is more dangerous than angina pectoris.
급성 심근 경색증은 협심증보다 더 심각합니다.

You need to further test.
추가 검사가 필요합니다.

I think you should be hospitalized.
당신은 입원이 꼭 필요합니다.

You need to be admitted into cardiology.
심장내과로 입원하여야 합니다.

Complete bed rest is recommended.
절대적인 침상안정이 필요합니다.

5) Lung (폐)

(1) 기본적인 질문

Do you have a cough?
기침이 있나요?

How long have you had a cough?
When did your cough begin?
언제 기침이 시작되었죠?

Did anything special bring it on?
원인이 되는 특별한 이유가 있나요?

What kind of cough is it?
기침이 어떤 종류이지요?

When does the cough occur?
언제 기침이 나오지요?

Do you cough quite often?
자주 기침을 하시나요?

Do you get any pain on breathing?
숨을 쉴 때 아프지는 않나요?

Do you get a pain in your chest when you cough?
기침을 할 때 가슴이 아프나요?

Do you get pain in your chest?
가슴이 아픕니까?

Have you had a recent cold?
최근에 감기에 걸린 적이 있나요?

Do you cough up phlegm?
Do you bring up any phlegm?
가래가 나오나요?

How much do you bring up phlegm?
얼마나 많이 나오지요?

When do you bring up phlegm?
언제 가래가 나오지요?

What color is it?
색깔은 어떻지요?

Are you coughing up thick yellow or red phlegm ?
기침에서 노랗거나 붉은 가래가 나오지는 않던가요?

Are you coughing up blood?
기침에 피가 나오지는 않던가요?

Have you ever coughed up blood or bloody sputum?
피가 섞인 가래를 뱉은 적이 있나요?

Do you have a fever with the shortness of breath?
숨쉬기 힘들면서 열은 없나요?

Does any position make it worse?
어떤 자세가 기침을 악화시키나요?

Do you have any difficulty with your breathing?
숨을 쉬는데 불편하지는 않나요?

Do you get short of breath?
Are you troubled by short of breath?
Have you had any shortness of breath?
숨쉬기 곤란하나요?.

Is it more difficult to breathe in or breathe out?
숨을 들이키거나 내쉴 때 언제가 더 힘들죠?

Does it hurt when you breathe in?
숨을 들이킬 때 아픈가요?

Have you ever had asthma or allergy?
천식이나 알러지를 앓은 적이 있나요?

Are you using a puffer for your asthma?
Do you use an inhaler for your asthma?
천식으로 분무기를 사용하나요?

How many puffs do you use per day?

하루에 몇 번 불죠?

Have you ever suffer from tuberculosis?

결핵에 걸린 적은 없습니까?

When was the last time you had a tuberculosis test?

결핵 검사를 마지막으로 한 때가 언제죠?

(2) Asthma (천식)

Your asthma seems to be getting better.

천식이 점점 좋아지는군요.

This could be worse at night and during cold or dry weather.

이것은 밤이나, 차거나, 건조한 공기를 마시면 더 악화될 수 있습니다.

Asthma is triggered by allergies.

천식은 알러지에 의해서 생기는 것입니다.

Many people with asthma are allergic to something in their environment.

천식이 있는 대부분의 사람들은 자신들의 환경에 있는 어떤 것에 알러지가 있습니다.

The most common causes of allergens are certain foods, pollens, dust and molds.

알러지의 가장 흔한 원인은 음식이나 꽃가루, 먼지와 곰팡이입니다.

Asthma results when a stimulus, such as an allergen, causes swelling of the tissues in the air passages of the lungs, making it difficult to breathe.

천식은 알러지의 원인물질이 폐로 가는 공기 통로의 조직에 부종을 일으켜 숨을 잘 쉴 수 없게 만듭니다.

Asthma is usually characterized by attacks of wheezing, coughing, and difficulty exhaling.
천식은 숨을 쉴 때 쌕쌕거리고 기침하고 내쉬기 힘드는 것이 특징입니다.

The main objective of asthma care and treatment is to keep you symptom free and healthy.
천식의 가장 중요한 치료 목적은 증상을 없애 건강하게 만드는 것입니다.

Getting rid of the things you are allergic to can help your asthma medicine work better.
알러지를 일으키는 원인을 제거하면 약이 더 잘 듣고 천식에 도움이 될 것입니다.

Asthma is rarely fatal if you take your medicine and follow my orders.
천식은 당신이 약을 먹고 제 말대로만 하면 위험하진 않습니다.

Drink plenty of water to keep your body hydrated and to thin mucous secretions.
몸에 수분이 충분하고 가래를 묽게 하기 위해 물을 많이 드십시요.

If certain material trigger a reaction, avoid those materials.
어떤 물질이 자극을 일으키면 그 물질들을 피하세요.

And when you have an attack, use your inhaler.
그리고 만약 발작이 일어나면, 약 분무기를 사용하세요.

You'd be better to take a flu vaccine shot.
독감 예방주사를 맞는 것이 좋을 것 같군요.

(3) Pneumonia (폐렴)

The chest X-ray suggests that you may have pnemonia.
흉부사진에서 폐렴이 의심되는군요.

X-ray shows lobar pneumonia.
엑스레이에서 대엽성 폐렴이 보입니다.

The homogeneous density at the right lower lung field indicates
　acute bacterial pneumonia.
우측 폐 하부에 있는 균질한 음영이 급성 박테리아성 폐렴을 말해줍니다.

Pneumonia is a serious infection of your lungs.
폐렴은 당신 폐의 감염을 의미합니다.

Acute pulmonary infection maybe caused by various organisms.
급성 폐렴은 다양한 균들에 의해 생깁니다.

Bacterial pneumonia can attack anyone.
박테리아 폐렴은 누구든지 올 수 있습니다.

The air sacs in the lungs filled with pus and other liquid.
폐의 공기 주머니에 고름과 다른 액체가 고입니다.

Oxygen has trouble reaching the blood.
산소가 피에 도달하기 힘들어집니다.

If there is too little oxygen in your blood, your body cells can't
　work properly.
만약 산소가 당신 피에 부족하면, 당신의 세포들이 일을 적절하게 할 수 없
　습니다.

Hospitalization is needed.
입원이 필요합니다.

It needs to be treated with intravenous antibiotics.
정맥 내 항생제 투여로 치료할 필요가 있습니다.

Early treatment with antibiotics can cure pneumonia.
항생제 초기 투여가 폐렴을 치료하게 합니다.

Besides antibiotics, you are given supportive treatment.
항생제 외에도 다른 부수적인 치료가 따릅니다.

You will need to take about two weeks off.
당신은 2주정도 쉬어야만 합니다.

I'm pretty sure that we can do best for you in the hospital.
당신이 병원에 있어야만 저희가 최선을 다할 수 있다고 생각합니다.

You are on powerful antibiotics.
당신은 지금 강한 항생제를 맞고 계십니다.

You will be discharged from the hospital in 2 weeks.
2주 내로 퇴원하게 될 것입니다.

(4) Lung Cancer (폐암)

I am afraid that I have some bad news.
미안하게도 나쁜 소식이 있습니다.

I think that you do have a problem with your lung.
제 생각에 당신의 폐에 이상이 있군요.

I think you maybe lung cancer.
제 생각에 이것은 폐암일 수도 있습니다.

This is a serious condition.
심각한 상태입니다.

Chest X-ray reveals the presence of the lung mass.
흉부 엑스레이에 폐의 종양이 나타나는군요.

You need CT scanning and bronchoscopic examination.
당신은 CT 스캔과 기관지경 검사가 필요합니다.

We need to do a few tests to confirm this diagnosis.
이 질병을 확진하려면 몇 가지 검사가 꼭 필요합니다.

Cough and hemoptysis occur owing to bronchial and lung lesion.
기침과 객혈은 기관지와 폐 병변 때문에 발생합니다.

Hoarseness is due to involvement of the recurrent laryngeal nerve owing to extension of a mass from the left lung.
쉰 목소리는 좌측 폐의 종양이 회귀 후두신경을 압박하여 발생되었습니다.

I'd like to take a few test.
몇 가지 검사를 하겠습니다.

CT scanning is significantly useful for detecting the presence of extrathoracic metastasis.
전산화 촬영 스캔은 흉부 밖으로의 전이유무를 아는데 매우 유용합니다.

Lung cancer may spread extensively within the thorax and metastasis widely through the body.
폐암은 흉부에서 몸 전체로 전이될 수 있습니다.

Brain, chest and abdominal CT scanning are needed for detecting the metastasis.
뇌, 흉부, 복부 CT 스캔이 전이 유무를 알기 위해 필요합니다.

Bronchogenic examination is an important technique in the diagnosis of bronchogenic tumor.
기관지경 검사는 기관지 암 검사에 아주 중요합니다.

Bronchial and lymph node biopsy may be obtained for cytologic evaluation.
기관지와 임파선 조직 검사가 세포 조직 평가를 위해 필요합니다.

I am concerned for your health.
전 당신의 건강에 대해서 책임이 있습니다.

The test are harmless and will give us more information to make a decision.
그 검사들은 해가 없고, 치료를 결정하는 데 도움을 줍니다.

Smoking is directly responsible for 87% of lung cancer cases and causes most cases of chronic bronchitis.
흡연은 폐암의 87%와 관계되고, 만성 기관지염을 일으키는 가장 흔한 원인입니다.

The smoking is bad for your health.
담배는 당신의 건강에 해롭습니다.

Cigarette smoking is the toughest addiction to break.
흡연은 끊기 참 어렵습니다.

But you have your fate in your own hands.
하지만 당신은 당신의 운명을 책임지고 있습니다.

Treatment depends on the location of tumor and whether the cancer has spread outside the lung.
치료는 종양의 위치, 폐 외부로의 전이 여부에 의해 정해집니다.

Chemotherapy is needed to destroy cancer cells.
항암제 치료가 암세포를 죽이기 위해 필요합니다.

Anti cancer medication will stop the growth of the cancer cells
   but the side effects are difficulty in eating and hair loss.

항암제는 암 세포의 증식을 멈추게 해주지만 식욕감퇴나 탈모의 부작용이
   있습니다.

Combination treatment with chemotherapy and radiation therapy
   is needed to reduce cancer lesion.

항암제와 방사선 치료 요법이 암 부위를 줄이기 위해 필요합니다.

I know experienced surgeon in this field.

나는 이 분야의 수술 전문가를 알고 있습니다.

I will send you to a specialist.

당신을 전문가에게 보내드리겠습니다.

We need to put you on a respirator.

호흡기를 달아야 할 것 같습니다.

(5) Dialogue

D : What's your main trouble?
   무엇이 가장 문제이지요?

P : I have shortness of breath.
   숨이 벅찹니다.

   I am unable to catch my breath.
   호흡을 할 수가 없어요.

D : You say you are breathless?
   숨을 쉴 수 없다는 뜻인가요?

P : Yes, I get puffed if I go upstairs.
   예, 이층만 올라가도 숨이 찹니다.

My symptoms have increased gradually over the past few days.

제 증상은 과거 몇 일 동안 계속 심해졌습니다.

D : Does anything special bring on this symptom?

이 증상을 일으킬 만한 일은 없나요?

P : It seems to be when I get a cold.

감기 걸린 다음부터 그런 것 같습니다.

D : Is your asthma normally under control?

당신의 천식은 잘 조절이 되고 있나요?

P : Yes, I use inhaler regularly.

예. 흡입기를 규칙적으로 사용하고 있습니다.

But I sometimes get breathless when I walk.

하지만 걸을 때 때때로 숨이 찹니다.

D : How many stairs can you climb without getting out of breath.

숨이 차지 않고 계단을 얼마나 오를 수 있죠?

P : About twenty.

20계단 정도입니다.

D : Do you smoke?

담배를 피시나요?

P : No.

아닙니다.

6) Digestive Organ (소화기관)

(1) 기본적인 질문

Do you get pain in your abdomen?
배가 아픕니까?

Have you had any belly pain?
배가 아프나요?

Do you have gastric or abdominal pain?
위나 배가 아픈가요?

Where does your belly hurt you?
배 어느 부위가 아프죠?

Do you feel nausea or vomiting?
오심이나 구토를 느끼나요?

Are you gonna throw up?
토할 것 같나요?

How much do you vomit?
얼마나 많이 토했죠?

How often do you vomit?
얼마나 자주 토했죠?

When did you vomit?
언제 토했죠?

Have you noticed any blood in your vomit?
토할 때 피 같은 것은 못 보셨나요?

What color is the vomit?

토한 것들의 색깔이 어떠했습니까?

Do you bring up acid?

신물이 넘어 오나요?

How about your digestion?

소화는 어떻습니까?

What kind of pain?

어떤 종류의 통증이죠?

What do you feel like?

어떻게 느끼시는데요?

How often do you get pain?

통증이 얼마나 자주 발생하죠.

Do you feel pain after meal?

식사 후 통증이 오나요?

Do certain foods bring on pain?

어떤 음식이 통증을 일으키나요?

Do you feel pain before meal?

식사 전에 통증이 오나요?

If you eat, do you feel better?

만약 먹으면 좋아지던가요?

How soon after?

얼마 후 그렇던가요?

Did you have any other symptoms with your stomach pain?

위통과 함께 다른 증상은 없었나요?

Have you ever diagnosed with stomach ulcer?

위궤양이라고 진단 받은 적이 있나요?

Does any particular food upset you?

배탈을 나게 한 어떤 특별한 음식이 있었나요?

Have you eaten a food that might be spoiled?

상한 음식을 먹지는 않았나요?

Do you have pain in the abdomen, especially after you eat foods
  that are difficult to digest?

특별히 잘 소화가 되지 않는 음식을 먹고 배가 아프지는 않았나요?

How are the bowel movements?

What about your bowel movements?

Bowel troubles?

화장실 가는 것은 어떻습니까?

Are the bowels all right?

Do you have any problem moving your bowels?

대변보는 것은 괜찮나요?

Difficult bowel movement?

Painful bowel movement?

Absent bowel movement?

Infrequent bowel movement?

어렵나요? 아프나요? 없나요? 불규칙한가요?

Do you have pain with your bowel movements?

Do you have pain while moving your bowel?

대변 눌 때 배가 아프나요?

Do you have pain without bowel movements?

대변을 보지 않아도 배가 아픈가요?

How many times did you have bowel movements today?
오늘 대변을 몇 번 보셨지요?

How often do you have bowel movements?
얼마나 자주 대변을 보시죠?

Do you often have fewer than three bowel movements each week?
일주일에 3번 미만으로 대변을 보십니까?

Do you often have a hard time passing stools?
대변을 보기 힘들 때가 있습니까?

Have you had chronic constipation?
만성적인 변비를 가지고 있나요?

Do you have any form of loose or watery stool?
Do you have diarrhea?
설사는 하지 않나요?

Since when have you had diarrhea?
언제부터 설사가 있었죠?

How often did you have diarrhea?
설사를 몇 번이나 했죠?

Do you have dry feces or hard feces?
대변이 마르고 딱딱하지는 않나요?

Do you have constipation?
변비가 있나요?

Have you noticed any changes in your urine or stool?
소변이나 대변에 어떤 이상은 없나요?

Do you ever have bloody stool?
Have you ever passed any bloody stool?
혈변을 눈 적은 없나요?

Do you ever have black stool?
Have you ever passed any black stool?
검은 변을 눈 적은 없나요?

What about color of stool?
대변이 무슨 색이죠?

Have you noticed an abnormal smell?
이상한 냄새는 나지 않던가요?

Are bowel movements gray, white or greasy in appearance?
대변이 회색이거나 하얗거나 기름지지는 않나요?

Do you get pain during passing your motions?
대변볼 때 통증이 있나요?

Do you take laxative?
변비약을 먹었나요?

Do you suffer from loss of appetite?
식욕이 없나요?

Do you feel muscle aches or headaches?
근육통이나 두통은 없나요?

Do you feel thirst or fatigue?
갈증이나 피곤함을 느끼십니까?

Do you feel abdominal swelling or bloating?
복부 팽만감이나 가스 찬 것을 느낍니까?

Do you have fever?
열이 나나요?

Have you lost any weight?
몸무게가 줄었나요?

Have you traveled recently to another country?
최근에 다른 나라로 여행을 갔다오지 않았나요?

Are you presently taking an antibiotics or other medicine?
최근에 항생제나 다른 약을 계속 복용하지는 않았나요?

Do you have itching around your anus?
항문 주변으로 가렵지는 않나요?

Have you recently had an ultrasound scan of your abdomen?
최근에 복부 초음파 검사를 하셨나요?

(2) Diarrhea (설사)

Diarrhea is a common problem that usually lasts a day or two and goes away on its own without any special treatment.
설사는 특별한 치료없이 하루 이틀 정도 지속되는 일반적인 증상입니다.

As long as diarrhea goes away on its own, laboratory test for the cause is not usually necessary.
설사가 저절로 멈추면 검사는 필요치 않습니다.

However, prolonged diarrhea can be a sign of other problems.
하지만 지속되는 설사는 다른 문제가 있다는 것입니다.

Acute diarrhea with a sudden onset is often caused by something eaten, such as food poisoning, viruses or bacteria as in infectious diarrhea or traveler's diarrhea.

갑자기 발생된 급성 설사는 식중독이나 바이러스나 박테리아 감염, 여행자 설사 같은 것들이 원인입니다.

Chronic diarrhea could be any of numerous problems such as inflammatory bowel disease, irritable bowel syndrome, diabetic diarrhea, certain medications, or various underlying intestinal diseases.

만성 설사는 염증성 장질환, 과민성 대장염, 당뇨병, 약물이나 여러 가지 장내 질환이 원인일 수 있습니다.

Some people are unable to digest lactose in milk.

어떤 사람들은 우유에 있는 락토스를 분해하지 못해 생기기도 합니다.

Medicines such as antibiotics, blood pressure medications, and antacids containing magnesium are reason for diarrhea.

항생제나 혈압약, 마그네슘이 있는 제산제가 설사의 원인이 될 수 있습니다.

Some people develop diarrhea after stomach surgery or removal of the gall bladder.

위 수술이나 담낭 제거술을 받은 환자에게서 설사가 있을 수도 있습니다.

The reason may be a change in how quickly food moves through the digestive system after stomach surgery or an increase in bile in the colon that can occur after gallbladder surgery.

그 이유는 위 수술 후 음식이 소화기관을 빨리 통과하거나, 담낭 수술 후 대장내 담즙이 많아져 생깁니다.

You may have food poisoning.

당신은 식중독일 가능성이 있군요.

Food poisoning usually causes flu-like symptoms with diarrhea.

식중독이 설사를 동반하는 독감 같은 증상들을 일으킵니다.

Signs of food poisoning usually occurs within 6 hours after eating and last one or two days.

식중독 증상은 음식을 먹은 후 6시간 내에 나타났다가 하루나 이틀 지속됩니다.

Just try to be a little bit patient.

좀 더 인내심을 가져야 합니다.

Bacteria are destroyed by normal cooking but toxin is heat stable.

박테리아는 요리할 때 파괴되지만 독소는 열에 파괴되지 않습니다.

Bacteria can grow in foods if they are not stored properly.

박테리아는 음식이 적절하게 저장되지 않으면 증식을 합니다.

People who visit foreign countries are at risk for traveler's diarrhea, which is caused by eating food or drinking water contaminated with bacteria, viruses, or sometimes parasites.

외국을 여행한 사람들의 설사는 주로 박테리아나 바이러스, 기생충이 감염된 물이나 음식을 먹어서 생깁니다.

Stool test and culture are needed to check for bacteria, parasites, or other signs of disease.

대변 검사나 배양이 박테리아나 기생충, 다른 질환의 여부를 알기 위해 필요합니다.

Blood tests can be helpful in ruling out certain diseases.

혈액검사가 다른 질환을 감별키 위해 필요합니다.

To find out if a food intolerance or allergy is causing the
diarrhea, I'd like to ask you to avoid milk products and other
foods to see whether the diarrhea responds to a change in diet.

음식에 대한 알러지나 반응을 보기 위해 우유 제품이나 다른 음식들을 먹지
말아 주세요.

I will uses a colonoscopy to look at the inside of the colon.

대장 안을 보기 위해 대장 내시경을 사용할 것입니다.

Diarrhea is not serious enough to need significant treatment.

설사는 치료가 필요 없을 정도로 경미하군요.

Replacing lost fluid to prevent dehydration is the only treatment
necessary.

탈수를 방지하기 위해 손실된 물만 보충해 주면 됩니다.

Diarrhea can cause dehydration.

설사는 탈수를 일으킬 수 있습니다.

Dehydration occurs when the body has lost too much fluid and
electrolytes.

탈수는 우리 몸이 너무 많은 전해질과 수분을 잃을 때 나타납니다.

Dehydration is particularly dangerous in children and the
elderly, and it must be treated.

탈수는 어린이나 노인에게는 위험하므로 치료되어야 합니다.

The fluid and electrolytes lost during diarrhea need to be
replaced promptly.

설사로 잃은 수분이나 전해질은 즉시 보충되어야 합니다.

Although water is extremely important in preventing
dehydration, it does not contain electrolytes.

비록 물도 아주 중요하지만, 물은 전해질이 없습니다.

To maintain electrolyte levels, you could have soups, which contain sodium, and fruit juices, which contain potassium.

전해질을 유지하려면 소금이 든 수프나 칼륨이 많은 과일 주스를 드세요.

I recommend a special rehydration solution that contains the nutrients children need.

어린이에게 필요한 영양소가 들어있는 보충액을 권유합니다.

You can buy this solution in the grocery store.

보충액은 가게에서 살 수 있습니다.

Anti-diarrheal medications that stop diarrhea may be helpful in some cases, but they are not recommended for people whose diarrhea is from a bacterial or parasite infection.

지사제가 도움을 주기는 하지만, 박테리아나 기생충 감염이 원인인 경우는 쓰면 안됩니다.

Until diarrhea subsides, try to avoid milk products and foods that are greasy, high-fiber, or very sweet. These foods tend to aggravate diarrhea.

설사가 멈추기 전까지는 유제품, 기름진 음식이나, 고 섬유질, 단 것을 먹지 마세요. 이와 같은 음식들은 설사를 악화시킵니다.

(3) Constipation (변비)

Your abdominal pain may merely be results of overeating, gas, or constipation.

당신의 복부 통증 원인이 단순히 과식이나, 가스, 변비 때문일 수도 있습니다.

The most common cause of constipation is a low fiber and high fat diet.

변비의 원인은 섬유질이 적고 지방이 많은 음식이 원인입니다.

People who eat plenty of high-fiber foods are less likely to become constipated.

섬유질이 많은 음식을 먹는 사람들에게는 변비가 적습니다.

Liquids like water and juice add fluid to the colon and bulk to stools, making bowel movements softer and easier to pass.

물이나 쥬스는 장에 수분을 공급하고 변의 양을 늘려 대변을 보기 쉽고 잘 나오게 합니다.

You try to drink enough of liquids and high fiber foods every day.

매일 충분한 양의 물과 고섬유질 음식을 드세요.

Liquids like coffee that contain caffeine seem to have a dehydrating effect.

카페인이 든 커피와 같은 음식은 탈수효과가 있습니다.

Lack of exercise can lead to constipation.

운동 부족도 변비를 만듭니다.

Some medications can slow passage of bowel movements.

어떤 약물들은 장운동을 느리게 합니다.

Irritable Bowel Syndrome (IBS) have spasms in the colon that affect bowel movements. Constipation and diarrhea often alternate, and abdominal cramping and bloating are common symptoms.

과민성 대장 증후군은 대장을 수축시켜 장운동에 영향을 줍니다. 변비와 설사가 반복되고, 복통이나 가스 찬 느낌이 주 증상입니다.

It often worsens with stress, but there is no specific cause or anything unusual.

스트레스에 의해 나빠지기도 하지만, 특별한 이유는 없습니다.

During pregnancy, women may be constipated because of hormonal changes or because the heavy uterus compresses the intestine.

임신 중, 여자들은 호르몬 변화나 자궁의 장 압박으로 변비가 올 수 있습니다.

Aging may also affect bowel regularity because a slower metabolism results in less intestinal activity and muscle tone.

나이가 들면 대사가 느려지며, 장의 운동과 힘이 떨어져 변비가 올 수 있습니다.

People often become constipated when traveling because their normal diet and daily routines are disrupted.

사람들은 종종 여행으로 규칙적인 식사가 안될 때, 변비가 생길 수 있습니다.

People who ignore the urge to have a bowel movement may eventually stop feeling the urge, which can lead to constipation.

화장실을 억지로 잘 안가는 사람에게도 변비가 생길 수 있습니다.

Some neurological, metabolic and endocrine disorders can slow the movement of stool through the colon.

어떤 신경학적, 대사적, 내분비적인 질환도 변비를 일으킬 수 있습니다.

A diet with enough fiber helps form soft, bulky stool.

충분한 섬유질 섭취가 대변을 부드럽게 해 줄 것입니다.

Life style changes can help treat and prevent constipation

생활을 변화시키면 변비치료와 예방이 될 것입니다.

Drink enough water and other liquids such as fruit and vegetable juices.

물이나 과일, 야채 쥬스 같은 것들을 마시세요.

Exercise regularly and reserve enough time to have a bowel movement.
규칙적으로 운동하고 화장실 보는 충분한 시간을 가지세요.

Most people who are mildly constipated do not need laxatives.
가벼운 변비는 약이 필요하지 않습니다.

I will prescribe some laxatives for a limited time.
몇 번 쓸 수 있게 완하제를 처방해 드리겠습니다.

I'll give you some medicine to loosen bowels.
변비약을 드리겠습니다.

(4) Gastroenteritis (위장염)

It could be a gas.
가스가 찼을 수도 있습니다.

It could be acute gastroenteritis.
급성 위장염 일 수 있습니다.

Many different viruses and bacterias can cause gastroenteritis.
많은 다른 종류의 바이러스와 박테리아가 위장염을 일으킵니다.

The possible causes of gastroenteritis are food poisoning, viral or bacterial digestive infection, traveler's diarrhea, parasites infection, food intolerance, other causes of diarrhea.
위장염의 가능한 원인은 식중독, 바이러스나 박테리아 감염, 여행자 설사, 기생충, 맞지 않는 음식이나 설사를 일으키는 원인 등입니다.

Nothing by mouth for six hours.
6시간 동안은 아무 것도 먹지 마세요.

Then sips of clear liquids.
그리고 깨끗한 물을 조금씩 먹으세요.

If your symptom is relieved, you can try a little food.
증상이 좋아지면 약간의 음식을 먹어보세요.

Bed rest and drink clear water to avoid dehydration.
휴식을 취하고 탈수 예방을 위해 깨끗한 물을 드세요.

You need to drink solutions which contains sodium, potassium.
나트륨이나 칼륨이 든 물을 마실 필요가 있습니다.

Avoid fried, spicy foods, fruits and vegetables.
튀긴 것이나, 맵거나, 과일, 야채를 피하세요.

Don't eat solid foods on the first day of the attack.
증상이 생긴 첫 날은 고형음식을 먹지 마세요.

Progress to gradual addition of solid foods and gradual return to
usual diet.
증상의 진행에 따라 천천히 고형음식이나 일상 음식을 먹도록 하세요.

I will prescribe some medications.
약을 처방해 드리겠습니다.

I'm going to give you an anti-spasmodic drug to take.
진경제를 먹도록 해 드리겠습니다.

If you don't improve, come back to me.
호전이 없으면 저에게 다시 오세요.

(5) Peptic ulcer (소화성 궤양)

It could be an ulcer.
궤양일 수 있습니다.

The most common peptic ulcer symptom is burning pain in the abdomen between the breastbone and the belly button.
위궤양의 가장 흔한 증상이 가슴과 배꼽 사이의 배가 타는 듯이 아픈 것입니다.

The pain often occurs when the stomach is empty, between meals and in the early morning hours, but it can occur at any other time.
통증은 위가 비었거나, 식간, 이른 아침에 자주 발생되나, 언제든 올 수 있습니다.

Pain may last from minutes to hours and may be relieved by eating food or taking antacids.
통증은 몇 분에서 몇 시간 올 수 있고, 음식이나 제산제에 의해 완화될 수 있습니다.

Sometimes ulcers bleed.
때로 궤양은 출혈을 일으킵니다.

Ulcers sometimes can lead to other problems.
궤양들은 가끔씩 다른 문제들을 일으킵니다.

These problems include bleeding, perforation or obstruction.
이 문제들이란 출혈이나 천공, 또는 폐쇄를 말합니다.

Ulcers can block food from going through the stomach.
궤양들은 음식이 위를 통과하는 것을 막을 수 있습니다.

This causes nausea, vomiting.

이때 오심과 구토 증상이 일어납니다.

The majority of peptic ulcers are caused by the H. pylori
  bacterium.

궤양의 대부분의 원인은 헬리코박터 파일로리 박테리아 때문입니다.

Some ulcers are caused by long-term use of non-steroidal anti-
  inflammatory agents.

일부 궤양은 비스테로이 소염제의 장기간 사용에 의해서도 옵니다.

Drug-induced ulcers usually heal once the person stops taking
  the medication.

약에 의한 궤양은 약을 중단하면 곧 좋아집니다.

I'll perform an endoscopy for a correct diagnosis.

정확한 진단을 위해 내시경을 하겠습니다.

I'll get a biopsy through the endoscopy.

내시경을 통해 조직검사를 할 것입니다.

To help the healing process and relieve symptoms, I will
  prescribe some antacids to neutralize the acid and medicines.

증상을 줄이고 치유를 위해 제산제와 약을 드리겠습니다.

In a few cases, cancerous tumors in the stomach or pancreas can
  cause ulcers.

때론 위나 췌장의 악성 암들이 궤양을 일으키기도 합니다.

Peptic ulcers are not caused by spicy food or stress.

소화성 궤양은 매운 음식이나 스트레스에 의해 생기지는 않습니다.

I will test you for H. pylori.

헬리코박터 파일로리에 대한 검사를 하겠습니다.

This test is important because treatment for an ulcer caused by
  H. pylori is different from that for an ulcer caused by other
  problem.
헬리코박터 파일로리에 의한 궤양의 치료는 다른 궤양과 다르므로 이 검사
  는 중요합니다.

H. pylori is diagnosed through blood, breath, stool and tissue
  tests.
헬리코박터 파일로리는 혈액, 호흡, 대변, 조직에 의해서 검사될 수 있습
  니다.

We can detect antibodies to H. pylori bacteria in blood test.
혈액에서는 헬리코박터 파일로리 항체를 발견할 수 있습니다.

Urea breath tests are mainly used after treatment to see whether
  it worked, but they can be used in diagnosis too.
요소 호흡 검사는 진단뿐만 아니라, 치료 결과를 보는데도 사용할 수 있습
  니다.

You should drink a urea solution.
당신은 요소가 든 약물을 마셔야합니다.

If H. pylori is present, it breaks down the urea, releasing the
  special carbon.
만약 헬리코박터 파일로리가 있으면 요소를 분해하여 특별한 탄소를 배출
  합니다.

The blood carries the carbon to the lungs, where you exhale it.
혈액이 탄소를 폐로 운반하면 당신은 그것을 호흡으로 내뱉게 됩니다.

The breath test is 96 percent to 98 percent accurate.
호흡 검사는 96%에서 98% 정확합니다.

Treatment usually involves a combination of antibiotics, acid suppressors and stomach protectors.

치료는 대개 항생제와 위산 억제제, 위 보호제가 함께 사용됩니다.

The most proven effective treatment is a 2-week course of treatment called triple therapy.

가장 효과가 있는 치료는 삼중치료로 불리는 2주 코스 치료입니다.

2-week triple therapy reduces ulcer symptoms, kills the bacteria, and prevents ulcer recurrence in more than 90 percent of patients.

2주간의 삼중치료는 궤양의 증상을 줄여주고, 박테리아를 죽이며, 90% 이상에서 재발을 막아줍니다.

Antibiotics used in triple therapy may cause mild side effects such as nausea, vomiting, diarrhea, dark stools, metallic taste in the mouth, dizziness, headache.

삼중 치료에서의 항생제는 때로 오심, 구토, 설사, 흑변, 금속 맛, 어지러움, 두통 등을 일으킵니다.

It is very important to continue taking all of this medicine until it is gone, even when you begin to feel better.

비록 당신의 증상이 좋아지더라도, 이 모든 약들을 계속해서 먹는 것이 아주 중요합니다.

I want to see you 2 weeks later.

2주 뒤에 보도록 하죠.

(6) Dialogue 1.

D : Do you feel much better?

　　좀 더 나아진 것 같아요?

P : No, terrible.

아뇨, 짜증이 나요.

D : How many times did you have bowel movements today?

오늘 대변을 몇 번 보셨지요?

P : I have had diarrhea four times today.

오늘 설사를 4번이나 했어요.

D : Do you have any pain now?

지금도 어디가 아픈가요?

P : I have mild lower abdominal pain.

아랫배가 약간 아파요.

D : Do you have pain with your bowel movements?

대변볼 때 통증이 있나요?

P : Yes.

그렇습니다.

D : Do you have bloody diarrhea?

피가 섞인 설사는 하지 않나요?

P : No.

아뇨.

D : You have traveller's diarrhea caused by contaminated food
and drink.

당신은 감염된 음식이나 음료수 때문에 생긴 여행자 설사입니다.

Medicine didn't seem to relieve your symptom.

약이 증상을 호전시켜주지 않았던 것 같군요.

P : Should I take more medicine?
약을 더 먹어야 하나요?

D : You need antibiotics.
당신에겐 항생제가 필요합니다.

I will write you a prescription.
당신에게 처방전을 써 주겠습니다.

These medicines can make you feel better.
이 약들이 당신의 증상을 호전시킬 것입니다.

P : Okay.
알겠어요.

D : If your symptoms doesn't feel like its going away after 3
days, you may need to run tests.
만약 당신의 증상이 3일 안에 좋아지지 않으면 몇 가지 검사가 필요합니다.

As long as you still have pain, don't eat any solid food or
drink large amount of liquids.
통증이 있는 동안은 고형의 음식이나 너무 많은 양의 물은 먹지 마십시오.

(7) Dialogue 2.

D : I'd like to know your bowel habits including frequency of
bowel movements, character of stools, presence of blood in
the stool.
당신은 화장실을 얼마나 자주 가고, 대변의 특징이나 대변에 피가 보이
는 지 알고 싶군요.

P : All is normal.
다 정상입니다.

But I have stomach pain on these days.
하지만 요즘 위통이 있어요.

D : Have you ever had endoscopic examination?
내시경 검사를 받은 적은 있나요?

P : I had a normal endoscopy three years ago.
3년 전에 내시경 검사가 정상이었습니다.

D : Can you describe your pain?
통증이 어떻던가요?

P : A burning pain.
타는 듯한 통증입니다.

It comes and goes for several days or weeks.
며칠이나 몇 주 간격으로 옵니다

It occurs 2 to 3 hours after a meal.
식후 2-3시간에 옵니다.

It is relieved by food and antacid medications.
식사를 하거나 제산제를 먹으면 좋아집니다.

D : How frequently do you have pain?
얼마나 자주 통증이 있죠?

P : It occurs when the stomach is empty.
공복에 아픕니다.

Night stomach pain wakes me up.

야간의 위통 때문에 여러 차례 잠에서 깹니다.

D : Do you have any other symptoms?

다른 증상은 없습니까?

P : Sometimes I had nausea and vomiting.

가끔씩 오심과 구토를 동반합니다.

D : This may be symptom of a gastritis or gastric ulcer.

이것은 위염이나 위궤양 증상일 수가 있습니다.

P : What causes gastric ulcer?

위궤양이 왜 생기죠?

D : A type of bacteria called Helicobacter pylori causes many ulcers.

헬리코박터 파이로리 라는 박테리아가 궤양을 일으킬 수 있습니다.

Also acid and other juices made by the stomach can contribute to ulcers by burning the lining of your digestive tract.

그리고 위에서 만들어지는 위산이나 다른 액이 위장 표피를 상하게 할 수도 있습니다.

P : Are stomach ulcers serious?

위궤양은 심각한 병인가요?

D : Not usually.

항상 그런 것은 아닙니다.

Now I would like to check your abdomen.

이제 당신의 배를 검사해보겠습니다.

Will you get undressed and lie on the table?

옷을 벗고 진찰대 위에 누워 주실래요?

P : Yes.

알겠습니다.

D : Could you show me with your finger the point where it hurts
   you most?

가장 아픈 곳을 손가락으로 가리켜 주실래요?

P : Here.

여기입니다.

D : Does it hurt where I touch?

제가 만지는 곳이 아픈가요?

P : Not so much.

많이 아프지는 않아요.

D : Which position makes you feel better?

어떤 자세가 통증을 줄여주던가요?

P : If I bend my body, I get a little relief from the pain.

몸을 구부리면 통증이 줄어들더군요.

D : To see whether symptoms are caused by an ulcer, I will do
   an upper gastrointestinal series and an endoscopy.

위궤양 때문인지 알기 위해, 상부 위장관 촬영과 위 내시경 검사를 해야
   될 것 같군요.

7) Liver (간)

(1) 기본적인 질문

Do you feel fatigue?
피곤함을 느낍니까?

Do you feel nausea or vomiting?
오심이나 구토를 느끼나요?

Do you have right upper quadrant abdominal discomfort or pain?
배 오른쪽 위가 아프거나 불편한가요?

What kind of discomfort?
어떤 종류의 불편함이죠?

Do you feel abdominal tenderness?
배를 누르면 아픈가요?

Did you ever have jaundice?
황달이 있었던 적이 있나요?

Did you have any other symptoms with your jaundice?
황달 외 다른 증상은 없었나요?

Do you feel itching sensation?
가렵지는 않나요?

Do you have aches, fever or chills?
통증이나 열, 오한을 느끼나요?

Do you experience unexplained weight loss?
이유 없이 체중이 감소하나요?

Have you lost any weight?
몸무게가 줄었나요?

Do you experience loss of appetite?
식욕이 없나요?

Do you have diarrhea?
설사를 하지는 않나요?

Do you have dark and foamy urine or pale feces?
검고 거품이 나는 소변이나, 색이 연한 대변을 보지는 않나요?

Are you presently taking an antibiotics or other medicine?
최근에 항생제나 다른 약을 계속 복용하지는 않았나요?

Did you have vaccine against hepatitis B?
B형 간염 예방 주사를 맞았나요?

(2) Hepatitis (간염)

I'm going to get some blood tests done to see what is causing
the symptom.
증상의 원인이 무엇인지 알기 위해 혈액 검사를 하겠습니다.

Lab tests show that the liver is not working well.
검사에서 간의 기능이 좋지 않습니다.

Many people infected with viral hepatitis have no symptoms.
대부분의 간염 환자들은 증상이 없습니다.

Five different viruses cause five different hepatitis, A-E.
5종류의 바이러스가 서로 다른 5종류의 간염을 일으킵니다.

A person who has had hepatitis A once is immune from further infections.

A형 간염을 걸렸던 사람은 추가 감염에서 면역이 됩니다.

Hepatitis B becomes a chronic infection in up to 10 percent of patients and can result in cirrhosis or liver cancer.

B형 간염은 환자 10%에서 만성이 되고, 간경화나 간암이 될 수 있습니다.

Hepatitis C is usually a mild disease, but is highly likely to result in chronic hepatitis and may cause cirrhosis or liver cancer.

C형 간염은 경미하지만, 만성간염이나 간경화, 간암이 될 수 있습니다.

Hepatitis D occurs as a co-infection with hepatitis B.

D형 간염은 B형 간염과 함께 감염이 됩니다.

Hepatitis E can cause severe acute symptoms, but doesn't result in chronic hepatitis.

E형 간염은 심한 급성 간염을 보이나, 만성으로 가지는 않습니다.

It may be necessary to examine symptoms that may be caused by complications of hepatitis and underlying causes of hepatitis.

간염의 합병증이나 간염의 원인을 알기 위한 검사가 필요합니다.

Your bilirubin is high, but it doesn't affect you.

빌리루빈이 높지만 해는 없을 것입니다.

The itching is due to retained bile salts in tissue.

가려움은 조직에 담즙산이 축적되어 생깁니다.

Like most viral diseases, no drug treatment is available.

대부분의 바이러스 질환처럼 특별한 치료가 필요 없습니다.

The symptoms can last a few weeks.

증상은 몇 주까지 갈 수 있습니다.

The only good news is that you recover without complications.

가장 좋은 것은 합병증 없이 회복되는 것입니다.

Immune globulin shots consist of antibodies against the hepatitis A virus kill the hepatitis A virus and can help prevent hepatitis A in people who have been exposed to the virus. But it is only effective within 14 days of exposure.

A형 간염에 대한 항체로 만든 면역 글로불린은 A형 바이러스를 죽이고 A형 간염에 노출된 사람에게 예방을 해줍니다. 하지만 노출 14일 이내에만 효과가 있습니다.

The vaccine against hepatitis B is administered as three shots over a period of months.

B형 간염 백신은 몇 달에 걸쳐 3번 맞습니다.

(3) Hepatoma (간암)

You may have liver cancer.

간암인 것 같군요.

Underlying possible causes of hepatoma are cirrhosis of the liver, alcoholic liver disease, chronic hepatitis B.

간암의 잠재적인 원인들은 간경화나, 알코올성 간염, 만성 B형 간염입니다.

The choice of treatment depends on the condition of the liver, the number, size, and location of tumors and whether the cancer has spread outside the liver.

치료의 선택은 간의 상태나 종양의 수, 크기, 위치, 간 외부로의 전이 여부에 의해 정해집니다.

Pain is a common problem for people with liver cancer.

통증이 간암의 일반적인 문제입니다.

The tumor can cause pain by pressing against nerves and other organs.

암은 신경이나 다른 기관을 눌러 통증을 일으킬 수 있습니다.

We will try to reduce your pain in several ways.

우리는 당신의 통증을 줄이기 위해 여러 방법을 사용할 것입니다.

Chemotherapy is needed to destroy cancer cells.

항암제 치료가 암세포를 죽이기 위해 필요합니다.

Anti cancer medication will stop the growth of the cancer cells but the side effects are difficulty in eating and hair loss.

항암제는 암 세포의 증식을 멈추게 해주지만 식욕감퇴나 탈모의 부작용이 있습니다.

Chemotherapy may cause discomfort and make a complications.

항암치료는 불편함을 야기하고 합병증을 만들 것입니다.

We will use chemoembolization or hepatic arterial infusion.

우리는 항암제를 이용해 혈전을 유도하거나 간동맥으로 주입할 것입니다.

We will insert a tube into the hepatic artery and inject an anticancer drug into the catheter.

우리는 튜브를 간동맥으로 넣어 항암제를 투여할 것입니다.

Microwave or LASER therapy can kill the cancer cells with heat.

마이크로파나 레이저 치료는 열로 암세포를 죽일 수 있습니다.

We will use ultrasound to help guide the probe.

우리는 프로브를 안내하기 위해 초음파를 이용 할 것입니다.

We will inject alcohol directly into the liver tumor to kill cancer cells.

우리는 암 세포를 죽이기 위해 알코올을 간암내로 직접 주입할 것입니다.

We will make an incision into the abdomen and insert a metal probe to freeze and kill cancer cells for cryotherapy.

우리는 냉동치료법을 위해 배에 절개를 가한 후, 금속프로브를 넣을 것입니다.

Radiation can help relieve pain by shrinking the tumor.

방사능 조사는 암을 줄어들게 해 통증을 완화시켜 줍니다.

Relaxation techniques such as listening to slow music or breathing slowly and comfortably can relieve your pain.

느린 음악을 듣거나, 숨을 천천히 쉬는 것들이 통증을 줄여줄 것입니다.

(4) Gallstone (담석)

Silent gallstones are usually left alone and occasionally disappear on their own.

증상이 없는 담석은 그냥 놔두고 스스로 없어지기도 합니다.

Silent stones do not necessarily require immediate treatment.

증상이 없는 담석은 치료가 바로 필요없습니다.

Usually only patients with symptomatic gallstones are treated.

증상이 있는 담석증만 치료가 필요합니다.

Cholesterol stones form when bile contains too much cholesterol, too much bilirubin, or not enough bile salts.

콜레스테롤 담석은 콜레스테롤, 빌리루빈이 너무 많거나 담즙산이 부족할 때 생깁니다.

Obesity is a major risk factor for gallstones, especially in women.

비만은 특히 여성에서 담석증의 위험인자 입니다.

I will prescribe certain medications to dissolve stones and to reduce pain.

담석을 녹여주는 약과 통증을 줄여주는 약들을 처방해 주겠습니다.

Extracorporeal shockwave lithotripsy can break up stones into tiny pieces that can pass through the bile ducts without causing blockages.

체외파 충격술이 담석을 작은 조각들로 부수어 담즙관을 통해 나오게 할 수 있습니다.

Surgical gall bladder removal procedure is needed.

외과적 담낭 절제술이 필요합니다.

Laparoscopic cholecystectomy is the most common treatment of gallstone with symptom.

내시경을 이용한 담낭절제술이 가장 일반적인 증상이 있는 담석증의 치료 방법입니다.

(5) Dialogue

D : Tell me what I can do for you today?

　제가 무엇을 도와드릴까요?

P : My body seems to be going bad on me.

　몸이 점점 더 안 좋아지고 있어요.

D : What exactly were your symptoms?

　당신의 증상이 정확히 어떤 것이지요?

P : The main problem I'm having is indigestion and fatigue.

주 증상은 소화불량과 피곤함입니다.

D : Well, your main trouble is indigestion and fatigue?

음, 소화불량과 피곤함이 당신의 주 증상이군요?

P : Yes. Sometimes abdominal discomfort is accompanied by nausea.

예. 때때로 복부 불쾌감이 오심과 함께 오기도 합니다.

D : The abdominal discomfort may be a sign of the result of something as harmless as gas.

복부 불쾌감은 가스 찼을 때와 같이 해가 없는 것 때문일 수도 있습니다.

OK. I want to ask you something.

알겠습니다. 제가 몇 가지를 물어보겠습니다.

Have you been eating all right?

먹는 것은 괜찮았나요?

P : About the same as usual, Doctor.

항상 비슷하게 먹어요.

D : How is your appetite?

식욕은 어떠세요?

P : Not good.

좋지는 않아요.

D : Do you have any problem with your bowel movements?

대변보는 것은 이상이 없습니까?

P : No.

없습니다.

D : Do you have a history of gastritis or gastric ulcer?
위염이나 위궤양을 앓았던 적이 있습니까?

P : No. I have always had an iron stomach.
없습니다. 제 위장은 튼튼합니다.

D : Have you ever used any medication?
어떤 약을 복용한 적은 있습니까?

P : I took an antacid.
제산제를 복용했습니다.

D : Have you ever been hospitalized?
병원에 입원했던 적은 있나요?

P : When I was a child, I had an operation for appendicitis.
어렸을 때 충수염으로 수술을 받았습니다.

D : Any other problem?
다른 문제는 없습니까?

P : I received Hepatitis B vaccine shot 2 weeks ago.
2주 전 B형 간염 백신을 맞았습니다.

4 *General & Chest Surgery*
(일반외과 & 흉부외과)

1) 외과적인 질문 (내과 분야별 질문 참조)

Have you ever had any injuries?
다친 적은 없나요?

Have you had any masses in your breasts?
유방에 혹이 있나요?

When did you first notice this lump?
언제 이 혹을 처음 발견하셨죠?

Did you experience any pain in your breast?
유방이 아픈 적이 있나요?

Do your breasts get sore before your period?
생리 전에 유방이 아픈가요?

Have you ever tried examining your breasts?
유방을 검사 해 본 적이 있나요?

Did you feel swelling in your neck?
목이 부은 것을 느끼나요?

Have you had any thyroid trouble?
갑상선에 문제가 있었던 적이 있나요?

Have you ever noticed any enlargement of lymph nodes?
임파선이 부은 적은 없었나요?

Have you noticed any lumps anywhere in your body?
몸에 혹 같은 것은 없나요?

Have you ever had a hernia?
탈장 같은 것은 없었나요?

Do you have shortness of breath?
숨이 가쁘나요?

Do you get any pain on breathing?
숨을 쉴 때 아프지는 않나요?

Do you have chest pain?
가슴이 아프나요?

Do you get a pain in your chest when you cough?
기침을 할 때 가슴이 아프나요?

Have you ever coughed up blood or bloody sputum?
피가 섞인 가래를 뱉은 적이 있나요?

Have you ever brought up blood?
피를 토한 적이 있나요?

Have you had any pain in your chest before?
전에도 가슴이 아픈 적이 있었나요?

Do you have a history of cardiac trouble?
심장에 문제가 있었던 적이 있습니까?

Do you get pain in your abdomen?
배가 아픕니까?

Where does your belly hurt you?
배 어느 부위가 아프죠?

Do you feel nausea or vomiting?
오심이나 구토를 느끼나요?

How often do you get pain?
통증이 얼마나 자주 발생하죠.

Have you ever passed any bloody stool?
혈변을 눈 적은 없나요?

Have you ever passed any black stool?
검은 변을 눈 적은 없나요?

Did you ever have jaundice?
황달이 있었던 적이 있나요?

Do you have fever?
열이 나나요?

Have you lost any weight?
몸무게가 줄었나요?

Have you ever noticed any edema in your legs?
다리가 부은 적이 없나요?

Do you have ---? or Do you feel ---?

Bleeding tendency
Any allergic history
Any surgery history
Any medical problem
Nausea and Vomiting

Abdominal discomfort or pain
Indigestion or burning sensation
Stomach bloating after meals
Gas or Feeling of fullness
Bloating or Feeling of abdominal fullness after meals
Diarrhea or Constipation
Fever
Loss of appetite
Weight loss
Anemia
Jaundice
Weakness or Fatigue
Abdominal hard mass
Abdominal fluid retention
Vomiting blood
Blood in stool or Black stool
Neck lump in the front of the neck near the Adam's apple
Neck nodule or Neck swelling
Hoarseness or Difficulty speaking
Difficulty swallowing or Difficulty breathing
Throat pain or Neck pain
Breast lump or thickening
Underarm lump
Breast changes or swelling
Nipple changes or discharge
Breast or Nipple tenderness
Lump near the anus or rectum
Sudden shortness of breath
Painful breathing
Sharp chest pain
Chest tightness
Rapid heartbeat

2) 수술 전후에 필요한 설명

Surgery is necessary for you to treat this problem.
Surgery should be considered to treat your problem.
문제를 치료하기 위해서는 수술이 필요합니다.

It's no big deal.
It's a simple surgery.
간단한 것입니다.

A lot of patients have had that surgery done.
많은 사람들이 그 수술을 받았습니다.

But we can't give a hundred percent guarantee that it would be
  okay.
하지만 괜찮을 것이라고 100% 보장하지는 못합니다.

Surgery is the best choice for treatment.
치료를 위해서는 수술이 최선의 선택입니다.

Most patients get better after operation.
대부분의 환자들이 수술 후 좋아집니다.

Several hours may be necessary to give you fluids and
  antibiotics and to prepare the operation.
수액과 항생제를 주고 수술을 준비하기 위해 몇 시간이 필요할 수 있습니다.

The anesthesiologist uses a general anesthetic technique
  whereby patients are put to sleep and made pain free in
  operation.
마취의사들이 수술 중 통증이 없고 잠을 재우기 위해 전신마취를 합니다.

Occasionally a spinal anesthetic may be used.
때때로 척추 마취를 하기도 합니다.

You feel better immediately after an operation.
수술 후 곧 좋아질 것입니다.

You'll get an operation tomorrow.
내일 수술을 받으실 겁니다.

The surgery was fine.
Surgery was a successful.
Operation was fine.
수술이 잘 되었습니다.

We're going to take the tube out of your throat.
당신의 목에서 튜브를 뺄 것입니다.

Take a deep breath in, and out.
숨을 크게 들이쉬고 내 쉬세요.

Take a deep breath and cough in order to free your lungs of any
    fluid build up that may occur due to the general anesthesia.
전신마취 때문에 당신의 폐에 액체가 고이지 않도록 숨을 크게 쉬고 기침을
    하세요.

Pain medicines can relieve pain but it make you drowsy.
진통제가 통증을 없애 주지만, 멍하게 만들 수 있습니다.

You are allowed to eat when the stomach and intestines begin to
    function again.
위와 장의 기능이 돌아오면 먹을 수 있습니다.

The first meal is a clear liquid diet.
처음 식사는 깨끗한 죽입니다.

If you tolerate this meal, the next meal usually is a regular diet.
이 음식을 먹고 괜찮으면 정상적인 음식이 나올 것입니다.

You can walk and resume your normal physical activities as
  soon as possible.
가능한 빨리 걷고 정상적인 활동을 시작하세요.

You can move around as much as you like.
당신이 하고 싶은 만큼 돌아다녀도 됩니다.

Movement is good for you.
움직이는 것이 당신에게 좋습니다.

You will be discharged from the hospital within 1 week after the
  operation.
수술 후 1주 이내에 퇴원할 수 있을 것입니다.

You are able to be back to your normal activities within 2 weeks.
2주 이내에 정상 생활로 돌아 갈 수 있을 것입니다.

You are able to return to work within three to four weeks after
  the operation.
당신은 수술 후 3-4주 이내에 정상적인 일을 할 수 있을 것입니다.

3) 수술 합병증에 대한 설명

Certain risks are present when any operation requires a general
  anesthetic and the abdominal cavity is opened.
전신 마취와 개복수술에는 몇 가지 위험이 따릅니다.

Severe bleeding can occur and coagulopathy rarely occur.
심한 출혈이 있을 수 있고, 혈액응고 이상이 드물게 올 수 있습니다.

Pneumonia and dyspnea often occurs.

폐렴이나 호흡이상이 올 수 있습니다.

Patients who smoke are at a greater risk for developing lung problems.

담배를 피우시던 분에게 폐에 문제가 생길 위험이 더 높습니다.

Thrombophlebitis, or inflammation of the veins, is rare but can occur if the patient requires prolonged bed rest.

장기간 침상에 있을 경우, 혈전이나 정맥염이 올 수 있습니다.

Adhesions is a known complication of any abdominal operation and adhesions can lead to intestinal obstruction.

복부 수술 후 합병증으로 유착이 올 수도 있고, 장폐색이 될 수도 있습니다.

Hernia is a complication of any incision of abdomen.

복부 수술 후 탈장이 올 수도 있습니다.

Peritonitis or infection in the abdomen often occurs.

복막염이나 복부 내 감염이 올 수 있습니다.

Sepsis complication rarely occurs.

폐혈증과 같은 합병증이 드물게 일어납니다.

The mortality rate of operation is estimated 5 % of operation.

수술 중 사망률은 약 5% 정도입니다.

Sometimes people continue to have problem even after surgery.

때때로 수술 후에도 계속적인 문제가 발생되기도 합니다.

We can't give a hundred percent guarantee that it would relieve all your symptoms.

수술 후 당신의 모든 증상이 좋아질 것이라고 100% 보장하지는 못합니다.

It's tough, but it's true.
답답하지만 사실입니다.

I want to tell you that we can't promise definitely.
확실히 약속할 수 없군요.

4) 수술환자 보호자에 대한 설명

The surgery was successful.
The surgery was a success.
수술은 성공입니다.

I am happy to tell you that patient is out of surgery, that everything went fine.
환자의 수술 모든 게 잘되어 끝났다고 말하니 기쁘군요.

The surgery lasted about two hours and that tumor was removed.
수술이 2시간 정도 걸려 종양이 제거 되었습니다.

Patient had a localized cancer.
환자는 국한된 암을 가지고 있었습니다.

We had performed total resection, taking out most of cancer region.
우리는 암의 대부분을 도려냈습니다.

There are no complications and full recovery is expected.
합병증은 없고 완전한 회복이 기대됩니다.

Patient will be in intensive care unit.
환자는 중환자실에 있을 것입니다.

I think the patient will be fine.

환자는 좋아질 것이라고 생각합니다.

Patient is expected to be hospitalized for 2 weeks, then go home
to recuperate.

환자는 2주정도 입원 후 집에 돌아가 회복하시면 될 것으로 생각됩니다.

We have some serious matters to discuss regarding patient's
condition.

환자의 상태에 대해 상의할 중요한 문제가 있습니다.

Patient's condition is very serious.

환자 상태가 아주 심각합니다.

Multiple organs are severe damaged.

많은 기관이 심하게 손상되어 있습니다.

They function not well.

그들의 기능이 좋질 않습니다.

Surgery is a risk.

수술은 위험한 것입니다.

The success rate is small.

성공률이 적습니다.

His chance of survival is small.

살 가능성이 적습니다.

Odds are about fifty-fifty.

확률은 50대 50입니다.

We will do everything we can.

우리가 할 수 있는 것은 다 하겠습니다.

5) 국소마취 수술 후 주의사항

You have just had a surgical procedure that will hopefully correct your problem.

당신은 바로 지금 치료를 위한 수술을 받았습니다.

You should experience no pain for the first few hours, because the area has been numbed with local anesthesia.

당신은 처음 몇 시간 동안은 국소마취로 무감각하기에 통증을 느끼지 않을 것입니다.

If you see blood coming through the bandage, don't be alarmed.

붕대를 통해 피가 나와도 놀라지 마십시오.

Elevate your wound site and wrap some toweling around the bandage.

상처 부위를 높게 올린 다음 수건으로 붕대 주위를 감으세요.

Keep the site elevated and notify the doctor if bleeding continues.

상처부위를 높게 하고도, 출혈이 계속되면 의사에게 알려 주세요.

Keep the bandage clean and intact until your next visit.

다음 진료 때까지 붕대를 깨끗하게 유지하세요.

For pain take the prescribed medication which the doctors has given to you as prescribed.

통증을 위해 의사가 처방해 준 약을 복용하세요.

Your next appointment is ＊＊＊.

당신의 다음 진료 시간은 ＊＊＊입니다.

If you have any question, call doctor ＊＊＊-＊＊＊＊.

만약 의문이 나는 사항이 있으시면, 의사에게 연락하세요.

Day or night at the following telephone number ✳✳✳-✳✳✳✳.
주간 또는 야간 전화 번호입니다.

If no answer at the above number or you have an emergency, you may call ✳✳✳-✳✳✳✳.
전화 번호에 응답이 없고 응급상황이면, 이곳으로 연락을 하실 수 있습니다.

6) Appendicitis (충수염)

Blood test, X-ray and abdominal ultrasound is neccessary for you to determine if there is an abnormal finding in your abdomen.
당신의 배에 어떤 이상이 있는지, 혈액 검사와 **X-ray** 검사, 초음파 검사가 필요합니다.

Laboratory results and ultrasonogram show inflamed and infected appendix.
혈액검사와 초음파에서 염증이 있고 감염된 충수돌기가 보이는군요.

The appendix is hollow pouch attached to the cecum, the beginning of the large intestine.
충수돌기는 대장의 시작부분 맹장에 있는 작은 길쭉한 주머니입니다.

There is need to perform appendectomy.
충수돌기 절제술이 필요합니다.

We will remove the appendix by using the traditional open procedure.
우리는 전통적인 방법으로 충수돌기를 제거할 것입니다.

Most incisions are less than 10 cm in length.
대부분 절개는 10cm 미만입니다.

We will perform appectomy via laparoscopy.

우리는 충수돌기 절제술을 복부내시경을 통해 할 것입니다.

Laparoscopic appendectomy needs only 1 inch incision in the abdomen.

복부 내시경을 이용한 충수돌기 절제술은 복부의 1cm 절개만 필요합니다.

One incision is near the umbilicus, or navel, and one is between the umbilicus and the pubis.

배꼽이나 주변에 1개의 절개를 하고, 다른 1개는 배꼽과 치골 사이에 합니다.

Two other incisions are smaller and are in the right side of the lower abdomen.

2개의 다른 절개는 작게 우측 하복부에 합니다.

We pass a camera and special instruments through these incisions.
With the aid of this equipment, we can perform appendectomy.

우리는 카메라와 특수 기구를 이 곳에 넣은 후, 이것들을 이용해 충수돌기 절제술을 합니다.

The appendix had ruptured.

충수돌기가 파열되었더군요.

We inserted the drain.

우리는 드레인을 넣었습니다.

Rubber tubes promote the flow of infection inside the abdomen to outside of the body.

고무튜브가 복부 내 감염을 밖으로 나오도록 도와줍니다.

Wound infections can do occur and an abscess may form in the abdomen as a complication of appendicitis.
충수돌기 절제술후 합병증으로 상처 감염이나 복부내 농양이 생길 수도 있습니다.

You may require admission for 5 days.
당신은 5일 간의 입원이 필요합니다.

The appendix was located in the posterior area of the abdomen.
충수돌기가 복부 후반부에 있었습니다.

7) Hemoperitoneum (혈복증)

Probably a lacerated blood vessel within the abdomen or internal organ trauma may lead to rapid bleeding.
아마도 복부나 내부 장기의 찢어진 혈관이 빠른 출혈을 일으키고 있는 것 같습니다.

The spleen and liver are common internal organs that may be traumatized, and cause a hemoperitoneum.
비장이나 간이 손상 후 복강내 출혈을 일으키는 가장 흔한 장기입니다.

Diagnostic peritoneal lavage is needed to determine if patient should have immediate operation.
환자가 응급 수술을 받아야 하는지 아닌지, 진단적 복강내 세정이 필요합니다.

We will make a nick in your belly so I can fill your abdomen with fluid.
당신의 배에 작은 절개를 내어 용액을 넣겠습니다.

Once it's full, we'll watch as the fluid drains out.
일단 다 차면 용액이 흘러나온 것을 관찰 할 것입니다.

If blood comes out, you have abdominal injuries.
만약 피가 나온다면 당신은 복부에 손상을 입은 것입니다.

After patient stabilizes, a CT of the abdomen should be obtained
  for detect bloody fluid.
환자가 안정되면 출혈을 알기 위해 복부 **CT**를 꼭 찍어야 합니다.

Abdominal CT is a good test to see if blood is present in the
  abdominal cavity.
복부 **CT** 촬영이 복부내 피가 있는 지 볼 수 있는 좋은 검사입니다.

If there is significant blood loss, we will consider angiography.
만약 심각한 출혈이 보이면, 혈관조영술을 고려할 수도 있습니다.

A hemoperitoneum is a potentially life threatening situation.
복강내 출혈은 생명을 위협하는 위험한 상황입니다.

Bleeding may lead to shock.
출혈은 쇼크를 일으킬 수 있습니다.

The rapid abdominal distension may also cause pressure on the
  diaphragm, and decrease ability to breathe comfortably.
빠른 복부 팽창은 횡격막에 압박을 가해 숨을 편하게 쉬지 못하게 합니다.

Intravenous fluids and blood transfusion should be given to
  maintain blood pressure and improve tissue perfusion.
혈압을 유지하고 조직으로 피가 잘 가게하기 위해 수액과 수혈이 필요합
  니다.

Hemoperitoneum occured when a car has hit patient.
차가 칠 때 복강내 출혈이 생겼습니다.

Exploratory surgery is the only way to obtain a diagnosis and treat the condition.

실험적 수술이 진단과 치료를 위한 유일한 방법입니다.

The spleen was ruptured by blunt trauma.

비장이 손상당해 파열되었습니다.

The surgical removal of the spleen should be done to stop bleeding.

비장제거술이 출혈을 멈추기 위해 행해져야 합니다.

The spleen has a role in the immune system and filtering foreign substances and worn-out blood cells from the blood.

비장은 면역과 혈액내 이물질이나 다 된 혈액 내 세포들을 거르는 역할을 합니다.

The patient needs to have emergency operation.

환자는 응급수술을 받아야 합니다.

We can't give a hundred percent guarantee that the patient would be okay.

환자가 괜찮을 것이라고 100% 보장하지는 못합니다.

8) Stomach Cancer (위암)

Fecal occult blood test is needed because stomach ulcer and cancer sometimes causes bleeding that cannot be seen.

위궤양이나 위암이 때때로 보이지 않는 출혈을 야기 시키므로 대변잠혈검 사가 필요합니다.

Upper GI series and endoscopy help us find tumors or other abnormal findings.

상부 위장관 X-ray 검사나 내시경 검사가 암이나 다른 이상이 있는지 발견 하도록 도와줍니다.

I'd like to perform an endoscopy for diagnosis.
진단을 위해 내시경을 해야겠습니다.

We can remove some tissue through the endoscopy.
우리는 내시경을 통해 일부 조직을 제거할 것입니다.

It could be an ulcer, but it's not typical.
궤양일 수 있지만 전형적인 것은 아닙니다.

A biopsy is the only sure way to know whether cancer cells are
  present.
조직검사가 암세포가 있는 지 해 볼 수 있는 유일한 검사입니다.

Pathologist will examine the tissue under a microscope to check
  for cancer cells.
병리학자가 현미경으로 암세포가 있는 지 검사할 것입니다.

We have some very serious matters to discuss regarding your
  disease.
당신의 병에 대해 상의할 중요한 문제가 있습니다.

I am afraid you have stomach cancer.
당신은 위암을 가지고 있습니다.

Treatments for your stomach cancer include surgery,
  chemotherapy, and/or radiation therapy.
위암에 대한 치료로는 수술이나 항암제, 또는 방사선 치료입니다.

Surgery is the most common treatment for stomach cancer.
수술이 위암 치료의 가장 일반화된 치료입니다.

The operation is called gastrectomy.
그 수술은 위절제술이라 불립니다.

We will remove part or all of the stomach, as well as some of the tissue around the stomach.

우리는 위의 일부나 전체와 위 주위 조직들을 제거할 것입니다.

Because cancer can spread through the lymphatic system, lymph nodes near the tumor are often removed during surgery so that the pathologist can check them for cancer cells.

위암은 임파선 조직을 통해 퍼지므로, 암 주위 조직의 임파선을 수술 중 제거하여 병리학자가 암세포를 검사할 것입니다.

If cancer cells are in the lymph nodes, tumor may have spread to other parts of the body.

만약 암세포가 임파선에서 발견이 되었다면, 종양은 몸의 다른 곳으로 전이되었을 수 있습니다.

We will connect the remaining part of the stomach to the esophagus or the small intestine after partial gastrectomy.

우리는 부분 위절제술 후 남은 위 부분을 식도나 소장과 연결시킬 것입니다.

After a total gastrectomy, we will connect the esophagus directly to the small intestine.

완전 위절제술 후 우리는 식도와 소장을 직접 연결할 것입니다.

Chemotherapy is needed to destroy remaining cancer cells.

항암제 치료가 남은 암세포를 죽이기 위해 필요합니다.

Combination treatment with chemotherapy and radiation therapy is needed to relieve symptoms and to destroy cancer cells that may remain in the area.

항암제와 방사선 치료 요법이 증상을 완화시키고, 남은 부위의 암세포를 죽이기 위해 필요합니다.

You may need to stay in the hospital while receiving chemotherapy.

항암제 치료를 받는 동안 입원할 필요가 있습니다.

You should come to the hospital regularly for radiation therapy.

당신은 방사선 치료를 위해 규칙적으로 병원에 와야 합니다.

Biological therapy (Immunotherapy) is a form of treatment that helps the body's immune system attack and destroy cancer cells.

생물학적(면역치료) 치료는 몸의 면역 시스템이 암세포를 공격하여 파괴하는 치료의 일종입니다.

9) Hepatoma (간암)

I'm afraid you have a liver cancer.

간암이군요.

We should consider your general health and age before operation.

우리는 수술 전에 당신의 전신 건강과 나이를 고려해야 합니다.

There is no evidence that the cancer has spread to the nearby lymph nodes or to other parts of the body.

암이 주위 임파선이나 다른 곳으로 퍼졌다는 근거는 없습니다.

It is a localized resectable liver cancer that can be removed during surgery.

수술 중 제거할 수 있는 국한된 간암입니다.

You need partial hepatectomy.

부분 간절제술이 필요합니다.

We will remove part of the liver and leave a part of normal liver tissue.
우리는 간의 일부를 제거하고 정상 간 조직의 부분을 남길 것입니다.

Remaining healthy tissue takes over the functions of the liver.
남은 건강한 조직이 간기능을 대체합니다.

Operation depends on how well the liver is working.
수술은 간 기능이 얼마나 좋은지에 따라 달려있습니다.

Surgical removal of the tumor is not possible because of poor liver function or the location of the tumor.
암 제거 수술은 간기능이 안 좋고 암의 위치 때문에 불가능합니다.

It is a localized unresectable cancer.
이것은 국한된 절제 불가능한 암입니다.

We will inject alcohol into the area around certain nerves in the abdomen to block the pain.
우리는 통증을 없애기 위해 복부의 신경 주위로 알코올을 집어넣을 것입니다.

Combination treatment with chemotherapy and radiation therapy is needed to reduce cancer lesion.
항암제와 방사선 치료 요법이 암 부위를 줄이기 위해 필요합니다.

Advanced liver cancer cannot be cured, so we can try to slow the progress of the disease with chemotherapy or radiation therapy.
이미 진행된 간암은 치료가 불가능하므로, 병의 진행을 늦추기 위해 항암제와 방사선 치료를 하도록 노력할 것입니다.

Cancer can recur after operation because undetected cancer cells remained somewhere in the body.
암은 어떤 곳에 발견되지 않는 암세포가 있을 수 있으므로 수술 후 재발할 수 있습니다.

Most recurrences occur within the first 2 years of treatment.
대부분 재발은 2년 안에 나타납니다.

Liver transplant may be required or the patient will die.
간이식이 필요할 것 같군요, 그렇지 않으면 환자는 죽을 것입니다.

Total hepatectomy with liver transplantation is an option only if the disease has not spread outside the liver and only if a suitable donated liver can be found.
간제거 후 이식술은 간 밖으로 전이가 되지 않고, 간 공여자가 있을 경우에만 할 수 있는 수술옵션입니다.

Unfortunately, the supply of transplant livers is extremely limited, and patient may face a long wait before a liver becomes available, and many do not survive long enough to reach this point.
불행하게도 간의 공여는 극히 제한적이기에, 간을 얻으려면 오랜 시간 기다려야 하는데, 환자가 그때까지 살아있기가 힘이 들 것입니다.

10) Gall Stone (담석)

Surgery to remove the gall bladder is the most common way to treat symptomatic gallstones.
담낭제거술이 증상이 있는 담석의 일반적인 치료입니다.

The standard surgery is laparoscopic cholecystectomy.
일반화된 수술은 내시경을 통한 담낭절제술입니다.

We make several tiny incisions in the abdomen and insert surgical instruments and a video camera into the abdomen.
우리는 복부에 몇 개의 작은 절개를 가한 후, 수술기구를 넣고 비디오 카메라로 복부를 볼 것입니다.

We can carefully separate the gall bladder from the liver through monitor.

모니터를 보면서 우리는 조심스럽게 간에서 담낭을 제거할 수 있습니다.

Because the abdominal muscles are not cut during laparoscopic surgery, you have less pain and fewer complications.

내시경 수술은 복부 근육에 절개를 가하지 않으므로 통증이나 합병증이 거의 없습니다.

Recovery usually involves only one night in the hospital, followed by several days of restricted activity at home.

병원에서 하루면 회복하고 집에서 며칠만 조심하면 됩니다.

If we discover any obstacles to the laparoscopic procedure, such as infection or scarring from other operations, the operating team may have to switch to open surgery.

만약 내시경 수술 도중 감염이나 다른 수술로 인한 상처가 발견되어 방해가 되면, 개복술로 바꿀 수 있습니다.

The most common complication in gall bladder surgery is injury to the bile ducts.

담낭 수술의 가장 흔한 합병증은 담관의 손상입니다.

An injured common bile duct can leak bile and cause a painful and potentially dangerous infection.

손상된 담관은 담즙이 새어나와 위험한 감염을 일으킬 수 있습니다.

Minor injury to bile duck can sometimes be treated nonsurgically, but major injury requires additional surgery.

담관에 일어난 작은 상처는 수술하지 않고 치료가 될 수도 있지만, 큰 상처는 추가 수술이 필요합니다.

11) Thyroid Cancer (갑상선 암)

I'd like to check the thyroid, voice box, and lymph nodes in the neck for unusual nodules or swelling.

나는 이상한 혹이나 부종이 없는 지, 당신의 목에 있는 갑상선과 성대, 임파선을 검사해 보겠습니다.

I'd like to test for abnormal levels of calcium and hormones in the blood.

혈액에서 칼슘과 호르몬 검사를 해봐야 할 것 같군요.

Ultrasonography is needed to see how many nodules are present, how big they are, and whether they are solid or filled with fluid.

초음파는 얼마나 많은 혹이 있고, 크기와, 액체의 유무를 보는 데 유용합니다.

Radionuclide scanning is necessary for you to make thyroid nodules show up on a picture and know whether thyroid cancer has spread to distant sites.

갑상선 혹이 잘 나오고, 갑상선 암이 다른 곳으로 잘 퍼졌는 지 보기 위해서는 방사선 동위 원소 검사가 필요합니다.

MRI or CT is needed to find out whether the cancer has spread to the lymph nodes or other areas within the neck.

목안의 다른 조직으로 암이 퍼졌는 지 보기 위해 **MRI**나 **CT** 촬영이 필요합니다.

Biopsy is the only sure way to know whether a nodule is cancerous.

조직 검사가 혹이 암인지 아닌지 보기 위한 가장 좋은 검사입니다.

We can remove a sample of tissue from a thyroid nodule with a thin needle.

우리는 작은 주사바늘을 통해 갑상선 혹 조직을 떼어낼 것입니다.

We will use an ultrasound device to guide the needle through the nodule.

우리는 혹으로 가는 바늘의 안내를 위해 초음파를 사용할 것입니다.

A pathologist will look at the cells under a microscope to check for cancer.

병리학자가 암 여부를 검사하기 위해 현미경으로 세포들을 관찰할 것입니다.

Diagnosis was difficult from the fine-needle aspiration, so surgical biopsy is needed during the operation.

바늘을 통한 진단이 어렵기 때문에 수술 중 조직검사가 필요합니다.

A pathologist then checks the tissue for cancer cells.

병리학자가 그 다음 암 세포를 검사할 것입니다.

If the diagnosis is thyroid cancer, we need to know the stage, or extent, of the disease to plan the best treatment.

만약 진단이 갑상선 암으로 나오면, 우리는 그 시기와 정도를 가장 최선의 치료를 위해 알 필요가 있습니다.

Depending on the type and stage, thyroid cancer may be treated with surgery, radioactive iodine, hormone treatment, external radiation or chemotherapy.

갑상선 암은 종류와 시기에 따라 수술, 방사선 요오드 요법, 호르몬 치료, 방사선 또는 항암제 치료를 합니다.

Surgery is the most common treatment for thyroid cancer.

수술이 갑상선 암의 가장 흔한 치료입니다.

We will remove all or part of the thyroid.

우리는 갑상선 일부 또는 전체를 제거할 것입니다.

The type of surgery depends on the type and stage of thyroid cancer, the size of the nodule and the patient's age.

수술은 갑상선 암의 종류와 시기, 혹의 크기, 환자의 나이에 따라 다릅니다.

Nearby lymph nodes are sometimes removed.

근처의 임파선은 종종 제거됩니다.

You need to take thyroid hormone pills to replace the natural thyroid hormone after operation.

당신은 수술 후 갑상선 호르몬을 대체해 줄 갑상선 호르몬 약을 먹어야 합니다.

12) Breast Cancer (유방암)

It is normal for the breasts to feel a little lumpy and uneven.

약간 멍울이 지고 불균형한 것은 정상입니다.

It is common for your breasts to be swollen and tender right before or during your menstrual period.

생리 전이나 생리 기간 중 커지고 아픈 것은 정상입니다.

A screening mammogram is the best tool available to find breast cancer before symptoms appear.

유방 X-선 검사가 증상이 나타나기 전 유방암을 발견할 수 있는 가장 좋은 방법입니다.

I'd like to check you regularly to watch for any changes.

어떤 변화가 있는 지 보기 위해 규칙적인 검사가 필요합니다.

Early breast cancer usually does not cause pain.

초기 유방암은 통증을 일으키지 않습니다.

I suspect this may be a tumor of breast.

유방암이 의심되는군요.

Lump in the breast and small nodules in the underarm area may be a sign of breast cancer.

팔 아래나 유방에 있는 혹은 유방암의 증상일 수 있습니다.

Nipple discharge and inverted nipple into the breast may be a sign of breast cancer.

젖꼭지에서 분비가 있거나 함몰이 된 것은 암의 증상일 수 있습니다.

I will examine your breast to know the size and texture of the lump and determine whether the lump moves easily.

혹의 크기와 느낌, 잘 움직이는 지 검사를 해 보겠습니다.

Mammograpm is needed to get important information about a breast lump.

유방 **X**-선 촬영은 유방 혹에 대한 중요한 정보를 줍니다.

Ultrasonogram is needed to know whether a lump is a fluid-filled cyst or a solid mass .

혹에 액체가 있는 지 알기 위해 초음파가 필요합니다.

Fine needle aspiration is needed to make a diagnosis.

진단을 위해 주사 바늘을 통한 조직검사가 필요합니다.

Tissue removed in a needle biopsy goes to a lab to be checked by a pathologist for cancer cells.

바늘로 떼어진 조직은 병리학자가 암이 있는지 보기 위해 검사실로 보내어집니다.

Surgical biopsy is needed to get a sample of a lump.

혹의 샘플을 얻기 위해 수술적 조직 검사가 필요합니다.

I am afraid you have a breast cancer.

유방암이군요.

Special laboratory tests can help determine whether hormones help the cancer to grow.

특별한 검사가 어떤 호르몬이 암을 자라게 했는 지 알 수 있게 합니다.

Surgery is the most common treatment for breast cancer.

유방암은 수술이 가장 일반적인 치료방법입니다.

It is common to use several treatment modalities concurrently with the goal of preventing recurrence.

재발 방지를 위해 몇 가지 치료방법이 함께 필요합니다.

After breast-sparing surgery, you should receive radiation therapy to destroy cancer cells that remain in the area.

유방을 남기는 수술을 받은 후에는, 남은 조직의 암세포를 죽이기 위해, 항암제 치료가 필요합니다.

Radical mastectomy is nessary for you.

당신에게는 광범위 유방 절제술이 필요합니다.

It is wide excision of the breast, adjacent muscles and axillary lymph nodes.

그것은 유방과 주위 근육, 액와부 임파선들을 모두 제거하는 수술입니다.

We will remove the whole breast and most of the lymph nodes under the arm and, often, chest muscles.

우리는 전체 유방과 팔 아래 대부분의 임파선, 그리고 때론 흉벽 근육을 제거할 것입니다.

Breast reconstruction is an option after mastectomy.

유방 제건술은 유방 절제술 후 옵션입니다.

You can discuss breast reconstruction with a plastic surgeon before having a mastectomy.

유방 제거술 동안 유방 재건술에 대한 것은 성형외과 의사와 상의하기 바랍니다.

Before surgery, radiation therapy, alone or with chemotherapy or hormonal therapy is needed to destroy cancer cells and shrink tumors.

수술 전, 암세포를 죽이고 크기를 줄이기 위해, 항암제 혹은 호르몬 치료가 병행되는 방사선 치료가 필요합니다.

Chemotherapy or hormonal therapy or biological therapy should be needed to destroy the remained cancer cell.

남은 암세포를 죽이기 위해, 항암제 또는 호르몬 치료, 또는 생물학적 치료가 필요합니다.

I recommend you to wear an elastic cuff to improve lymph circulation.

나는 당신에게 임파선의 흐름을 좋게하기 위해 탄력 압박대를 착용하기를 권합니다.

Lymphedema after surgery can be prevented or reduced with exercises and by resting with the arm propped up on a pillow.

수술후 임파선 부종은 운동이나 베개 위로 팔을 올림으로써 줄이거나 예방할 수 있습니다.

Regular follow up exams are important after breast cancer treatment.

유방암 치료 후 규칙적인 검사가 중요합니다.

You should perform monthly breast self-examinations and have a mammogram every 1 to 2 years.

당신은 매달 유방 자가 검사를 하고, 1-2년에 한 번 유방X-선 검사를 받아야 합니다.

When doing a breast self-exam, it's important to remember that each woman's breasts are different, and that changes can occur because of aging, the menstrual cycle, pregnancy, menopause, or taking birth control pills or other hormones.

유방 검사를 하는 동안 여자들의 유방은 각각 다르고, 나이나 생리 주기, 임신, 폐경, 피임약이나 호르몬 등에 의해 다를 수 있음을 기억해야 합니다.

13) Breast Self-Exam (유방 자가 검사)

Woman should perform breast self exams starting at age 20.

여성들은 20세부터 유방 자가 검사를 시작해야 합니다.

It is estimated that one out of every eight women will be diagnosed with breast cancer in her life time.

8명의 여성중 한 명이 자신의 일생 중 유방암으로 진단되고 있습니다.

The best way to beat it is to find it early.

가장 좋은 치유법은 빨리 발견하는 것이지요

This makes monthly brest self-exams all the more important.

이것은 유방 자가 진단이 더욱 중요함을 일깨워줬습니다.

Look at each breast and nipple to check for swelling, lumps, dimpling, or skin change.

각 유방의 부종이나 혹, 함몰이나 피부 변화를 검사하세요.

Put your left hand over your head and gently press into the skin of your breast using the pads of the first 3 fingers of your right hand.

당신의 왼손을 머리위로 올리고 오른손가락 3개로 유방의 피부를 누르며 검사하세요.

Move your finger pads in a circle as you feel your breast tissue.

당신의 유방 조직이 느껴지도록 손가락으로 원을 그리며 검사하세요.

Start at the outer part of your breast and slowly move around it in a clockwise direction.

유방 바깥쪽에서 시계방향으로 검사하세요.

Squeeze your nipple to check for liquid coming from it.

젖꼭지를 짜서 액이 나오는지 보세요.

Check your other breast the same way.

다른 쪽 유방도 같은 방법으로 검사하세요.

14) Colorectal Cancer (대장, 직장암)

There are often no symptoms for colorectal cancer in its early stages, which is why screening tests are important.

대장 및 직장암은 초기에 증상이 없으므로 스크린 검사가 중요합니다.

Bright red or very dark blood in the stool may be a sign of the polyp or cancer.

대변에 선홍색이나 검은 혈액이 있으면 폴립이나 암의 증상일 수 있습니다.

Fecal occult blood test is needed to check for hidden blood in the stool.
대변 잠혈 반응 검사는 변내의 감추어진 혈액을 검사하기 위해 필요합니다.

Because of an increased risk of colorectal cancer in older adults, I should do barium enema and colonoscopy to rule out a diagnosis of cancer.
나이 든 성인에서의 대장암, 직장암의 위험률 증가 때문에 암을 감별하기 위해 바륨관장이나 대장경 검사를 하겠습니다.

Barium enema is needed to see the colon and rectum on the X-rays.
바륨 관장은 X-선으로 대장과 직장을 보기 위해 필요합니다.

Colonoscopy is necessary for you to look at the rectum and the entire colon.
직장과 전체 대장을 보기 위해 대장 내시경이 필요합니다.

If polyps are found, they can be removed.
만약 폴립이 보이면 그들은 제거될 수 있습니다.

Treatment for colorectal cancer depends mostly on the size, location, and extent of the tumor, as well as a person's overall health.
대장이나 직장암의 치료는 암의 크기나 전이 정도, 환자의 전체적인 건강에 따라 결정됩니다.

Surgery to remove the tumor is the most common treatment for colorectal cancer.
암을 제거하는 수술이 대장암, 직장암의 일반적인 치료입니다.

Patient continues to have bowel problems after operation.
수술 후에도 계속적인 장운동 문제가 발생됩니다.

Radiation therapy before surgery is needed to shrink a tumor so that it is easier to remove.

암의 크기를 줄여 쉽게 제거되도록 수술전 방사선 치료가 필요합니다.

We will remove the tumor along with part of the healthy colon or rectum and nearby lymph nodes and reconnect the healthy portions of the colon or rectum.

우리는 건강한 대장이나 직장을 따라 주위 임파선과 함께 암을 제거한 후, 직장과 대장의 정상인 부분을 연결할 것입니다.

When we cannot reconnect the healthy portions, a temporary or permanent colostomy is necessary.

만약 우리가 건강한 부분으로 연결하지 못한다면, 일시적이거나, 또는 영구적인 대장조루술이 필요합니다.

Colostomy is a surgical opening through the wall of the abdomen into the colon.

대장 조루술은 복벽을 통해 대장의 개구부를 만드는 수술입니다.

After a colostomy, you have to wear a special bag to collect body waste.

대장 조루술 후 배출물들을 모으기 위한 특별한 백을 차야 합니다.

Chemotherapy will be given to destroy any cancerous cells that may remain in the body after surgery.

항암제가 수술 후 몸 안에 남아있는 암세포를 파괴하기 위해 투여될 것입니다.

Radiation therapy is needed to destroy any cancer cells that remain in the treated area.

방사선 치료가 치료받은 부위에 남은 암세포를 파괴하기 위해 필요합니다.

15) Hemothorax & Pneumothorax (혈흉 및 기흉)

Diminished breath sound on the right side.
오른 쪽 호흡음이 줄어들었군요.

You may have got pneumothorax.
기흉일 수가 있습니다.

No breath sounds on the right side.
오른쪽에 호흡음이 없군요.

Your symptom may be due to hemothorax.
당신의 증상은 혈흉 때문입니다.

I wanna chest X-ray.
흉부 사진을 찍어야겠습니다.

X-ray is back.
필름이 나왔습니다.

The chest X-ray suggests that you may have hemothorax.
흉부사진에서 혈흉이 의심되는군요.

I'll give you O_2.
산소를 주겠습니다.

Take a deep breath through the mask.
마스크로 숨을 깊게 들이쉬세요.

I'll get an arterial blood gas.
동맥 혈액 가스 검사를 할 것입니다.

Delayed hemothorax can occur at some interval after blunt chest trauma.
가슴을 다친 후, 지연성 혈흉이 올 수도 있습니다.

A small hemothorax may often remains unnoticed in chest X-ray.

작은 혈흉은 흉부 X-ray에서 안보이기도 합니다.

Such small collections rarely need treatment.

그와 같이 작은 것은 치료를 안 해도 됩니다.

Accumulation of blood within the chest results from injury to intrathoracic structures or the chest wall.

흉부에 피가 고인 것은 흉곽 내 구조물이나 흉벽에 손상이 와서 생깁니다.

Blood will be evacuated through tube.

피는 튜브를 통해 빼내어질 것입니다.

It should be drained by tube thoracostomy.

흉곽내 삽관으로 빼내야만 합니다.

Sometimes injury of the arteries may produce a persistent bleeding.

때때로 동맥의 손상이 계속적인 출혈을 일으킬 수도 있습니다.

This is considered a massive hemothorax.

이것은 심한 혈흉입니다.

Surgical exploration should be performed.

시험적 수술이 필요합니다.

Empyema complication may develop from infection in a retained collection of blood.

농흉 합병증이 남아있는 혈액에 감염이 생겨 올 수 있습니다.

It requires surgical drainage.

이것은 수술적 배농술이 필요합니다.

We suspect pneumothorax because you suddenly develop
  shortness of breath.
갑자기 호흡곤란이 온 곳으로보아 기흉이 의심됩니다.

A chest X-ray is the best way to confirm that you have a
  pneumothorax.
흉부 **X-ray** 검사가 기흉의 가장 좋은 진단법입니다.

The X-ray shows the pneumothorax as a dark area in the chest.
X-ray에서 가슴의 검은 부분이 기흉을 나타냅니다.

A CT scan may be needed in some cases to find a small
  pneumothorax.
컴퓨터 단층 촬영이 작은 기흉을 진단하기 위해 필요할 수도 있습니다.

A pneumothorax is a collapsed lung.
기흉은 폐가 찌부러진 것입니다.

A pneumothorax occurs when air escapes from the lungs.
기흉은 폐의 공기가 빠져나와 생깁니다.

A spontaneous pneumothorax can develop in people who don't
  have any obvious lung disease.
자연적인 기흉은 특별한 폐의 병이 없더라도 생길 수 있습니다.

Once the cause of pneumothorax is treated, a collapsed lung
  usually will return to normal within 2 or 3 days.
일단 기흉의 원인이 치료만 되면 폐는 2-3일 안에 좋아집니다.

Recovering from a collapsed lung may take up to several weeks.
찌부러진 폐가 회복되려면 몇 주가 필요할 것입니다.

We need to do needle decompression.
You need needle decompression.

Needle decompression is needed.

주사 감압이 필요합니다.

Removal of the air from the pleural cavity with a needle and syringe is needed.

주사바늘과 실린지로 흉곽내 공기를 빼야 합니다.

Removal of the air from the pleural cavity by inserting a chest tube is needed.

흉부 튜브를 넣어 흉곽내 공기를 빼야합니다.

We'll insert tube into your chest.

당신 흉부로 튜브를 넣을 것입니다.

This procedure gonna help you breathe.

이 시술이 당신이 숨을 쉴 수 있게 해 줄 것입니다.

Sometimes damaged or scarred portions of lung should be removed by operation to allow the pneumothorax to heal.

때로는 기흉을 치료하기 위해 수술로 손상 당하거나 흉이 있는 폐의 일부를 수술로 제거해야 합니다.

Your condition require surgery.

수술이 필요합니다

I recommend surgery.

수술을 권유합니다.

I'll put you on a surgical schedule.

수술 스케줄을 잡겠습니다.

16) Dialogue 1.

D : When did you first start with abdominal pain?
복부 불쾌감이 언제부터 시작되었지요?

P : About three weeks ago.
약 3주전부터입니다.

D : Does anything do help your pain?
어떤 것도 통증에 도움이 안되던가요?

P : I usually just wait it out and it goes away.
저는 항상 통증이 사라질 때까지 기다립니다.

D : Do you have intense pain even without a bowel movement?
대변을 보지 않을 때도 배가 무척 아픈가요?

P : Yes.
예.

D : Do you ever vomit?
토하지는 않았습니까?

P : No, but I have had chronic belching.
아닙니다. 하지만 자주 트림이 나옵니다.

D : Is everything else all right? Digestion, bowel movements, urination?
소화나 대변, 소변은 정상인가요?

P : I've got no trouble.
아무 문제가 없습니다.

D : Do you have black bowel movements?

검은색 변을 보지는 않습니까?

P : No, my stool is dark brown.

아뇨, 대변 색깔은 짙은 갈색입니다.

D : What do the stool look like? well-formed?

대변 모양은 어떻죠? 대체로 잘 뭉쳐져 있나요?

P : Yes.

예.

D : Do you have blood in your bowels?

대변에 피가 있던가요?

P : No.

아닙니다.

D : Do you have a small tender lump near the rectum?

직장 주변에 작고 아픈 혹이 있습니까?

P : No.

없습니다.

D : Did you have recently had an endoscopy and an ultrasound scan of your abdomen?

최근에 내시경이나 복부 초음파 검사를 받았습니까?

P : Yes, and results was all right.

예 결과는 정상이었습니다.

D : Have you any other trouble?

다른 이상한 것은 없나요?

P : No.
없습니다.

D : I think we need to do further testing.
좀 더 검사를 해봐야겠군요.

P : OK.
알겠습니다.

17) Dialogue 2.

D : I am afraid the lump is a breast cancer.
죄송하게도 그 혹은 유방암입니다.

I know this is bad news for you.
이것이 당신에게는 나쁜 소식이라는 것을 압니다.

Do you know what cancer is?
암이 무엇인 지 아시죠?

P : Yes. Shall I lose my breast?
예. 가슴을(유방을) 잃어야 하나요?

D : Yes. We can't let this go on any longer, because the cancer will spread.
예. 더 이상 그냥 두면 안 됩니다. 왜냐하면 암이 퍼질 것이기 때문입니다.

Your life could be at risk.
생명이 위험해질 수도 있어요.

P : What do I do now?
이제 어떻게 하죠?

D : Surgery is necessary for you.
수술이 필요할 것 같군요.

P : I can't afford the breast surgery myself.
저 혼자서는 유방 수술을 할 수가 없습니다.

   May I choose medication instead of surgery?
   수술 대신 약으로 대신하면 안됩니까?

D : The only way to treat this is by an operation.
이것을 치료한 유일한 방법은 수술입니다.

P : What is the name of the surgery that I need?
제게 필요한 수술이 무엇이죠?

D : Surgery is radical mastectomy.
수술은 광범위 절제술입니다.

   It is wide excision of the breast, adjacent muscles and
   axillary lymph nodes.
   그것은 유방과 주위 근육, 액와부 임파선들을 모두 제거하는 수술입니다.

P : Will I need chemotherapy?
항암제 치료가 필요합니까?

D : Chemothrapy is needed with the goal of preventing
   recurrence.
   재발 방지를 위해 항암제 치료가 필요합니다.

P : What kind of complications will I have after operation?
수술 후 무슨 합병증이 올 수 있죠?

D : Side effects of treatment cause fatigue, hair loss, nausea, vomiting, lymphedema, anemia and neutropenia.

치료 부작용은 피로감, 탈모, 오심, 구토, 임파 부종, 빈혈, 적혈구 감소증 등입니다.

P : Okay, I have made up my mind to have surgery.

알겠습니다. 수술을 하기로 결정했습니다.

18) Dialogue 3.

D : You just relax.

긴장을 푸세요.

Try and control your breathing.

호흡을 조절하세요.

P : I don't know how to get on with my life?

어떻게 살아야 할지 모르겠습니다.

D : What happened?

무슨 일이지요?

Calm down.

진정하세요.

We're gonna take care of you.

곧 치료해 드리겠습니다.

P : I need more help with self care than doctor can give me.

의사들이 해 주는 것보다 나 자신의 도움이 더 필요합니다.

I had the surgery and my colon removed.

수술을 받고 대장을 절제했습니다.

I can't endure permanent colostomy.
영구적인 인공항문 상태를 견딜 수가 없습니다.

I feel so alone.
난 혼자인 것만 같아요.

D : There is a nonprofit organization you can find support from other people who have had this kind of surgery.
당신과 비슷한 수술을 받은 사람들로부터 도움을 받을 수 있는 비영리 단체가 있습니다.

There are many informations available for you.
당신에게 도움이 될 정보가 많을 것입니다.

P : I'd like to return to my career and participating in activities with my friends.
저는 제 직업을 다시 되찾고, 친구들과 함께 활동하고 싶습니다.

D : Uncover your arm, please.
팔을 걷어 주실래요?

P : What's that?
그게 무엇이지요?

D : This will relax you and make you feel a little calm.
이 것이 당신의 긴장을 풀어주고 진정시키게 해 줄 것입니다.

P : No. I don't want.
필요 없습니다.

D : Quite harmless.
안전합니다.

Lie back, Please.
누우세요.

Calm down.

진정하세요.

P : OK.

알겠습니다.

D : All done.

다 되었습니다.

P : I don't feel any different.

별 이상을 못 느끼겠는데요.

D : It may take a little time to make effect.

효과가 나타나려면 조금 시간이 걸립니다.

Now try to get some relaxation.

진정하도록 노력해 보세요.

5 *Obstetrics and Gynecology*
(산부인과)

1) 부인과적 질문

Are you on your period?
생리중인가요?

When did your period start?
언제 생리가 시작되었죠?

When was your last period?
마지막 생리가 언제였죠?

Do you have regular periods?
Are your periods regular?
May I ask you if your periods are regular?
생리는 규칙적인가요?

Are you missing your period?
생리를 걸렀나요?

When was the period before that?
그 전의 생리는 언제였지요?

Have your periods always been regular in the past?
과거에 생리는 항상 규칙적이었나요?

When did your periods first start?
When was your first period?
How old were you when your periods started?
언제 생리가 처음 시작했죠?

How do you feel before your periods start?
생리 전 어떻게 느끼죠?

How long do your periods last?
How many days do you have?
How long do you have periods?
생리가 얼마나 지속되죠?

How many days have you been bleeding?
얼마동안 출혈이 있었죠?

Are your periods heavy?
생리가 많나요?

How much do you lose?
How much do you bleed?
얼마나 나오죠?

Do you have much flow each time?
항상 양이 많나요?

How many pads do you use each day?
매일 생리대를 얼마나 쓰죠?

Do you have menstrual cramp?
Do you have abdominal pain?
생리통이 있나요?

Where does your belly hurt you?
배 어느 부위가 아프죠?

Do you get pain in your lower abdomen?
아랫배가 아픕니까?

Have your periods become more painful?
생리 중 점점 더 아프던가요?

Do you use pads as well as tampons?
생리대와 탐폰을 같이 쓰나요?

When was the your last cervical smear?
자궁경부 검사를 마지막으로 한 적이 언제죠?

Have you had regular cervical smears?
정기적으로 자궁경부검사를 하나요?

Do you get any bleeding after intercourse?
Is there any bleeding during sex?
성교 중 출혈이 있나요?

Do you still see your periods?
Do you have your periods?
아직도 생리중인가요?

Have you stopped having periods?
생리가 멈추었나요?

Do you get hot flushes?
얼굴이 화끈거린 적이 있나요?

Do you have vaginal discharge?
질분비가 있나요?

Do you have vaginal bleeding without menstruation?
생리도 없이 출혈이 있나요?

How long have you had this discharge?
얼마나 오래 이 분비가 있었죠?

How often do you get it?
얼마나 자주 있죠?

How much is there?
얼마나 많나요?

What color is it?
색깔은 어떻죠?

Does it contain clots? mucus? pus?
응집된 것이나 점액질, 농이 있던가요?

Do you have any itching sensation?
간지러운가요?

Have you ever been pregnant?
임신한 적은 있나요?

When did you have sex last?
최근에 섹스는 언제 하셨죠?

Do you use an intra-uterine device(IUD)?
자궁내 피임기구는 쓰지 않습니까?

Are you taking pill?
Do you take any contraception?
피임약을 먹고있습니까?

Have you ever had any abortion?
유산한 적이 있었나요?

Have you ever had D&C?
인공중절수술을 받은 적이 있었나요?

Why did you have a D & C?
왜 D&C 수술을 받았죠?

Do you have any history of ectopic pregnancy?
자궁 외 임신을 한 적이 있나요?

Do you have ---? or Do you feel ---?

Menstrual changes
Irregular periods
Missed periods
Abnormal menstrual bleeding
Amenorrhea - absence of periods
Sore nipples
Morning sickness
Nausea or Vomiting
Vaginal discharge
Vaginal odor
Blood in urine or stool
Vaginal irritation or itching
Itching or red vulva
Vaginal discomfort
Vaginal dryness
Urination discomfort
Pain during intercourse
Lower abdominal pain or cramps
Fever
Facial flushing
Bladder control problems
Emotional problem

2) 산과적 질문

Are you pregnant?
임신하셨나요?

How far along?
얼마나 되었죠?

How long have you been pregnant?
임신한 지 얼마나 되었죠?

When is your baby due?
When is your due date?
언제가 분만일이죠?

When the contraction's start?
언제 진통이 시작되었죠?

Can you feel the baby move?
아기가 움직이는 것을 느끼나요?

Are you having contractions?
자궁 수축이 있나요?

How frequent are the contractions?
자궁 수축이 얼마나 자주 있죠?

Are you missing your period?
생리를 걸렀나요?

How long has it been since your last period?
마지막 생리후 얼마나 되었죠?

Could you be pregnant?

임신 가능성이 있나요?

When was your last periods?

마지막 생리가 언제였죠?

Have you had sexual intercourse?

섹스를 하였나요?

When was your last contact?

마지막 섹스가 언제였죠?

Have you taken a pregnancy test?

임신 검사를 해 보셨나요?

Is this your first pregnancy?
Is this your first child?

초산인가요?

Have you ever been pregnant?

임신 한 적이 있나요?

Have you been pregnant three times?

3번째 임신하셨나요?

When was the date of your last delivery?

마지막 분만이 언제였죠?

Have you had any cramps or bleeding?

배가 아프거나 출혈한 적이 있나요?

Any cramping? Any vaginal bleeding?

배가 아프거나 출혈은 없었나요?

Do you have swelling and tenderness over the breast?
유방 위가 붓고 아픈가요?

Have you ever had any spontaneous abortion?
Have you ever had any miscarriage?
자연유산이 있었나요?

Have you ever had D&C?
인공중절수술을 받은 적이 있나요?

Have you ever had a C-sec?
제왕 절개술을 받은 적이 있나요?

Do you have any history of ectopic pregnancy?
자궁 외 임신을 한 적이 있나요?

How many times have you been pregnant?
몇 번 임신을 하셨죠?

Did you have preeclampsia before?
전에 임신 자간증에 걸린 적이 있나요?

How many children do you have?
아이들이 몇 명이나 있죠?

How old are they?
아이들이 몇 살이죠?

Did you have a normal delivery?
Were your children delivered vaginally?
Were they all full term and spontaneous delivery?
정상분만이었나요?

Was your child delivered by C-section?
제왕절개술로 태어났나요?

Did you have any trouble during pregnancy?
임신 중 이상은 없었나요?

Was labour induced or did it start by itself?
분만이 유도되었나요 아니면 자연적으로 시작되었나요?

How long were you in labour?
분만 시간이 얼마였죠?

Did you have any complications when you had delivery?
분만 중 어떤 부작용은 없었나요?

3) 분만실에서 필요한 표현

Let's try a deep breath.
숨을 깊게 쉬세요.

Blow through your mouth.
입으로 부세요.

Contractions are 2 minutes apart.
자궁 수축이 2분 간격으로 있군요.

Let's hook her up to a fetal monitor.
태아 모니터를 연결합시다.

Fetal heart tone are good at 160.
태아 박동이 160으로 좋군요.

Full dilated, 100% effaced.
경부가 완전히 열리고 100% 준비되었군요.

Your baby's head is engaged in the canal.
아이 머리가 산도에 진입했습니다.

The membrane isn't ruptured yet.
아직 양수가 터지지 않았군요.

We'll do an amniotomy to rupture it.
양수를 터트릴 것입니다.

Membrane is ruptured.
양수가 터졌습니다.

Labour is starting.
분만이 시작되었습니다.

We need to deliver.
분만을 해야겠습니다.

It's OK. You're going to be fine.
괜찮습니다. 곧 괜찮아질 겁니다.

Breathe. Just breathe.
숨을 쉬세요.

Blow through the pain.
호흡을 통해 통증을 내 쉬세요.

Please lie down on the table.
침대에 올라가 누우실래요?

Could you please put your legs into stirrups.
두 발을 다리 받침대 위에 올려 주세요.

We are gonna push on the next one. OK?
다음에 힘을 주서야합니다. 아시겠죠?

It's time to start to push.
힘 주실 시간입니다.

One, Two, Three. Push. Push.
하나, 둘, 셋. 힘주세요. 힘주세요.

Keep going push.
계속 힘주세요.

One more push. That's right.
한 번 더 힘주세요. 맞아요.

Seeing a head here.
여기 머리가 보이는군요.

We are gonna get her out.
곧 나오려고 합니다.

Good push. One more push.
좋습니다. 한 번 더 힘주세요.

Your baby is gonna come out.
아이가 곧 나오려 합니다.

Okay. Head is coming.
좋습니다. 머리가 나오고 있습니다.

Stop pushing.
그만 힘주세요.

Shoulders are clear.
어깨가 나왔습니다.

Good. You did a good job.
좋습니다. 잘했습니다.

Clamp. Cut. There you go.
묶고, 자르고, 자 여기 있습니다.

You did it.
해냈군요.

You have a beautiful little girl.
당신은 이제 예쁜 딸을 갖게 되었습니다.

4) Pregnancy (임신)

I'll do urine test to verify your pregnancy.
임신을 확인하기 위해 소변 검사를 하겠습니다.

Your pregnancy urine test is positive.
임신 반응 소변검사는 양성입니다.

When a woman becomes pregnant, her body starts to produce a
  hormone called hCG (Human Chorionic Gonadotropin).
여성이 임신을 하게 되면 체내에서 HCG란 호르몬을 분비하게 됩니다.

hCG hormone give the positive result on both urine and blood
  pregnancy tests.
hCG 호르몬은 소변과 혈액에서 양성으로 나옵니다.

The sensitivity for pregnancy test on the first day of a missed
  period is 90 percent.
생리가 지나친 첫날 임신 반응 검사의 민감도는 90%입니다.

The accuracy on one week after the first day of the missed
  period is 97 percent.
생리가 지난 일주일 후 임신 반응 검사의 정확도는 97%입니다.

First morning urine is the ideal sample as it contains the most concentrated presence of hCG.

아침의 첫 소변에 hCG 농도가 높아 가장 좋습니다.

Hold the test stick in your stream of urine and hold it for at least six seconds so that adequate urine contacts the absorbent end.

검사 막대를 잡고 소변에 6초 정도 있어 끝 부분 흡수가 잘 되도록 해야 합니다.

A positive result can be seen as quickly as 40 seconds.

결과는 빠르면 40초안에 볼 수 있습니다.

I will tell you when the baby is due.

언제 아기가 분만될지 말해 드리겠습니다.

Add 9 months and 7 days to the first day of your last menstrual period.

당신의 마지막 생리 날에서 9개월과 7일을 더합니다.

Your expected delivery date will be around -.

당신의 분만일은 -주변입니다.

Many pregnancy symptoms are very similar to those that occur right before menstruating.

임신 후 많은 증상들이 생리 전의 증상과 비슷합니다.

Eating a protein and carbohydrate at bedtime tends to lessen the nausea that occurs in the morning.

자기 전 단백질이나 탄수화물이 아침의 구토를 줄여주는 경향이 있습니다.

Breasts may be very tender, swollen and start to enlarge.

유방이 붓고 아프며 커질 수 있습니다.

Your nipples may start to darken in color, become more erect and be extremely sensitive.

젖꼭지 색깔이 어두워지고 곧게 서며 민감해집니다.

The uterus puts pressure on your bladder making you feel the need for more frequent urination.

자궁이 방광을 눌러 소변을 자주 누게 됩니다.

Leg cramps are often more common in pregnancy.

임신을 하면 다리에 쥐가 더 잘납니다.

Light bleeding (spotting) may occur approximately 8 - 10 days from ovulation.

작은 출혈은 배란 후 8-10일째 보일 수 있습니다.

The spotting is caused from implantation which is when the fertilized egg burrows into the endometrial lining.

작은 출혈은 수정된 난자가 자궁 내막을 파고들어 갈 때 생깁니다.

Ultrasonogram is needed to assess the condition of baby.

아기 상태를 평가하기 위해 초음파가 필요합니다.

I'll get an ultrasound.

초음파를 하겠습니다.

It's a good position.

자세는 좋군요.

Baby seems very active.

아기가 잘 움직이는군요.

Movement is good.

움직임이 좋습니다.

Head is okay.
머리는 괜찮군요.

Looks like a large baby.
아기가 큰 것 같군요.

Weight is on the high side.
몸무게가 높은 편이군요.

You need to be scheduled for ultrasound.
초음파 검사 스케줄을 잡겠습니다.

I will schedule an ultrasound exam every 12 weeks.
12주 간격으로 초음파를 예약해 드리겠습니다.

Ultrasounds will be combined with amniocentesis to validate a
diagnosis.
진단을 확인하기 위해 초음파와 함께 양수천자가 함께 행해질 것입니다.

As a pregnant woman, you need more nutrients to help your
baby grow and be healthy.
임산부로써 아기 건강과 자신의 건강을 위해 좀 더 많은 영양이 필요합니다.

You may have developed gestational diabetes during your
pregnancy.
임신에 의한 당뇨병에 걸린 것 같습니다.

Your blood pressure is a little elevated.
혈압이 조금 올라갔군요.

Your hypertension is probably related to the pregnancy.
당신의 고혈압은 아마도 임신과 관련이 있을 수 있습니다.

You could have preeclampsia.
당신은 전자간증일 수 있습니다.

You have a disorder of late pregnancy known as eclampsia.
당신은 자간증입니다.

The blood vessels spasm, causing lack of oxygen to the brain,
  which leads to the seizure.
혈관들이 수축되고, 산소가 뇌로 가는 것이 부족해, 발작이 일어납니다.

We are gonna relax them with medicine.
우리는 약으로 증상을 완화시킬 것입니다.

You might have an ectopic pregnancy.
자궁외 임신 일 수 있습니다.

We'll do ultrasound.
초음파를 하겠습니다.

You need surgery right away.
지금 즉시 수술이 필요합니다.

It's serious.
이것은 심각합니다.

5) Cervical Cancer (자궁경부암)

I suspect this may be cervical cancer.
자궁암이 의심되는군요.

Pap smear will be done by using a piece of cotton stick to gently
  scrape the outside of the cervix to pick up some cells that can
  be examined under a microscope.
작은 면봉으로 자궁경부 외부를 긁어 세포를 떼어내 현미경으로 검사할 수
있게 팝 검사가 행해질 것입니다.

You may feel some pressure, but you usually do not feel pain.

약간의 압박감을 느끼나 통증은 없을 것입니다.

Most cervical cancers can be caught early with regular screening.

대부분의 암은 규칙적인 검사에 의해 발견이 됩니다.

Early stages of cervical cancer have no symptoms.

자궁경부암의 초기 증상은 없습니다.

A Pap smear can detect pre-cancerous and cancerous cells on the cervix.

팝 검사가 자궁경부의 암 이전 세포나 암 세포를 발견하게 합니다.

If the Pap test abnormality is unclear, we may repeat the test to ensure accuracy.

팝 검사가 불명확할 경우, 정확하게 하기 위해 검사를 반복할 것입니다.

Since the Pap test showed a significant abnormality, I'd like to perform a test called a colposcopy.

팝 검사가 의미 있을 정도로 이상을 보여 질확대경을 통해 검사를 해야겠습니다.

I will use a magnifying instrument to view the tissue surrounding the vagina and cervix to check for any abnormalities.

질과 자궁 주위의 조직에 이상이 있는 지 보기 위해 확대경을 이용할 것입니다.

I will remove a small amount of cervical tissue for biopsy.

조직검사를 위해 경부에서 약간의 조직을 떼어 낼 것입니다.

Biopsy is the only sure way to know whether the abnormal cells indicate cancer.

조직검사가 암을 나타내는 세포를 보는데 가장 확실한 방법입니다.

Treatments for cancer of the cervix depend on the stage of disease, the size of the tumor, and a woman's age, overall physical condition, and desire to have children.

자궁경부암의 치료는 병의 시기와 크기, 나이와 몸의 상태, 아기를 가지려 하는 지에 의해 결정됩니다.

Treatment for cervical cancer during pregnancy may be delayed, depending on the stage of the cancer and how many months of pregnancy remain.

임신 중 자궁경부암의 치료는 암의 시기와 임신의 남은 기간에 따라 늦추어 질 수도 있습니다.

Possible early stage treatments are Cryosurgery, Diathermy, Laser surgery, Electrocoagulation.

초기치료는 냉동, 열, 레이저 치료, 전기소작법 등입니다.

Hysterctomy is needed to remove the cancer.

암을 제거하기 위해 자궁적출술이 필요합니다.

Sometimes people continue to have problem even after hysterectomy.

때때로 자궁적출술 후에도 계속적인 문제가 발생되기도 합니다.

We consider giving chemotherapy and radiation therapy to treat for invasive cervical cancer.

자궁경부암을 치료하기 위해 항암제와 방사선 치료를 고려하고 있습니다.

Combination treatment with chemotherapy and radiation therapy is needed to relieve symptoms and to destroy cancer cells that may remain in the area.

항암제와 방사선 치료 요법이 증상을 완화시키고, 남은 부위의 암세포를 죽이기 위해 필요합니다.

6) Abnormal Menstruation (생리불순)

Heavy menstrual periods, bleeding between periods, and bleeding after menopause are common symptoms of endometrial hyperplasia.

생리가 많거나 생리기간 중간에 출혈이 있거나, 폐경 이후 출혈이 자궁내막 증식증의 일반적인 증상입니다.

Oral contraceptives or dilatation and curettage will help to treat the endometrial hyperplasia

피임제나 D&C가 자궁내막 증식증을 치료하는데 도움을 줍니다.

I will prescribe birth control pills.

피임제를 처방해 드리겠습니다.

Oral contraceptives reduce the pain and the amount of bleeding.

피임제가 통증과 출혈의 양을 줄여 줄 것입니다.

To prevent endometrial hyperplasia from developing into cancer, I'd like to recommend surgery to remove the uterus.

자궁내막 증식증이 암으로 변하기 전에 자궁 적출술을 권유합니다.

If you're experiencing a lot of irregular periods or heavy bleeding during the period, you need to increase your iron intake.

생리가 불규칙하거나 생리 중 출혈이 많을 경우 철분 섭취를 많이 해야 합니다.

Vitamin C will help with the absorption of iron.

비타민 C가 철의 흡수를 도와 줄 것입니다.

Over the count pain medications will reduce the menstrual cramp.

일반 진통제가 생리통을 줄여줄 것입니다.

In younger women who are having menopausal symptoms, and
in women who have had a hysterectomy but still have one or
both of their ovaries, follicle stimulating hormone(FSH) level
blood test may be useful to confirm menopause.

생리가 없거나 자궁적출술을 받아 난소가 하나 또는 둘 있는 여자에게는 폐
경이 되었는지 알기 위해 **FSH** 호르몬 검사가 유용합니다.

I'll review the test results.

결과를 검토해 보겠습니다.

I want to see you next week.

다음 주 보도록 하죠.

7) Vaginitis (질염)

Vaginitis is caused by bacterial, yeast, parasite infection or
vaginal allergies

질염은 박테리아나 곰팡이 기생충, 질 알러지에 의해서 생깁니다.

The cause of vaginitis cannot be adequately determined solely
on the basis of symptoms or a physical examination.

질염의 원인은 이학적 검사만으로 증상을 확인할 수 없습니다.

Vaginal fluid tests or vaginal swab should be done.

질분비물에 대한 검사가 필요합니다.

I will do a vaginal examination.

질 검사를 하겠습니다.

Please flex your knees and separate apart.

무릎을 구부리고 벌려 주실래요?

There is a pus around the cervix and vagina.
경부 주위와 질에 고름이 있군요.

I will send this sample to the laboratory.
이 샘플을 검사실로 보낼 것입니다.

We will do a culture for infection.
균 배양 검사를 할 것입니다.

Laboratory tests allowing microscopic evaluation of vaginal
fluid are required for a correct diagnosis.
질분비물의 현미경 검사가 정확한 진단을 위해 필요합니다.

I'll give you a shot of antibiotics.
항생제 주사를 드리겠습니다.

I will prescribe anti-inflammatory vaginal creams to treat
inflammation without any underlying infection.
감염이 없는 질염 치료를 위해 소염제 연고를 처방해 드리겠습니다.

I will prescribe antibiotics for treatment of bacterial infections.
박테리아 감염 치료를 위해 항생제를 처방해 드리겠습니다.

8) Dialogue 1.

D : What's your problem?
무슨 문제가 있으시죠?

P : I missed my period once.
월경을 한 번 걸렀습니다.

And I had irregular menstrual cramp.
그리고 불규칙한 생리통이 있었습니다.

D : Do you have breast tenderness or abdominal fullness?

유방이 아프거나 배가 찬 느낌은 없나요?

P : No.

없습니다.

D : Have you ever been pregnant?

임신한 적은 있나요?

P : No.

없습니다.

D : Did you do an at-home pregnancy test?

집에서 하는 임신 테스트를 해 보셨나요?

P : I am not pregnant.

임신은 아닙니다.

I have irregular periods.

생리가 불규칙해요.

D : When was your last period?

마지막 월경이 언제였습니까?

P : 40 days ago.

사십 일 전이었습니다.

D : Are you married?

결혼은 하셨나요?

P : No.

아닙니다.

D : How old are you now?

지금 몇 살이시죠?

P : Twenty-six.

스물 여섯입니다.

D : How old were you when your periods started?

첫 월경이 시작된 게 몇 살이죠?

P : Eleven.

열 한살입니다.

D : Did you ever have an abnormal discharge or bleeding between your periods?

월경기간 사이에 이상한 분비물이나 출혈은 없었나요?

P : No.

아닙니다.

D : Do you have much flow each time?

항상 월경의 양이 많습니까?

P : Yes.

예.

D : Do you have pain or burning with urination?

소변 볼 때 아프거나 화끈거리지는 않나요?

P : No, but I urinate frequently.

아닙니다. 하지만 소변은 자주 봅니다.

D : Is your urine cloudy?

소변이 탁하나요?

P : No.

아닙니다.

D : I would now like to do vaginal examination.
이제 질 검사를 해보겠습니다.

P : Yes.
알겠습니다.

D : Could you please put your legs into stirrups.
두 발을 다리 받침대 위에 올려 주세요.

Please pull yourself down to the end of the table.
몸을 진찰대 아래까지 오도록 내려주세요.

Just relax.
긴장을 푸세요.

Now I am checking your uterus with my hands.
이제 당신의 자궁을 손으로 검사하겠습니다.

Please relax to feel your uterus with my finger.
자궁을 내 손가락으로 느낄 수 있게 긴장을 풀어주세요.

9) Dialogue 2.

D : Any other hospitalizations?
다른 일로 입원한 적은 없습니까?

P : I have had a D&C.
임신중절 수술을 받았었습니다.

D : When did your pelvic pain begin?
골반통증이 언제부터 시작되었죠?

P : It began in january of this year.
금년 일 월부터 시작되었습니다.

D : Do you still see your periods?
아직 월경이 있으십니까?

P : No, they finished three years ago.
아뇨 3년 전에 끝났습니다.

D : Do you have a foul-smelling vaginal discharge?
질분비물이 냄새가 나지는 않습니까?

P : No.
아닙니다.

D : Have you ever had any vaginal diseases?
성병에 걸린 적은 있었습니까?

P : No.
없습니다.

D : Are you sexually active now?
성적으로는 정상입니까?

P : Well.
글쎄요.

D : How frequently do you have sex?
얼마나 자주 하죠?

P : Twice a week.
일주일에 두 번 합니다.

D : Do you have any pain or discomfort during intercourse?
성교도중 통증이나 불편함이 있습니까?

P : Pardon me?
예?

D : OK, I can see that it's hard for you to talk about this.
알겠습니다. 아마도 이것에 대해 말하기 힘드시겠군요.

P : I was having pain during sexual intercourse.
성교통이 계속 있었습니다.

D : Does the pain affect your sex life?
통증이 성생활에 지장을 주던가요?

P : Absolutely.
정말로 그렇습니다.

D : Dyspareunia can have many causes.
성교통은 여러 가지 원인이 있을 수 있습니다.

P : I have vaginal dryness.
질 분비물이 잘나오지 않습니다.

D : I think it's important to discuss with your husband.
남편과 상의하는 것이 중요하다고 생각해요.

6 *Pediatrics*
(소아과)

1) 소아과적 질문 (내과 분야별 질문 참조)

How old is your baby?
How old is your child?
아이가 몇 살이죠?

How much does your baby weigh?
아기의 몸무게가 얼마죠?

Has your child been vaccinated as scheduled?
아이가 스케줄대로 예방 접종을 받았나요?

Does your baby have fever?
아기가 열이 있나요?

Did your baby vomit?
아기가 토하던가요?

Did your baby have fits?
아기가 발작을 했나요?

When did your baby start having fits?
언제 발작을 시작했죠?

Does your baby have cold symptoms?
아기에게 감기 증상은 없던가요?

Does your baby seem to have diarrhea?
아기가 설사를 하는 것 같던가요?

Is the bowel movement mostly yellow and runny?
변이 노랗거나 묽던가요?

Does your baby have hard bowel movements?
아기가 대변을 잘 누지 못하나요?

Does your baby cry before bowel movements?
변을 보기 전에 울던가요?

Can you recall about your child's immunization?
아이의 예방 접종에 대해 기억이 나나요?

Did you have any problems with pregnancy or birth?
임신중이나 분만시 어떤 문제는 없었나요?

Has you child had any surgery or hospitalization?
아이가 수술을 받거나 입원한 적이 있나요?

Is there any mass or lump on your baby?
아이에게 혹이나 멍울이 없던가요?

Is there any changes in behavior?
행동에 어떤 변화가 있던가요?

Does your child have earache or sore throat?
아이가 귀가 아프다거나 목이 아프다고 하지는 않던가요?

Is there symptom that fever comes and goes over several days?
열이 며칠 간격으로 왔다갔다하지는 않던가요?

Does your child have any sign of dehydration such as ---?
다음과 같은 탈수 증상들이 있나요?

: as follows
Irritability
Not eating as well as usual
Weight loss
Not urinating as often as usual
Urine is darker than usual
Fast heartbeat
Dry mouth
Thirst and eager to drink when something is offered
Sunken eyes
No tears when crying
Skin isn't as springy as usual

2) 어린이, 아기의 체온을 측정할 때

Place the thermometer's tip under the tongue and leave it there
   for 2 minutes.
체온계 끝을 혀 밑에 넣고 2분간 두세요.

Don't let your child bite on the thermometer.
체온계를 물지 않게 하세요.

Don't speak while it's in your mouth.
입안에 있는 동안은 말하지 마세요.

Place the thermometer under your child's armpit and fold arm
   across chest.
체온계를 당신 아이의 겨드랑이에 놓고 팔을 가슴 쪽으로 붙이세요.

Wait for the beef.
신호가 울릴 때까지 기다리세요.

I will check the temperature rectally.
체온을 직장에서 측정하겠습니다.

I will insert thermometer half an inch into the rectum.
체온계를 직장 안으로 반 인치 넣겠습니다.

Hold the thermometer still for 2 minutes.
2분간 체온계를 유지해 주세요.

Temperatures taken by rectum usually run 1° higher than those taken orally.
직장 내 체온은 구강 측정보다 대부분 1도 높습니다.

3) 어린이를 다룰 때

How old are you?
몇 살이니?

Do you attend school?
학교에 다니니?

Do you like school?
학교가 좋니?

Why don't you like it?
왜 안 좋아?

What are your best at school?
어떤 과목을 제일 잘하니?

What's your favorite subject?

어떤 과목이 제일 좋니?

Do you like other children?

다른 애들이 좋니?

Do you have friends?

친구들은 있니?

Do you read much?

책을 많이 읽니?

What kind of things do you read?

어떤 책을 읽니?

How many brothers and sisters have you?

형제가 몇 명이니?

How old is he?

그가 몇 살이니?

Is there a problem?

문제가 있니?

Put one finger on the spot where it hurts most.

가장 아픈 곳에 손가락 하나를 대봐.

Would you like to help me?

나 좀 도와줄래?

Show me where it hurts?

어디가 아픈지 보여줄래?

Open your mouth for me.

날 위해 입을 열어봐.

Let's take a look.
자 보자.

You did a good job.
잘했어.

They look good.
좋은데.

You're not feeling so great?
지금 몸이 좋지 않니?

Would it be all right if I examine you?
검사해봐도 되겠니?

You don't have to worry.
걱정하지마.

Give me a feel on the forehead.
이마 좀 만져 볼께.

I'm gonna listen to your chest.
가슴 좀 들어볼께.

Take a deep breath for me.
날 위해 숨을 깊게 들이 쉬어봐.

You are doing great.
잘하고 있어.

Let me look at your belly.
배 좀 보자.

Does that hurt?
아프니?

Are you gonna throw up?

토할 것 같니?

Don't worry.

걱정하지마.

We will get you fixed up right now.

지금 바로 낫게 해줄께.

Tiny prick.

조금만 따끔 할거야.

Very good.

잘했어.

Your fever seems come down.

열이 내린 것 같다.

It's back to normal.

정상으로 되었군.

4) Immunization (예방 접종)

Routine immunizations are necessary to keep your child healthy.

당신 아이의 건강을 위해 정기적인 면역이 필요합니다.

I'll give you a chart of immunization schedule.

예방접종 스케줄표를 주겠습니다.

I will make an appointment for your child according to
  recommended schedule for immunizations.

권장되는 면역 스케줄에 따라 당신 아이의 진료 예약을 해 드리겠습니다.

It will begin after birth.

태어난 후 시작됩니다.

After receiving vaccines, some children will have a mild fever and sore muscles.

백신을 맞고 나서 어떤 아이들은 미열이 나고 근육이 아플 수 있습니다.

Mild fever may be treated with acetaminophen syrup.

미열은 아세트 아미노펜 시럽으로 치료가 될 것입니다.

Sore muscles may be helped with a cold compress placed over the injection site.

주사를 맞은 곳에 얼음찜질을 하면 근육통증이 좋아질 것입니다.

I'll give you the child development booklet which has many tips on raising baby.

성장아기에 관한 정보가 많은 아기 성장 책자를 드리겠습니다.

5) Fever (고열)

Your child has probably got the flu.
It's probably just a flu.

아이가 독감에 걸린 것 같군요.

We'll run some tests.

몇 가지 검사를 하겠습니다.

Your kid will be fine.

아이는 괜찮아 질 것입니다.

Kids recover fast.

어린이들은 빨리 회복됩니다.

Fevers are a sign that the body is fighting an infection.
열은 몸이 감염과 싸우는 증상입니다.

Febrile seizure is due to high fever.
열성경련은 고열 때문입니다.

The first thing we need to do is bring fever down.
첫 번째 우리가 해야할 일은 열을 없애는 것입니다.

The main goal to treat is to make your child feel better.
치료의 주요 목적은 아이를 좀 더 편하게 해주는 것입니다.

Medications won't make them go away faster.
약들이 치료가 빨리 되게 하지는 않습니다.

Inserting rectal acetaminophen is a good method.
항문에 아세트 아미노펜을 넣는 것은 좋은 방법입니다.

Acetaminophen syrup and a lukewarm bath or massage will help lower a fever.
아세트 아미노펜 시럽과 미지근한 물로 목욕, 또는 마사지하는 것이 열을 낮추어 줄 것입니다.

Don't give your child aspirin.
아스피린을 주지 마세요.

Aspirin has been associated with Reye's syndrome, a rare disease of the brain and liver.
아스피린은 뇌나 간을 손상시키는 라이 증후군을 일으킬 수 있습니다.

Give the acetaminophen syrup before the bath or massage.
목욕 또는 마사지 전에 아세트 아미노펜 시럽을 먹이세요.

If the bath is given alone, your child may start shivering as his or
   her body tries to raise its temperature again.
목욕만 하게되면 다시 아이가 체온을 올리기 위해 떨 수가 있습니다.

Don't use alcohol or cold water for baths or massage.
알코올이나 찬 물로 목욕이나 마사지를 하면 안됩니다.

Give your child plenty to drink for preventing dehydration.
아이가 탈수가 되지 않도록 많은 물을 먹이세요.

Keep your child still and quiet.
아이를 조용한 환경에 있게 해주세요.

Dress your child in light pajamas so that body heat can escape.
몸의 열이 쉽게 나가도록 가벼운 잠옷을 입히세요.

If your child is chilled, put on a blanket but remove it when the
   chills stop.
만약 아이에게 오한이 들면 담요를 덮었다가 오한이 사라지면 다시 벗기
   세요.

Runny nose, cough, headache and muscle aches may bother
   your child during a cold.
감기가 있는 동안 콧물, 기침, 두통, 근육통들이 아이를 괴롭힐 수 있습니다.

It will get better with time.
시간이 가면서 점점 좋아질 것입니다.

Tonsils are swollen.
편도선이 부었군요.

We'll take a throat swab.
균 검사를 해보겠습니다.

I'm going to get some blood tests done to see what is causing the symptom.

증상의 원인이 무엇인지 알기 위해 혈액 검사를 하겠습니다.

I'll prescribe antibiotics syrup.

항생제 시럽을 처방해 드리겠습니다.

If your child don't improve, come back to me.

만약 아이에게 호전이 없으면 저에게 다시 오세요.

I want to see your child tomorrow.

내일 당신의 아이를 보도록 하죠.

Your child is dehydrated.

당신의 아이는 탈수가 있군요.

I'd like to start your child on fluids.

아이에게 수액을 먼저 주고 싶습니다.

I'd like to put your child in the hospital.

아이를 입원시켜야 할 것 같군요.

Your child needs to get fluid through the vein for preventing dehydration.

탈수를 방지하기 위해 정맥으로 수액 투여가 필요합니다.

I think it is best if we got a spinal tap to rule out meningitis.

뇌막염 감별을 위해 척추천자를 하는 것이 가장 좋을 것 같군요.

In order to know the diagnosis, we're gonna have to do a lumbar puncture.

진단을 알기 위해 요추천자를 할 것입니다.

It will rule out anything serious.

심각한 병을 감별 할 수 있을 것입니다.

I can't say at this point, whether your child is all right or not.
지금 이 시점에서는 아이가 괜찮을지 어떨지 말하기 힘듭니다.

Spinal tap is negative.
척추천자는 음성입니다.

So we can rule out meningitis.
그래서 뇌막염은 제외할 수 있을 것 같습니다.

Your child gonna be fine.
당신의 아이는 좋아질 것입니다.

Your child is coming around quite well.
아이가 좋아진 것 같군요.

Fever seems come down.
열이 내린 것 같습니다.

6) Croup (크루프)

Croup is an infection that causes the trachea and larynx to swell.
크루프는 기관지나 후두가 부어서 생깁니다.

Croup is usually part of a cold.
크루프는 감기의 일종입니다.

Croup symptoms most commonly occur in children 1 to 3 years old.
크루프 증상은 대개 1-3세에 많이 발생됩니다.

Croup causes a fever, hoarseness and a barking cough.
크루프는 열과 쉰 목소리, 짖는 듯한 기침을 일으킵니다.

Croup cause a crowing noise when your child breathes in
   through the narrowed windpipe.
크루프는 좁아진 기관으로 숨을 쉴 때 소리가 날 것입니다.

Croup usually lasts 5 to 6 days.
크루프는 보통 5 내지 6일간 지속됩니다.

Symptoms may be worse at night.
증상이 밤에 악화될 수도 있습니다.

Most children with mild croup can be treated at home.
크루프를 앓은 대부분의 아이들이 집에서 치유됩니다.

You should make your child as comfortable as possible.
당신의 아이가 가능한 편하도록 해주세요.

Make sure that your child gets plenty of rest and plenty to drink.
당신의 아이가 충분히 쉬고 많은 물을 먹이도록 하세요.

Acetaminophen syrup will relieve pain and lower fever.
아세트 아미노펜 시럽이 통증과 열을 줄여 줄 것입니다.

If your child has a mild attack of stridor, try having him or her
   breathe moist air.
만약 숨을 쉬기 힘들면 습한 공기로 숨을 쉬게 하세요.

Run hot water in the shower to steam up the bathroom and sit in
   there with your child.
목욕탕에 뜨거운 물을 틀고 수증기를 만든 다음 그곳에 함께 있으세요.

Use a mist vaporizer in the room.
방안에서 가습기를 이용하세요.

7) Bronchiolitis (세기관지염)

Bronchiolitis is a lung infection that can be caused by several kinds of viruses.

세기관지염은 여러 가지 바이러스에 의해서 생기는 폐의 감염입니다.

Children under age 2 get this illness in the winter and the early spring.

2세 이하의 어린이들이 겨울이나 초봄에 잘 걸립니다.

Most children are sick for about a week and then get well.

대부분의 아이들이 1주일 정도 아팠다가 회복됩니다.

Your child will probably have a runny nose and a slight fever for 2 to 3 days.

당신의 아이는 콧물이 나고 2-3일간 약간의 열이 있을 것입니다.

Then your child may begin to cough, breathe fast and wheeze for another 2 or 3 days.

그 후 기침을 하고 또 2-3일간 숨을 빨리 쉬고 새끈 거릴 것입니다.

Have your child drink plenty liquids.

많은 물을 먹이세요.

Use a mist vaporizer in the bedroom while the child is sleeping.

아이가 자는 동안 가습기를 이용하세요.

Run hot water in the shower to steam up the bathroom and sit in there with your child if he or she is coughing hard and having trouble breathing.

아이가 숨을 쉬기 힘들어하면 욕탕에 뜨거운 물을 틀고 그곳에서 함께 있으세요.

I will prescribe a liquid medicine to help with the cough and fever.

기침과 열을 내리기 위한 물약을 처방해 드리겠습니다.

I want to see your child again in 24 hours.

24시간 이내에 다시 보길 원합니다.

Make sure to wash your hands after you take care of your sick child to avoid spreading the virus to others.

바이러스를 다른 사람에게 퍼트리지 않도록 손을 깨끗이 씻으세요.

Your child is really working hard to breathe.

당신의 아이가 숨을 쉬기 힘들군요.

I'd like to put your child in the hospital.

병원에 입원을 시켜야 할 것 같습니다.

Your child should get oxygen while in the hospital.

병원에 있는 동안 산소를 마셔야 할 것 같습니다.

Your child can also get extra liquids through the veins which will help prevent dehydration.

탈수 예방을 위해 정맥으로 수액 투여가 필요합니다.

8) Vomiting & Diarrhea (구토, 설사)

Vomiting and diarrhea can be caused by viruses, bacteria, parasites, foods that are hard to digest.

구토나 설사는 바이러스나 박테리아, 기생충, 소화시키기 어려운 음식 때문에 생깁니다.

Vomiting and diarrhea can be harmful to children because they can cause dehydration.

구토나 설사는 어린이들에게 탈수를 일으키므로 위험할 수 있습니다.

Encourage your child to drink water and sports drinks.

물과 스포츠 음료를 먹이도록 하세요.

Oral rehydration solution which contains the right mix of salt, sugar, potassium and other elements will help replace lost body fluids.

소금, 설탕, 칼륨 등 전해질이 든 수분 보충제는 손실된 수분을 보충하는데 도움이 됩니다.

If your child keeps vomiting, wait 30 to 60 minutes after the last time he or she vomited, and then give him or her a few sips of oral rehydration solution.

만약 당신의 아이가 토하기 시작하면 다 토한 후 30 내지 60분 후에 수분 보충제를 조금씩 먹이도록 하세요.

Small amounts every few minutes may stay down better than a large amount all at once.

작은 양을 조금씩 먹이는 것이 많은 양을 한꺼번에 먹이는 것보다 좋습니다.

Drinks that have caffeine in them shouldn't be given because caffeine increases the amount of water and salt the body loses.

카페인은 몸의 수분과 염분을 소실시키므로 카페인이 든 것은 먹이지 마세요.

Even though eating may cause the amount of diarrhea to increase, your child will be able to get some food.

비록 먹는 것이 설사를 증가시켜도 약간의 음식은 먹을 수 있습니다.

If you are breast-feeding, keep breast-feeding.

만약 수유 중이면 계속 수유를 하세요.

Children should begin eating within 1 day after starting to take fluid.

물을 먹기 시작하면 하루 이내에 음식을 먹을 수 있도록 하세요.

Avoid foods with a lot of sugar and fat, such as ice cream, pudding and fried foods.

아이스크림, 푸딩, 튀긴 음식처럼 설탕이나 지방이 많이 든 음식은 피하세요.

Medicine to stop diarrhea usually isn't needed.

설사를 멈추는 약은 일반적으로 필요하지 않습니다.

If it's caused by an infection, diarrhea is a way for the body to get rid of the infection.

만약 감염이 있다면 설사는 몸이 감염을 제거하기 위한 반응입니다.

Giving medicines that stop diarrhea may interfere with the body's efforts to heal.

지사제는 몸이 나으려는 것을 방해할 수 있습니다.

Since the dehydration is severe, your child may need to be given fluids intravenously to replace fluids lost through vomiting or diarrhea.

탈수가 심하여 구토나 설사로 손실된 수액을 정맥으로 보충해 줄 필요가 있습니다.

Abdominal pain may merely be results of overeating, gas, or constipation.

복부 통증 원인이 단순히 과식이나, 가스, 변비 때문일 수도 있습니다.

9) Dialogue

D : Hi there.
안녕.

P : Hi.
안녕하세요.

D : Put one finger on the spot where it hurts most.
가장 아픈 곳을 손가락으로 집어봐.

P : Here.
여기에요.

D : Your problem is tummy aches.
배가 아픈가보구나.

How often get them?
얼마나 자주 아프니?

P : Nearly every day.
거의 매일 아파요.

D : Is it a sharp pain?
날카롭게 아프니?

P : Like daggers.
칼로 찌르는 것 같아요.

D : Do you get them just after eating?
먹은 후 아프니?

P : No.
아닙니다.

D : Do you get them just after going to bed?
잠을 잘 때 아프니?

P : Yes.
예.

D : Would you slip off your dress and shoes?
옷과 신발을 벗을래?

I'll just have a look at your tummy.
배만 살펴볼게.

OK. We're gonna make you better.
됐어. 곧 안아프게 해줄께.

Mother. Have your child ever been hospitalized due to any
serious illnesses or operations?
당신의 아이가 어떤 심한 질환이나 수술로 입원한 적이 있나요?

M : No.
없습니다.

D : Any other medical problems in the past
어떤 다른 질환은 없나요?

M : No.
없습니다.

D : How are his bowel movements?
배변 습관은 어떤가요?

M : Irregular.
불규칙합니다.

D : I think it is nervous tension that is upsetting his stomach.
위를 자극하는 신경성인 것 같습니다.

7 Orthopaedics
(정형외과)

1) 정형외과적 질문

Where is your pain?
어디가 아프시죠?

Do your joints ache?
Do you get pain in your joints?
관절이 아프나요?

Do your muscles ache?
Do you get pain in your muscles?
근육이 아프나요?

Where in your body does it hurt?
Where does your body hurt you?
몸 어느 부분이 아프나요?

How did you hurt?
How did you get hurt?
어떻게 다쳤어요?

Is there any deformity?
어떤 변형이 있나요?

Do you have redness or swelling?
붉거나 부종이 있나요?

Do you feel any pain here?
여기가 아픈가요?

When did accident happened?
언제 일어난 것이죠?

How long have you had it?
얼마나 오랫동안 아팠어요?

How frequently do you have pain?
얼마나 자주 통증이 발생하죠?

Are one or more joints swollen and tender?
하나 나 여러 개의 관절이 붓거나 아프지는 않나요?

Do you have any swelling in your joints?
당신의 관절에서 부은 곳은 없나요?

Do you have any pain or stiffness in any joint?
관절이 아프거나 굳어지는 곳은 없나요?

Do the joints feel stiff?
관절들이 굳어지는 느낌이 있나요?

Is the pain worse in the morning?
아침에 통증이 더 심해지던가요?

How long does the stiffness last?
굳어지는 느낌이 얼마나 되었죠?

Does the pain stay in one region?
통증이 한 곳에만 머무릅니까?

Which joints have a problem?
어떤 관절들이 아프시죠?

Have you any pains in your joints?
관절이 아프지 않으세요?

How about when you walk or excercise?
걷거나 운동할 때는 어떻습니까?

Have you ever had fractures of bones?
골절이 있었던 적은 없습니까?

Have you ever had rheumatoid arthritis?
류마티스 관절염을 앓았던 적은 없습니까?

When did you get these multiple joint pains?
언제부터 이러한 다발성 관절통이 있으셨죠?

Did you have any swelling in your joints?
관절이 부었던 적이 있습니까?

If you go out into the cold, do your fingers change colour and
  become painful?
만약 찬 곳으로 나가면, 손가락의 색이 변하거나 아프기 시작하나요?

Does your neck hurt?
목이 아프나요?

Does your back hurt?
허리가 아프나요?

Does the pain come with motion?
움직이면 아프나요?

Did the pain come from a repeated motion?
통증이 자주 움직여서 오던가요?

Does the movement make the pain more severe?
움직이면 통증이 더 심하던가요?

Do you have back pain with leg pain?
다리와 함께 허리가 아픈가요?

Do you have tingling sensation in your arms or legs?
팔이나 다리가 저리지는 않나요?

Do you have any radiating pain in your arms or legs?
팔이나 다리에 방사통은 없습니까?

Do you have any weakness in your arms or legs?
팔이나 다리가 약한가요?

Can you feel me touching them?
제가 만지는 것을 느끼시나요?

Wiggle your fingers and toes.
손가락, 발가락을 움직여 보세요.

Squeeze my hand.
제 손을 쥐어보세요.

Push down with you toes on my hand like a gas pedal.
차 페달 밟듯이 발가락으로 제 손을 눌러 보세요.

Bend your elbows and knees.
팔꿈치와 무릎을 구부려 보세요.

Pull your arms.
팔을 당겨 보세요.

Do you have a history of knee joint locking?
무릎을 굽혔다가 펴지지 않은 경우가 있었나요?

Are you being worked too hard in your job or exercise?
당신은 지금 혹시 무리한 일이나 운동을 하고 있습니까?

Do you have any history of falling or trauma?
넘어지거나 다친 적이 있습니까?

Did you fall (slip, trip)?
넘어졌나요?

Did your pain begin with a fall, a twisting injury or when you
lifted an object?
떨어지거나 허리를 삐거나 물건을 든 다음부터 아픈가요?

Do you have numbness or pain extending down your leg?
다리로 뻗치는 무감각이나 통증은 없나요?

Did you have sudden pain with minimal motion or a minimal
fall?
조그만 움직임이나 넘어진 다음 갑자기 아프나요?

2) Sprain or contusion (염좌)

It looks swollen.
부어있군요.

X-ray examination is necessary for you to rule out bone fracture.
뼈에 골절이 있는지 보기 위해 방사선 검사가 필요합니다.

A technician will take X-ray in radiology room.
방사선과 기사가 엑스레이 방에서 찍을 것입니다.

I will explain to you after X-ray is developed.
엑스레이가 현상이 되면 당신에게 설명해 드리겠습니다.

I have the results of your X-rays.
당신의 엑스레이 결과를 보았습니다

There is no bone fracture line in this film.
이 필름에서는 뼈의 골절은 보이질 않군요.

Application of the cold pack is necessary to reduce swelling and
　 pain.
부종과 통증을 줄이기 위해 얼음찜질이 필요할 것 같군요.

Reduction of the temperature of subcutaneous tissue and muscle
　 requires 20 to 30 minutes of exposure.
피하조직과 근육의 온도를 낮추기 위해 20분 내지 30분간의 얼음찜질이 필
　 요합니다.

Frostbite does not occur from a short-term application.
잠깐동안의 얼음찜질로는 동상이 걸리지 않습니다.

But it should not be continuously applied to skin for more than
　 30 minutes.
그러나 30분 이상 피부에 직접 얼음찜질을 하면 안됩니다.

Keep ice pack wrapping with towel directly on the lesion, 20 to
　 30 minutes, several times a day for 3 days.
얼음찜질을 수건에 감싸서 다친 곳에 대고 한 번에 20분 또는 30분 씩, 하루
　 에 예닐곱 번, 3일 간 해 주세요.

I'll put a splint(cast) on.
I'm gonna put a splint(cast) on.
부목(깁스)을 하겠습니다.

I'll get somebody to put a splint(cast) on your arm(leg).
다른 사람에게 팔 (다리)에 부목(석고)을 하도록 시킬 것입니다.

3) RICE 요법

*Rest(안정)

You may need to rest your ankle.
발목을 사용하지 말고 쉬세요.

You should crutches for several days to stand your foot.
발로 설 때 목발을 며칠 간 이용하세요.

*Ice(얼음찜질)

Using ice packs can decrease the swelling and pain.
얼음찜질은 부종과 통증을 줄여줍니다.

Keep using ice for up to 3 days after the injury.
상처에 3일간 얼음찜질을 사용하세요.

*Compression(압박)

Wrapping your ankle may be the best way to avoid swelling and
bruising.
부종과 멍을 줄이는 가장 좋은 방법이 발목을 감는 것입니다.

*Elevation(올림)

Raising your ankle to or above the level of your heart will help
prevent the swelling from getting worse and will help reduce
bruising.
부종이 빠지고 멍이 줄어들도록 심장보다 높게 발목을 올려 좋으세요.

4) After Ice Packing (얼음찜질 후)

After the first 2 or 3 days, you may put heat on the injury to help
ease the pain.
2-3일 후에는 따뜻한 찜질이 통증을 줄여줄 것입니다.

Don't use the strained muscle while you still have pain.
통증이 없어질 때까지 늘어난 근육을 쓰지 마세요.

Wrap the injured area with an elastic bandage for a few days.
며칠 간 손상당한 곳에 탄력붕대를 감으세요.

You may use over the counter medicines for pain.
통증을 위해 약국에서 타이레놀과 같은 약을 사 먹어도 됩니다.

If you need a splint, wear the splint.
부목이 필요하면 부목을 해야합니다.

5) Fibromyalgia (섬유근막동통)

I see no evidence that the trouble interfering with normal
neurological function.
정상 신경기능에 이상을 일으키는 증상은 없군요.

Maybe you are suffering from overuse syndrome.
아마도 당신은 과사용 증후군 인 것 같군요.

You should understand why your problem occurring.
당신의 문제가 왜 생겼는 지 이해하는 것이 좋을 것 같군요.

Chronic pain is often associated with severe activity.
만성 통증은 종종 무리한 활동과 같은 요인으로 생길 수도 있습니다.

Myalgia usually results from over-use.
근육통은 너무 많이 사용해서 오는 것입니다.

Your level of exercise is really more than it can take.
당신의 운동 레벨은 몸이 받아들일 수 있는 이상입니다.

You would like to make a rest and relaxation plan.
당신은 휴식과 여유를 갖는 게 좋을 것 같군요.

That is very important.
그것은 중요해요.

I recommend you to quit the sports for 4 weeks and reduce the work.
나는 당신이 4주정도 운동을 중지하고 일의 양을 줄이기를 권유합니다.

Sometimes it will be necessary to have a physical therapy.
때로는 물리치료가 필요할 수도 있습니다.

You should keep trying to rest your body.
당신은 무리하지 않도록 계속 노력해야 합니다.

Recurrence of symptoms depends on the activity.
통증의 재발은 활동과 관계됩니다.

If you need medicine to ease the pain, try Tylenol.
만약 통증을 줄이기 위해 약이 필요하다면 타이레놀을 드세요.

I'm going to give you an anti-inflammatory drug to take.
진통제를 먹도록 해 드리겠습니다.

I want you to get some physical therapy.
나는 당신이 약간의 물리치료를 받길 원합니다.

If you feel much better, you may do some activity.
만약 점점 더 좋아질 경우, 조금씩 활동을 시작하셔도 좋습니다.

Then I'd like to see you again in 2 weeks.
그리고 2주안에 보도록 하죠.

I recommend for you to stretch out before and after you work.
일하기 전 후에 스트레칭 운동을 하기를 권합니다.

It will take several weeks to heal over.
치료가 되려면 수 주일이 걸릴 것 같습니다.

6) Fracture (골절)

I'm afraid you have a fracture.
골절이 되었군요.

Your pain is from fracture.
당신의 통증은 골절 때문입니다.

The X-ray shows that your bone is broken.
엑스레이에서 골절이 보입니다.

You have a fracture of your arm (leg).
Your arm (leg) is broken.
팔 (다리)이 부러졌군요.

It looks like a non-displaced fracture.
전위가 없는 골절 같군요.

You need a cast.
You should get a cast.
You have to wear a cast.

You're gonna need cast.

깁스를 해야 합니다.

This fracture requires manipulative reduction to prevent deformity.

이 골절은 기형을 방지하기 위해 뼈를 맞추어주어야 합니다.

After that procedure, the fracture should be immobilized with a splint for several days until the swelling subsided.

그 다음 골절부는 부기가 빠질 때까지 며칠 간 반깁스로 고정시켜주어야 합니다.

A fiberglass cast can be applied several days later.

그 후 며칠 뒤, 합성섬유 석고로 고정할 수 있습니다.

A fiberglass cast is useful to immobilize most fractures.

합성섬유 캐스트는 대부분의 골절에 도움이 됩니다.

Sometimes complications can be associated with cast.

때로는 석고 후 합병증이 발생될 수도 있습니다.

Due to the pressure, skin problem and infection can be hidden under a cast.

압박 때문에, 피부 이상이나 감염이 될 수도 있습니다.

If you feel any discomfort, it is best to remove it to check for pressure sore or other problems.

만약 당신이 불편하다면, 석고를 제거하고 압박창상이나 다른 이상이 있는지 검사해야 됩니다.

Try to elevate your injured site.

다친 부위를 올리도록 노력하세요.

Sometimes chronic pain may result from ligament injury.
간혹 인대 손상으로 만성 통증이 올 수도 있습니다.

Other possible complications include post traumatic arthritis and motion limitation.
다른 가능한 합병증은 외상 후 관절염이나 운동 장해입니다.

You may need to wear a cast for several weeks.
당신은 아마도 몇 주정도 깁스를 해야 될 것 같군요.

It will take several weeks to heal over.
치료가 되려면 수 주일이 걸릴 것 같습니다.

You will probably be able to return to your sport in three months.
당신은 아마도 3개월 내에 운동을 할 수 있을 것입니다.

Wear the cast until your follow up examination.
다음에 올 때까지 깁스를 하세요.

Keep your cast dry.
깁스는 건조한 상태로 유지하세요.

While bathing, protect it with a plastic bag.
목욕하는 동안은 플라스틱 백으로 보호하세요.

If your cast gets a little wet, it can be dried with a hair dryer.
만약 깁스가 젖으면 드라이기로 말리세요.

Do not try to scratch the skin under the cast by pushing a sharp object.
날카로운 것으로 피부 아래를 긁지 마세요.

Check the skin around the cast every day.
매일 석고 주변 피부를 관찰하세요.

7) HNP (추간판 탈출증)

I'll raise your leg.
다리를 들겠습니다.

Tell me if this hurt.
아프면 말해주세요.

I don't see any sign of a slipped disc.
디스크 증상은 없군요.

Just a muscle strain.
근육 염좌이군요.

Back pain is usually caused by muscle strain.
요통은 대부분 근육 염좌 때문에 옵니다.

Back strain may occur while you are lifting, or happen during a
  fall.
허리 염좌는 물건을 들거나 넘어질 때도 올 수 있습니다.

Since most herniations involve the bottom two discs in the
  spinal, the pain usually begins in the lower back.
대부분의 디스크는 척추 아래 2개 부분에 오므로 아래 요추부가 아픕니다.

The bulging disc in this location exerts pressure on the sciatic
  nerve, and sharp pain may follow that nerve all the way down
  the leg and into the foot.
튀어나온 디스크가 좌골신경을 누르므로 다리와 발이 아픕니다.

MRI is needed to make a precise diagnosis and to point the site
  of the slipped disc.
정확한 진단과 탈출된 디스크 위치를 보기 위해 **MRI**가 필요합니다.

The first goal of treatment is to relieve pain by decreasing the muscle spasm.

첫 번째 치료 목적은 근 수축을 줄여 통증을 완화시키는 것입니다.

Apply heat pack and rest for up to three days.

뜨거운 찜질과 함께 3일 정도 쉬세요.

After improvement, begin abdominal muscle strengthening exercises to prevent future recurrences.

증상이 호전되면 재발을 방지하기 위해 복근 강화 운동을 하세요.

I'll prescribe pain killers muscle relaxants.

진통제와 근이완제를 처방해 드리겠습니다.

Most slightly slipped discs respond well to this kind of treatment.

대부분 약간만 생긴 디스크는 이 것들로 치료가 됩니다.

Since the pain does not respond to these therapies, surgery is needed.

통증이 이와 같은 방법에 반응이 없으므로 수술이 필요합니다.

We may have to remove the disc material.

디스크를 제거해야 될 것 같군요.

The best way to treat slipped disc is operation.

추간판 탈출증의 가장 좋은 치료는 수술입니다.

When the disc is removed, the pressure on the nerve is released, and this may rapidly relieve pain.

디스크가 제거되면, 신경의 압박이 풀리고, 통증을 줄여줄 것입니다.

The surgery involves a small incision in the skin over the spine, the removal of some ligament and bone material and the removal of some of the disc material.

이 수술은 척추 위에 조그만 절개를 가해 약간의 인대와 뼈와 디스크를 제거하는 것입니다.

Discectomy can now be performed arthroscopically, that is through a smaller incision using specialized tools under local anesthesia.

디스크 제거술은 지금 관절경을 통해 국소마취로 특수한 기구를 이용하여 할 수 있습니다.

After surgery you may feel pain at the site of the incision, and the original pain may be completely relieved immediately after surgery.

수술 후 수술부위는 아플 수 있지만, 원래 통증은 수술 후 바로 좋아 질 것입니다.

Sometimes you continue to have pain even after disc removal.

때때로 디스크 제거 후에도 계속적인 통증이 발생되기도 합니다.

Walking will allow you to maintain mobility in your spine as well as decrease the risk of scar tissue forming at the operative site.

걷는 것은 척추의 운동을 유지시켜 수술부위의 흉터가 생기는 것을 줄여줍니다.

Physical therapy may help your recovery.

물리치료가 회복을 도와 줄 것입니다.

8) Osteoporosis (골다공증)

Bones tend to lose strength with advancing age.
뼈는 나이가 듦에 따라 강도가 약해집니다.

You may have osteoporosis.
당신은 골다공증일수 있습니다.

I want you to have a bone density scan.
골밀도 검사를 받으시길 권유합니다.

I'd like you to have BMD done before I see you again.
골밀도 검사를 하고 나서 다시 보아야 할 것 같군요.

Bone densitometry compares your bone density to the peak bone density that someone of your same sex should have reached at about age 20 to 25, when it is at it's highest.
골밀도 검사는 안전하고 아프지 않는 검사로 20세나 25세 등 골밀도가 가장 높은 나이의 같은 성별의 사람과 당신의 골밀도를 비교하는 검사입니다.

It is a safe and painless X-ray technique.
안전하고 아프지 않은 X-ray 검사법입니다.

In the five to seven years after menopause, woman can lose as much as 20% of their bone mass.
폐경 후 5년에서 7년이 지나면 여자들은 자기 뼈의 20%를 잃을 수 있습니다.

Osteoporosis is most common in woman who have gone through menopause.
골다공증은 폐경기 후의 여성에게 아주 흔합니다.

One early sign is a backache.
초기 증상 중 하나가 요통입니다.

Osteoporosis is a disease of progressive bone loss.
골다공증은 뼈가 점차적으로 소실되는 병입니다.

Every one loses bone with age.
모든 사람이 나이가 듦에 따라 뼈가 소실됩니다.

Osteoporosis is an important factor for bone fractures.
골다공증은 골절의 중요한 요소입니다.

One in two women and one in five men over age 65 will sustain
bone fractures due to osteoporosis.
65세 이상의 여성들 중 2명에 1명이, 남성들 중 5명에 1명이 골다공증으로
골절상을 입습니다.

People who suffer from back pain may need to be screened for
osteoporosis.
요통을 호소하는 환자들은 골다공증에 대해 검사할 필요가 있습니다.

Because lost bone cannot be replaced, treatment for osteoporosis
focuses on the prevention of further bone loss.
소실된 뼈는 보충할 수 없으므로, 골다공증에 의한 치료는 뼈의 추가적 손
실을 막는데 있습니다.

Exercise has been its potential role in the prevention of heart
disease and osteoporosis.
운동은 심장병과 골다공증 예방에 중요한 역할을 합니다.

But exercise will not prevent all of the bone loss, it can
minimize bone loss.
하지만 운동이 뼈 소실을 전부 막아주지는 못하고 최소화 시켜줍니다.

Avoiding smoking and excess alcohol consumption can help
prevent osteoporosis.
흡연과 과도한 음주를 피하면 골다공증 예방에 도움이 됩니다.

You need calcium and vitamin D to keep your bones healthy.

당신은 뼈의 건강을 위해 칼슘과 비타민 D의 복용이 필요합니다.

Although calcium can't prevent gradual bone loss after menopause, it continues to play an essential role in maintaining bone quality.

비록 칼슘이 폐경 후 점진적인 뼈의 소실을 막지는 못하지만, 칼슘은 뼈의 밀도를 유지하는데 중요한 역할을 합니다.

Vitamin D helps your body absorb calcium.

비타민 D는 칼슘흡수를 돕습니다.

9) Degenerative Arthritis (퇴행성 관절염)

The problems you've been having are due to a condition called degenerative osteoarthrits.

당신이 가지고 있는 문제는 퇴행성 골관절염 때문입니다.

Osteorthritis means inflammation of the joint.

관절염은 관절의 염증을 말합니다.

It causes pain and limits movement of the joints that are affected.

이환 부위에 통증과 관절운동 장해가 오지요.

It is common in older people because they have been using their joints longer.

노인들이 관절을 오랫동안 써왔기 때문에 노인들에게 흔합니다.

People who have jobs that require the same movement over and over are also at risk.

반복되는 운동을 많이 하는 직업을 가진 사람들도 위험성이 있습니다.

No cure for osteoarthritis has been found.
골관절염에 대한 치료는 없습니다.

But some medicines and regular exercise will help you to protect
your joint and control pain.
하지만 일부 약이나 운동이 당신의 관절을 보호하고 통증을 조절해 줄 것입
니다.

I will write you a prescription, such as anti-arthritis medicines.
소염제를 처방해 드리겠습니다.

I want you to take the medicine three times a day after meal.
당신은 약을 하루에 세 번 식후에 복용하시기 바랍니다.

It will help you to abate your pain.
그 약이 당신의 통증을 줄어줄 것입니다.

10) Rhematoid Arthritis (류마토이드 관절염)

The primary symptoms of rheumatoid arthritis is pain and joint
stiffness in the morning.
류마티스 관절염의 초기 증상이 통증과 아침에 심해지는 관절 강직입니다.

The cause of rheumatoid arthritis is unknown, however the
condition involves an attack on body by its own immune cells.
류마티스 관절염의 원인은 알려져 있지 않지만, 자신의 면역과정에 관여하
는 세포가 자신의 몸을 공격하는 것과 관계가 있습니다.

Blood test, X-rays and analysis of joint fluid help in the
diagnosis of rheumatoid arthritis.
혈액 검사, X-선 검사, 관절액 검사가 류마티스 관절염 진단에 도움이 됩니다.

I'm going to get some blood tests done to see what is causing the pain.

통증의 원인이 무엇인지 알기 위해 혈액 검사를 하겠습니다.

A rheumatic factor test is positive in your blood test.

류마토이드 인자가 당신의 피검사에서 양성입니다.

The erythrocyte sedimetation rate(ESR) is also elevated.

적혈구 침강 속도도 올라갔습니다.

ESR measures the amount of inflammation when an arthritis problem is present.

그것은 관절염이 있을 때 염증의 정도를 측정하는 것입니다.

Chronic inflammatory disease may affect multiple joints.

만성 염증이 여러 관절에 영향을 미치는 것 같습니다.

You suffer from rheumatoid arthritis.

당신은 류마티스 관절염을 앓고 있습니다.

I have been trying to treat this symptom with NSAID but it hasn't responded to treatment.

이 증상을 치료하려고 **NSAID** 약을 썼지만, 치료에 반응을 하지 않는군요.

As you can see, anti-inflammatory drug doesn't seem to be working.

당신도 알다시피 소염제 약은 소용이 없는 것 같군요.

I will prescribe prednisone.

스테로이드를 처방해 드릴게요.

Prednisone at high dose is complicated by many side effects including osteoporosis, weight gain, diabetes, hypertension and aseptic necrosis of bones.

많은 양의 스테로이드는 골다공증, 체중 증가, 당뇨병, 고혈압, 무혈성 괴사증과 같은 합병증을 일으킵니다.

However it may be used in lower dosages to help control the inflammation of the joint.

하지만 적은 용량은 관절염증을 줄이기 위해 사용될 수도 있습니다.

Anti-cancer drug will be also used in lower dosages on once a week.

항암제를 적은 용량으로 일주일에 한 번 사용할 것입니다.

11) Dialogue

D : What can I do for you?

무슨 일로 오셨죠?

P : I have got a leg pain.

다리가 아픕니다.

D : Let me see your leg.

어디 다리를 제가 한번 볼까요?

P : OK.

알겠습니다.

D : Oh! There is an infected pocket of pus.

아! 감염된 종기 주머니가 있군요.

P : Sometimes I put ice on my knees.

때때로 얼음을 무릎에 올려놓기도 합니다

But my pain didn't seem to go away.
하지만 통증이 사라지질 않더군요.

D : This is abscess.
이것은 농양입니다.

P : I can't seem to do anything.
아무것도 못하겠어요.

D : I will cut a small hole around abscess to let the pus drain out now.
제가 지금 고름이 나오도록 조그만 절개 구멍을 뚫겠습니다.

P : No. Doctor. I never want to have surgery.
아닙니다. 의사 선생님. 저는 수술은 하지 않겠습니다.

D : We have to cut open the abscess and allow the pus to drain.
농양을 절개하여 고름이 나오도록 해야 합니다.

It's no big deal.
별거 아닙니다.

It's minor.
사소한 것입니다.

8 *Neurology and Neurosugery*
(신경과, 신경외과)

1) 신경과적 질문

Do you get pain in your head?
머리가 아픕니까?

Where in your head does it hurt?
Where does your head hurt you?
머리 어느 부분이 아프지요?

How did you get hurt?
어떻게 다쳤죠?

Did you hurt your head?
머리를 다쳤나요?

Did you hit your head?
머리를 부딪쳤나요?

Have you ever had any injuries on your head?
머리를 다친 적이 없나요?

Have you had any nausea or vomiting?
오심이나 구토를 하였나요?

Did you lose your consciousness?
의식을 잃었었습니까?

Do you remember when you had an accident?
사고났을 때가 기억나나요?

Have you ever had a head injury before?
Do you have any history of head trauma?
전에 머리를 다친 적이 있나요?

Have you injured your head or been knocked out recently?
최근에 머리를 다치거나 맞은 적이 있나요?

How far did you fall?
얼마나 높은 곳에서 떨어졌지요?

Do you have headaches?
Do you suffer from headaches?
두통이 있나요?

When was the first time you had headaches?
두통을 느낀 처음이 언제죠?

Do you have frequent headaches?
머리가 자주 아프나요?

Are you dizzy?
어지러운가요?

Are you dizzy when you stand up?
일어날 때 어지러운가요?

When do you feel dizziness?
언제 어지러움을 느끼죠?

How long does the dizziness last?
어지러움이 얼마나 지속되죠?

How often do you have headaches?
얼마나 자주 두통이 있지요?

When did you first develop headaches?
언제 처음 통증이 생겼죠?

Where is the pain?
In which part of the head do you get the pain?
(One-side or both sides of the head, Frontal, Occipital)
어디가 아프시죠?

How long do the headaches last?
두통이 얼마나 지속되죠?

Are there worse in the morning or evening?
아침이나 저녁에 악화되나요?

What kind of medicine do you usually take to relieve your
  headaches?
두통을 없애기 위해 무슨 약을 먹었죠?

When did the seizure start?
언제부터 경련을 했죠?

Have you ever had the seizure in the past?
과거에 경련을 한 적이 있나요?

How often do you have the seizure?
얼마나 자주 경련을 하죠?

What triggered the seizure?
어떤 것이 경련을 일으키죠?

Do you ever feel sick?
메스꺼운 적이 있나요?

Do you have a fever?
열은 있나요?

Do you have stiff neck?
목이 뻣뻣하지는 않으세요?

Have you ever had this kind of headache in the past?
과거에도 이런 종류의 두통이 있었습니까?

Do you have a history of high blood pressure?
고혈압 경력은 있나요?

Do you have pressure around your eyes?
눈 주위에 압박감 등은 없습니까?

Do you have any problem with your hearing and seeing?
듣거나 보는데 문제가 있나요?

Have you been having any problems with your memory?
기억에 문제가 있지는 않나요?

Can you feel me touching them?
제가 만지는 것을 느끼시나요?

Have you noticed any numbness, tingling or weakness in your limbs?
팔 다리가 감각이 없거나 저리거나 약해진 것을 느끼나요?

Do you have ---? or Do you feel ---?

Weakness
Vision problems or Light sensitivity
Hearing problems or Sound sensitivity
Pain over one eye

Blurred vision
Speech difficulty
Weakness or change of feeling in the arms or legs,
Tingling face
Confusion
Seizure or convulsion
Personality changes
Cognitive problems
Memory loss or problem
Gait problems
Balance or coordinate problems
Hallucinations
Behavioral problems
Disorientation

2) Headache (두통)

Many of diseases may be potential underlying causes of headache.

많은 질환들이 두통의 잠재적인 원인입니다.

I'd like to hear a full your medical history, such as past head trauma, diseases and the use of medications.

당신의 전체적인 과거병력, 즉 두부 손상이나 질병, 약의 사용 등에 대해서 알고 싶군요

I'd like to order a blood test to screen for thyroid disease, anemia, or infections.

나는 갑상선 질환이나 빈혈, 감염을 보기 위해 혈액검사를 의뢰하겠습니다.

X-rays and CT are needed to rule out a brain tumor or blood clots.

X-선과 CT가 뇌종양과 출혈 응집을 알기 위해 필요합니다.

MRI is important diagnostic tools in cases of headache to find brain tumor, brain lesion or other disease.
MRI가 두통의 경우에 뇌종양이나 뇌병변, 그 외의 질환을 발견하기 위한 중요한 기구입니다.

Electroencephalogram(EEG) is neccessary for you to measure brain activity.
EEG가 뇌활동을 측정하기 위해 필요합니다.

Angiogram is needed to detect an abnormal ballooning of a blood vessel.
혈관조영술이 뇌혈관의 팽창을 보기 위해 필요합니다.

An eye exam is needed to check for weakness in the eye muscle or unequal pupil size.
눈근육 약화와 동공 크기를 측정하기 위해 눈 검사가 필요합니다.

Not all headaches require medical attention.
모든 두통이 의학적으로 민감한 것은 아닙니다.

Aspirin or acetaminophen at the start of an attack will reduce the headache.
증상 시작할 때 아스피린이나 아세트 아미노펜을 먹으면 두통이 줄어들 것입니다.

Alcohol beverages and cigarette smoking often make headaches worse.
술이나 담배는 종종 두통을 악화시킵니다.

If you take a hot bath, it will reduce your headaches.
뜨거운 목욕을 하면 두통이 줄어들 겁니다.

Regular exercise can also reduce the frequency and severity of headaches.

규칙적인 운동이 두통의 빈도와 정도를 줄여줄 수 있습니다.

Temporary relief can be obtained by using cold pack on the painful side of the head.

머리 아픈 곳에 찬 찜질을 하면 일시적으로 통증이 줄어들 수 있습니다.

Small amounts of caffeine may be useful if taken in the early stages of headache.

두통 초기에 카페인을 먹으면 두통이 줄어들 수 있습니다.

Bed rest, darkened room and quiet will help reducing your headache.

침상 안정, 어두운 방, 조용함이 두통을 줄이는 데 도움을 줄 것입니다.

Self-regulation treatments(Biofeedback) and relaxation training which patients learn to relax the mind and body will help you.

몸과 마음을 편안하게 하는 스스로 조절하는 치료와 훈련이 당신을 도와줄 것입니다.

You have to concentrate your mind and body for relaxation.

당신의 마음과 몸이 편안해지도록 집중하세요.

You must be motivated to get well.

좋아진다는 확신을 가지세요.

I'll prescribe some medicines to control the headaches.

두통을 조절해 줄 약들을 처방해 드리겠습니다.

If you don't improve, come back to me.

호전이 없으면 저에게 다시 오세요.

I want to see you next week.

다음 주 보도록 하죠.

3) Stroke (뇌졸중)

CT or MRI must be performed to find out what kind of stroke it is to treat it correctly.

어떤 종류의 뇌졸중인 지 발견하고 정확히 치료하기 위해 CT 나 MRI 가 필요합니다.

CT and MRI are useful for determining if a stroke is caused by a blockage or by bleeding in the brain.

CT나 MRI는 뇌졸중이 뇌 안의 혈액차단이나 혹은 출혈에 의한 것인지 알기 위해 유용합니다.

EEG (electroencephalogram) is needed to record the electrical impulses and sensory processes of the brain.

EEG가 뇌의 전기파와 감각 과정을 기록하기 위해 필요합니다.

Doppler ultrasound test shows any changes in the blood flow to the brain.

도플러 초음파 검사는 뇌로 가는 혈액 흐름의 변화를 보여줍니다.

A stroke happens when part of your brain is not getting enough blood and stops working.

뇌졸중은 당신의 뇌가 충분한 혈액 공급을 받지 못하거나 기능이 없을 때 발생됩니다.

Depending on the part of the brain that is damaged, a stroke can cause sudden weakness or numbness of your face, arm, or leg on one side of your body.

손상 받은 뇌의 위치에 따라, 당신의 얼굴, 팔, 다리의 한쪽이 갑자기 둔해지고 약해집니다.

Medication is the most common treatment for stroke.

약물치료가 뇌졸중의 가장 일반적인 치료입니다.

Strokes caused by blood clots can be treated with clot-busting drugs.

혈액응집에 의한 뇌졸중은 응고를 없애는 약으로 치료될 수 있습니다.

TPA (tissue plasminogen activator) must be given within 3 hours of the start of a stroke to be effective.

TPA는 뇌졸중 3시간 이내에 써야 효과가 있습니다.

This is why it is so important for a person having a stroke to get to a hospital fast.

이것이 왜 뇌졸중 환자가 병원에 빨리 오는 것이 중요한 가의 이유입니다.

Anticoagulants such as warfarin, and antiplatelet agents such as aspirin interfere with the blood's ability to clot and can play an important role in preventing stroke.

와파린과 같은 항응고제나 아스피린과 같은 항혈소판제가 피의 응고 능력을 방해해 뇌졸중의 예방에 중요한 역할을 합니다.

Surgery is needed to repair vascular damage in the brain.

뇌 안의 혈관 손상을 회복시키기 위해 수술이 필요합니다.

We will place a metal clip at the damaged blood vessels.

우리는 손상된 혈관에 금속 클립을 고정시킬 것입니다.

For most stroke patients, physical therapy is the cornerstone of the rehabilitation process.

대부분의 뇌졸중 환자에게 재활과정이 중요합니다.

Exercise and training help the stroke patient relearn everyday activities.

운동과 훈련이 뇌졸중 환자가 일상 생활을 배우는데 도움을 줍니다.

Rehabilitation should begin as soon as possible after the patient is stable.

재활과정은 환자가 안정되면 바로 시작해야 합니다.

4) Epidural Hemorrhage (경막외 혈종)

Skull radiographs reveal a fracture crossing the vascular shadow of skull.

두개골 X-선이 두개골의 혈관음영을 가로지르는 골절선을 보입니다.

CT can make confirmation of brain injury.

CT가 뇌손상을 확진할 수 있습니다.

CT shows an acute epidural hematoma.

CT가 급성 경막외 출혈을 보이는군요.

The lens-shaped appearance is hematoma.

랜즈 모양이 혈종입니다.

Not all cases of acute EDH require immediate surgical evacuation.

급성 경막외 출혈 모두가 다 수술적 제거가 필요한 것은 아닙니다.

If a lesion is small and the patient is in good neurological condition, it is reasonable to observe the patient with frequent neurological examinations.

만약 병변이 적고, 환자의 신경증상이 좋으면 환자의 신경증상을 자주 관찰하며 지켜보는 것이 합리적입니다.

Early follow-up scanning assesses for further increase in hematoma size prior to deterioration.

의식을 잃기 전 초기 재촬영은 혈종의 크기가 증가하는 지 알게 해 줍니다.

If a rapid size increase is noted, then surgery is indicated.
만약 크기가 증가하면 수술이 필요합니다.

EDH continues to expand until the mass effect of the hemorrhage itself results in an increased intracranial pressure, a decreased level of consciousness, and a possible herniation syndrome.
경막외 출혈이 계속되면 혈종의 압박효과로 두 개 내압이 오르고 의식이 나빠지며 뇌가 한쪽으로 치우치게 됩니다.

A midline shift of the ventricular system exists.
뇌실의 중심이 이동되었습니다.

It is a life-threatening state.
이것은 생명이 위독한 상황입니다.

This hemorrhage requires immediate surgical evacuation.
이 출혈은 빨리 수술적 제거가 필요합니다.

Surgery is the opening the skull over the site of hemorrhage.
수술은 출혈이 있는 두개골 부위를 여는 것입니다.

After removing the hematoma, we will try to coagulate the bleeding vessels.
혈종을 제거한 후, 우리는 출혈을 일으키는 혈관을 응고시키도록 노력할 것입니다.

Sometimes patient continues to have problem even after hematoma removal.
때때로 혈종 제거 후에도 계속적인 문제가 발생되기도 합니다.

Patient has to be in ICU.
환자는 중환자실에 있어야만 합니다.

Patient has some brain swelling right now.

환자는 지금 뇌가 부어있습니다.

Patient is in coma.

환자는 혼수상태에 있습니다.

We have to wait and see how much he wakes up?

그가 얼마나 회복이 될지 기다려야만 합니다.

Patient should be managed in the ICU with a monitored setting until patient improves.

환자가 좋아질 때까지 중환자실에서 모니터하며 치료를 받아야 합니다.

Follow-up CT scans will be performed to determine the extent of clot evacuation and to evaluate for delayed hematomas.

혈종의 제거 정도와 지연성 혈종의 여부를 알기 위해 **CT** 재촬영이 행해 질 것입니다.

5) Brain Tumor (뇌종양)

We have some serious matters to discuss regarding your headache.

당신의 두통에 대해 상의할 중요한 문제가 있습니다.

You have a brain tumor.

뇌종양입니다.

The most frequent symptoms of brain tumors are headaches, nausea, vomiting, seizure.

뇌종양의 가장 흔한 증상들은 두통과 오심, 구토, 발작입니다.

Headaches that tend to be worse in the morning and ease during the day.

두통은 아침에 나빠졌다가 낮에 좋아지는 경향이 있습니다.

I'd like to check your muscle strength and nerve reflexes.

당신의 근력과 신경반응을 검사하겠습니다.

Skull x-rays show changes in the bones of the skull.

두개골 X-선이 두개골의 뼈의 변화를 보여주는군요.

Several laboratory tests include the EEG and the spinal tap is needed.

EEG를 포함한 몇 가지 검사와 척수천자가 필요합니다.

CT or MRI is neccessary to diagnose the brain tumor and a special dye may be used to enhance the brain tissue for checking differences.

CT와 MRI가 뇌종양을 진단하는데 필요하며, 뇌조직의 차이를 보기 위해 조영제가 사용되어 질 것입니다.

A biopsy is needed to determine the type of cancer cells.

암세포의 종류를 알기 위해 조직검사가 필요합니다.

Brain tumors are treated with surgery, radiation therapy and chemotherapy.

뇌종양은 수술과 방사선 치료, 항암치료로 치료됩니다.

Steroid treatment is needed to reduce the brain swelling.

스테로이드 치료가 뇌부종을 감소시키기 위해 필요합니다.

Anticonvulsant medicines will be injected to prevent or control seizures.

항경련제가 발작을 예방하고 치료하기 위해 주입될 것입니다.

If hydrocephalus is present, you may need a shunt to drain the cerebrospinal fluid.

만약 뇌수종이 발생하면 뇌척수액을 빼주는 수술이 필요합니다.

A shunt is a long, thin tube placed in a ventricle of the brain and then threaded under the skin to the abdomen.

수술은 가늘고 긴 튜브를 뇌실에 두고, 관을 피부 밑으로 하여 복부로 빼주는 수술입니다.

Excess fluid is carried away from the brain and is absorbed in the abdomen.

과다한 수액은 뇌에서 나와 복부로 흡수됩니다.

Surgery is the usual treatment for most brain tumors.

수술은 뇌종양의 일반적인 치료입니다.

To remove a brain tumor, we will make an opening in the skull.

뇌종양을 제거하기 위해 우리는 두개골을 열 것입니다.

Whenever possible, we will attempt to remove the entire tumor.

가능하면 우리는 모든 종양을 제거하려 노력할 것입니다.

However, if the tumor cannot be completely removed without damaging vital brain tissue, we will remove as much of the tumor as possible.

하지만 만약 종양이 생명중추 조직에 손상을 주지 않고 완전히 제거가 안될 것 같으면 가능한 많이 제거할 것입니다.

Partial removal helps to relieve symptoms by reducing pressure on the brain and reduces the amount of tumor to be treated by radiation therapy or chemotherapy.

부분 제거술은 증상을 완화시키고 뇌의 압력을 줄여주며 방사선과 항암 치료받을 암의 크기를 줄여 줍니다.

Stereotactic radiosurgery is another way to treat brain tumor.
입체적 방사선 수술 치료는 뇌종양의 다른 치료 방법입니다.

Radiation reaches the exact location of tumor without damaging other brain tissue from many angles.
방사선이 여러 각도에서 나와 암의 정확한 위치에 도달할 것입니다.

Combination treatment with chemotherapy and radiation therapy is needed to relieve symptoms and to destroy cancer cells that may remain in the area.
항암제와 방사선 치료 요법이 증상을 완화시키고, 남은 부위의 암세포를 죽이기 위해 필요합니다.

6) Dialogue

D : What brings you to me?
어디가 아프셔서 오셨죠?

P : I have this terrible symptom.
저는 증상이 좋질 않습니다.

D : Can you tell me about your symptom?
당신의 증상에 대해서 말해 주실래요?

P : My main problem is dizziness.
저의 주 증상은 어지러움입니다.

D : Have you had a cough?
감기에 걸리셨었나요?

P : No. Dizziness interferes with my business.
아닙니다. 어지러움이 제가 일을 못하도록 합니다.

D : How long have you had your symptom?

증상이 얼마나 오래되었지요?

P : I have had symptom for two weeks.

증상이 있는 지 2주가 되었어요.

It's been getting worse now.

지금은 더 나빠지고 있어요.

I feel that the room is spinning.

방이 빙빙 도는 것 같이 느껴집니다.

D : How often are the attacks?

얼마나 자주 어지럽죠?

P : Everyday.

매일 어지러워요.

D : What other symptoms do you experience with this problem?

다른 증상은 없습니까?

P : Sometimes I feel nauseous.

가끔씩 매스껍기도 합니다.

D : Chest pain or shortness of breath?

가슴 통증이나 호흡장애는 없습니까?

P : No, Just when I go up stairs, I get winded, and I have to lean
on the banister.

아닙니다. 단지 이층에 올라갈 때 숨이 차서 난간을 잡아야 합니다.

D : I'd like to hear a full your medical history, such as past
diseases and the use of medications.

당신의 전체적인 과거력, 즉 질병이나 약의 사용 등에 대해서 알고
싶군요.

9 *Ophthalmology*
(안과)

1) 안과적 질문

Are you having any problems with your eye?
Do you get any kind of problems with your eyes?
당신의 눈에 이상이 있습니까?

Do you have eye pain?
눈이 아프나요?

Do you have blurred vision?
눈이 흐린가요?

Do you have vision change?
시력의 변화가 있나요?

Have you noticed any change in your vision?
시력에 변화가 있나요?

When did this problem begin?
언제 이 문제가 생겼죠?

Both eyes? one eye?
두 눈 모두인가요? 한 눈인가요?

How would you rate the severity of your symptoms?
당신의 증상이 얼마나 심하죠?

What seems to make your symptom go away?

어쩔 때 증상이 사라지죠?

What other symptoms do you experience with this problem?

이 문제와 함께 다른 증상들도 있나요?

Have you seen another doctor?

다른 의사에게 진료 받은 적 있나요?

Have you ever worn glasses?

안경을 쓴 적이 있나요?

Can you see very well without glasses?

안경 없이 잘 볼 수 있나요?

Do you have difficulty reading the book?

책을 읽기 힘든가요?

Are you near-sighted or are you far-sighted?

근시인가요, 원시인가요?

Have you ever had any medical attention to your eyes?

당신의 눈에 대해 의학적으로 주의를 받은 적이 있나요?

Did you have any surgery, injuries, or serious infections?

어떤 수술을 받았거나 상처 또는 감염된 적이 있나요?

Did you have any inflammation in your eyelids?

안검에 염증이 있었나요?

Can you see clearly and comfortably both far away and close up?

먼 곳이나 가까운 곳을 명료하고 편안하게 볼 수 있나요?

Have you ever worn an eye patch?
아이 패치를 쓴 적이 있나요?

Have you ever used any medication for your eyes?
당신의 눈을 위해 약을 쓴 적이 있나요?

Do you take any eye drops?
안약을 썼나요?

Have you ever been told that you have cataracts, glaucoma or any other eye disease?
백내장이나 녹내장, 또는 다른 눈 질환이 있다고 들은 적이 있나요?

Have you ever had any eye injuries?
눈을 다친 적이 있나요?

Have you experienced any of the following symptoms in your eyes?
다음과 같은 증상들을 눈에서 경험한 적이 있나요?

Do you have ---? or Do you feel ---?

Eye pain or discomfort
Pink or Redness
Irritated eye
Eye discharge
Watering eyes
Swollen eyelid
Gritty or Itchy eye
Vision changes
Double vision
Blurred vision.
Sandy feeling
Tearing

Flashes of light
Floaters
Halos around lights
Frequent and severe headaches
Light sensitivity
Short-sightedness
(Difficulty seeing distant objects)
Far-sightedness
(Difficulty focusing on near objects)
Cloudy or foggy vision
Night glare or Poor night vision.
Colors that seem faded.
Gradual vision deterioration
Peripheral vision deterioration
Difficulty adjusting to brightness
Tender eyeball
Hard eyeball
Eyelid small red lumps
Multiple eyelid lumps
Enlarging eyelid pumps
Corneal scarring
Progressively dimming vision

2) 안경과 관련된 질문

How long have you been wearing glasses?
얼마나 오랫동안 안경을 썼지요?

When did you wear them?
언제 안경을 썼지요?

What were they for?
무엇을 교정하려고 안경을 썼지요?

What type of lenses do you wear?

어떤 종류의 렌즈를 쓰나요?

Are they for distance, near, or both?

안경은 원시? 근시? 혹은 난시를 위한 건가요?

When and why did you stop wearing them?

언제, 왜 안경쓰시는 걸 그만 두었지요?

Can you see clearly with glasses?

안경으로 깨끗하게 볼 수 있나요?

When was your last eye exam? By whom?

마지막 눈 검사를 언제 하셨지요? 누구에게요?

When were your glasses last changed?

최근에 언제 안경을 바꾸셨죠?

Do you wear contact lens?

콘택트 렌즈를 끼나요?

How often do you replace them?

얼마나 자주 갈아 끼우죠?

How many hours a day do you wear?

하루에 얼마나 끼우죠?

Have you ever had any eye inflammation?

눈에 염증이 있었던 적은 없나요?

3) 안과적 검사

I'll test your visual acuity.
시력 검사를 하겠습니다.

The vision test (Visual acuity test) is always done at a distance of twenty feet.
시력 검사는 항상 20피트 떨어져 검사합니다.

Stand on the line and read the eye chart.
선 위에 서서 챠트를 읽어주세요.

Look at straight ahead.
앞을 똑바로 보세요.

I'll look into each eye.
각 눈을 검사하겠습니다.

First, cover your left eye with paddle.
가리개로 왼쪽 눈앞에 막으세요.

Can you see these letters?
이 글자들이 보이나요?

Read from left to right.
왼쪽에서 오른쪽으로 읽으세요.

OK. Cover your right eye.
오른쪽을 가리세요.

Can you read this?
이것을 읽을 수 있으세요?

You're finished.

끝났습니다.

Please follow my finger with your eyes without moving your head.

I want you to follow my finger with just your eyes.

머리를 움직이지 말고 손가락을 따라 보세요.

We will examine your eyes.

눈을 검사하겠습니다.

Ophthalmoscopy requires dilating the pupils for the best view inside the eye.

검안경은 눈 안을 잘 보기 위해 동공을 확장시켜야 합니다.

I will place drops into your eye to dilate the pupil.

동공을 열기 위해 안약을 눈 안에 떨어뜨릴 것입니다.

Getting your eyes dilated is painless.

눈이 확장되어도 통증은 없습니다.

Dilating drops works on iris muscle and opens the pupil.

동공을 확장시키는 약은 홍채에 작용해서 동공을 엽니다.

After the examination, your vision may remain blurred for several hours.

검사 후에 몇 시간 동안 눈이 어릴 수 있습니다.

Bring a pair of dark sunglasses and a friend.

선글라스를 가져오고 친구를 데려 오세요.

Please sit here in front of the machine.

이 기계 앞으로 앉으세요.

Please rest your chin here and look straight ahead.
이곳에 턱을 대고 앞을 똑바로 보세요.

Keep your eyes open.
눈을 뜨세요.

Look at the marker on the screen.
스크린에 있는 표시를 보세요.

Look at the blinking light.
깜박거리는 불빛을 보세요.

The intraocular pressure is measured with a tonometer.
눈 안의 압력은 안압계로 측정합니다.

You will feel a soft pressure.
부드러운 압력을 느낄 것입니다.

The slit lamp is used to view the anterior structures of the eye such as the cornea, iris, and lens.
슬릿 램프는 각막, 홍채, 랜즈와 같은 눈 앞쪽의 구조물을 보는데 이용합니다.

Fundus photography are necessary to see the condition of the optic nerve, vitreous, macula, retina and its blood vessels.
안저 사진 검사는 안 신경, 초자체, 반문, 망막, 혈관들의 상태를 보기 위해 필요합니다.

Amsler Grid test is used to assess the center of the retina.
Amsler Grid 검사는 망막 중앙을 평가하는데 유용합니다.

Are you able to see the corners and sides of the square?
사각형의 코너나 주변을 볼 수 있나요?

Do you see any wavy lines?

틀어진 선이 보이나요?

Are there any holes or missing areas?

구멍 같이 잘 보이지 않는 부분이 있나요?

If the lines of grid do not appear straight and parallel or there are missing areas, I will examine the retina.

만약 그리드 선이 직선이 아니거나 잘 안 보이는 부분이 있으면 망막을 검사해 보겠습니다.

4) Conjunctivitis (결막염)

Red or pink eye is an infection of the conjunctiva.

충혈된 붉은 눈은 결막의 감염입니다.

Conjunctivitis is usually painless and does not adversely affect vision.

결막염은 통증이 없고 시력에 역효과를 일으키지는 않습니다.

If treatment is delayed, the infection may worsen and cause corneal inflammation and a loss of vision.

만약 치료가 늦어지면, 감염이 악화되어 각막에 염증이 생기고 시력을 잃을 수 있습니다.

Symtoms of viral conjunctivitis are watery discharge, irritation, and red eyes.

바이러스성 결막염의 증상은 물과 같은 분비물과 껄끄러움, 충혈입니다.

Infection usually begins with one eye, but may spread easily to the other eye.

감염은 한 쪽에서 시작되나 다른 쪽으로 쉽게 퍼져 나갑니다.

Allergic conjunctivitis usually affects both eyes and symptoms are itching, tearing and swollen eyelids.

알러지성 결막염은 양측이 동시에 발생하며, 증상은 가렵고 눈물이 나며 눈꺼풀이 붓는 것입니다.

Typical symptoms of bacterial conjunctivitis are stringy discharge that may cause the lids to stick together, especially after sleeping.

박테리아성 결막염의 가장 특징적인 증상은 잠을 잔 후 두텁고 끈적거리는 분비물입니다.

Like the common cold, there is no cure for viral conjunctivitis.

감기처럼 바이러스성 결막염의 치료는 특별하게 필요 없습니다.

The symptoms can be relieved with cool compresses and artificial tears.

증상은 얼음찜질과 안액으로 호전될 수 있습니다.

I will prescribe topical steroid drops to reduce the discomfort from inflammation.

염증으로 생긴 불편함을 줄이기 위해 스테로이드성 안약액을 처방해 드리겠습니다.

You should use one drop 4 times a day.

하루에 4번 한 방울씩 사용하세요.

Viral conjunctivitis usually resolves within 3 weeks.

바이러스성 결막염은 항상 3주 이내로 좋아집니다.

Cool compression and artificial tears may relieve discomfort in allergic conjuctivitis.

얼음찜질과 안액은 알러지성 결막염의 불편함을 줄여줄 것입니다.

I will prescribe non-steroidal anti-inflammatory medications, antihistamines and topical steroid drops.
비스테로이드성 소염제와 항히스타민제, 스테로이드성 안약을 처방해 드리겠습니다.

I will prescribe antibiotic eye drops or ointments to treat bacterial conjunctivitis.
박테리아성 결막염을 치료하기 위해 항생제 안약이나 연고를 처방해 드리겠습니다.

Warm washing will help to remove crusting and discharge.
따뜻한 물에 씻는 것이 눈의 딱지와 분비물을 제거하는데 도움을 줄 것입니다.

Eye drops will make the itching go away.
안약이 가려움을 없애 줄 것입니다.

To avoid spreading infection, avoid touching the face and wash hands frequently.
감염이 퍼지는 것을 막기 위해 눈을 만지지 말고 손을 자주 씻으세요.

Don't share towels and do not reuse handkerchiefs.
수건을 나누어 쓰지 말고, 손수건을 다시 사용하지 마세요.

Avoid shaking hands.
악수를 하지 마세요.

5) Myopia, Hyperopia, Astigmatism (근시, 원시, 난시)

Both genetic and environmental factors play a role in the presence and progression of myopia.
유전적, 환경적 요인이 근시의 발생이나 진행에 관계됩니다.

Close reading, watching and work is the main cause of acquired nearsightedness.

가깝게 읽고, 보고, 일하는 것이 후천성 근시의 중요한 원인입니다.

Myopia occurs when light entering the eye focuses front the retina.

근시는 눈에 들어 온 빛이 망막 앞에 맺혀 생깁니다.

If myopia is combined with astigmatism, you can experience headaches.

만약 난시와 함께 있으면, 두통이 있을 수 있습니다.

Farsighted people usually have trouble seeing up close, but may also have difficulty seeing far away as well.

원시를 가진 사람은 가까운 곳을 잘 보지 못하지만, 먼 곳 역시 잘 보지는 못합니다.

Hyperopia occurs when light entering the eye focuses behind the retina, instead of directly on it.

원시는 눈에 들어온 빛이 망막에 맺히지 않고, 뒤쪽에 맺혀 생깁니다.

Farsightedness is caused by a cornea that is flatter, or an eye that is shorter, than a normal eye.

원시는 각막이 정상보다 얇거나, 눈이 짧아 생깁니다.

Astigmatism means that the cornea is oval like a football instead of spherical like a basketball.

난시는 농구공처럼 둥글지 않고, 축구공처럼 울퉁불퉁해 생깁니다.

This causes light to focus on more than one point in the eye, resulting in blurred vision at distance or near.

이런 이유로 빛이 눈 안 한 곳에 모이지 않고, 여러 곳에 생겨 먼 곳과 가까운 곳이 흐리게 보입니다.

Astigmatism often occurs along with nearsightedness or farsightedness.

난시는 종종 근시나 원시와 함께 발생됩니다.

This problem can be corrected with glasses, contact lenses, or surgically.

이러한 문제는 안경, 콘택트 렌즈, 수술로 치유될 수 있습니다.

The most common surgery used to correct this problem is LASIK(Laser in situ keratomileusis) and it is a procedures to reshape the cornea.

이 문제를 치료하는 가장 일반적인 수술이 각막의 모양을 다시 만들어주는 라식 수술입니다.

6) Cataract (백내장)

Cataract is a clouding of the lens.

백내장은 렌즈가 혼탁해져 생깁니다.

A cataract starts out small.

백내장은 조그맣게 시작합니다.

The most common symptoms of a cataract are cloudy vision problems with light.

백내장의 가장 흔한 문제는 빛과 함께 흐린 시야입니다.

Headlights seem too bright at night, glare from lamps, feel very bright sunlight or a halo around lights.

밤에 헤드라이트가 밝게 보이는 것 같고, 불빛이 반짝거리고, 햇볕이 눈부시거나, 빛 주위로 달무리가 보입니다.

Cataracts tend to grow slowly, so vision gets worse gradually.

백내장은 천천히 진행하므로 시력도 천천히 나빠집니다.

You need surgery to remove the cataract.

백내장을 없애기 위해 수술이 필요합니다.

Cataract surgery is very successful in restoring vision.

백내장 수술은 시력을 되찾는데 아주 성공적인 수술입니다.

During surgery your lens is taken out and a plastic lens, like a contact lens, is put in.

수술동안 렌즈가 제거되고 콘택트 렌즈 같은 플라스틱 렌즈가 끼워집니다.

The plastic lens stays in your eye all the time.

플라스틱 렌즈는 항상 당신의 눈에 있게 될 것입니다.

Cataract surgery helps you see clearly again.

백내장 수술은 당신의 눈을 다시 잘 보게 해 줄것입니다.

7) Glaucoma (녹내장)

Glaucoma is a disease caused by increased intraocular pressure resulting either from a malformation or malfunction of the eye's drainage structures.

녹내장은 눈의 배출조직의 기능이나 구조에 이상이 생겨 안압이 높아지는 질병입니다.

Objects in front may still be seen clearly, but objects to the side may be missed.

눈앞에 있는 물체가 잘 보이지만, 주변의 물체는 안 보일 수 있습니다.

As the glaucoma worsens, the field of vision narrows.

녹내장이 안 좋아질수록 시야는 좁아집니다.

You need to make several follow-up visits to have your pressure monitored.

안압의 계속적인 측정을 위해 몇 번 더 오셔야 합니다.

Left untreated, an elevated IOP causes irreversible damage the optic nerve and retinal fibers resulting in a progressive, permanent loss of vision.

치료를 안 하고 놔두면, 올라간 안압이 시신경과 망막의 섬유조직에 상처를 주어 점차 영구적으로 시력을 잃게 됩니다.

Early detection and treatment can slow, or even halt the progression of the disease.

조기 발견과 치료가 병의 진행을 막아주고 멈추어줍니다.

I will prescribe some medications to control the eye pressure in the form of eye drops and pills.

안압을 조절해 줄 약을 안약이나 경구용으로 처방해 드리겠습니다.

Some medicines can cause headaches or burning and redness in the eyes.

어떤 약은 두통과 충혈, 눈의 화끈거림을 일으킬 수 있습니다.

Surgery is indicated when medical treatment fails to lower the pressure satisfactorily.

수술은 약물치료로 효과적인 안압을 떨어뜨리지 못했을 때 필요합니다.

The objective of glaucoma operation is to allow fluid to drain from the eye more efficiently.

녹내장의 수술 목적은 좀 더 효과적으로 액체를 배출하게 끔 하는 것입니다.

Laser surgery(laser trabeculoplasty) helps fluid drain out of the eye.

레이저 수술이 액체를 눈 밖으로 배출하는 데 도움을 줄 것입니다.

You must put drops in the eye for several weeks after the operation to fight infection and swelling.

수술 후에 감염과 부종을 막기 위해 몇 주간 안약을 넣어야 합니다.

In many cases, you will need to keep taking glaucoma drugs even after laser surgery.

많은 경우에 있어서 당신은 레이저 수술 후에도 녹내장 약을 계속 먹어야 합니다.

Keep in mind that while glaucoma surgery may save remaining vision, it does not improve sight.

녹내장 수술은 남은 시력은 보호하지만, 시력을 더 좋게 만들지는 않다는 것을 명심하셔야 합니다.

8) Dialogue

P : Will eye surgery be painful?

눈 수술은 아픈가요?

D : No.

아닙니다.

P : Will I feel anything during surgery?

수술 중 무언 가를 느끼나요?

D : Most patients feel only gentle pressure.

약간의 압박감만 느낍니다.

P : What do I see during surgery?

수술 중 무엇을 보고 있나요?

D : You only see the bright lights of the microscope.

현미경의 밝은 불빛 만 볼 것입니다.

P : How soon may I leave after surgery?
  수술 후 언제쯤 갈 수 있죠?

D : You may leave within a few hours after the surgery.
  수술 후 몇 시간 안에 갈 수 있습니다.

P : May I drive myself home?
  혼자 집으로 운전해도 되나요?

D : No. bring your friend.
  안됩니다. 친구를 데려 오세요.

10 *Ear, Nose, Throat*
(이비인후과)

1) 이비인후과적 질문

Do you have a pain deep in the ear?
귀 안쪽 깊은 곳이 아프나요?

Do you hear fluid in your ear?
귀 안에서 물 흐르는 소리가 느껴지나요?

Do you feel water in your ear?
귀에 물 있는 게 느껴지나요?

Do you have ringing in your ears?
Do you hear ringing?
Have you experienced any ringing in your ears?
귀울림이 있나요?

Do you have a ringing in one or both ears?
귀울림이 한쪽 또는 양쪽에서 있나요?

Which ear is worse?
어느 쪽이 더 나쁘죠?

What does the noise sound like?
What does it sound like?
어떤 소음이 들리나요?

Do you have good hearing?
잘 들리나요?

Do you feel pressure that can't be cleared with swallowing?
삼키는 것으로 좋아지지 않는 귀 안의 압박감 같은 것이 있나요?

Do you have thick drainage from the ear canal?
귀에서 진한 분비물이 나오나요?

Do you have pus coming from your ears?
귀에서 고름이 나오나요?

Do you have pain behind your ear?
귀 뒤쪽이 아프나요?

Do you have tenderness when you touch the bone behind ear?
귀 뒤의 뼈를 만지면 아프나요?

Does your ear hurt when I pull on the ear?
귀를 잡아당기면 아프나요?

Do you have swelling of the outer ear?
귀 바깥쪽이 부었나요?

How often does ear pain occur?
귀 통증이 얼마나 자주 발생하죠?

Did your ear pain start with hit to the ear?
Did the pain start after a blow to the ear?
귀를 맞은 다음부터 아프기 시작했나요?

Do you have hearing loss?
귀가 잘 안 들리나요?

Do you have hearing loss in one or both ears?
한쪽 또는 양쪽에서 귀가 잘 안 들리나요?

Can you hear well what others say?
다른 사람들이 말할 때 잘 들리나요?

Have you been exposed to loud noises at work?
Are you working around loud noises?
일할 때 소음에 계속 노출되나요?

Has your hearing loss occurred gradually as you have aged?
나이가 들면서 점차 귀가 안 들리던가요?

Do you wear a hearing aid?
보청기를 사용하시나요?

Do you have bouts of dizziness?
갑자기 어지러운 적이 있나요?

Do you feel dizziness?
어지럽나요?

Do you have a cough or runny nose?
기침을 하거나 콧물이 나나요?

Do you have frequent nosebleeds?
자주 코피가 나나요?

Do you have sore throat?
Do you get a pain in your throat?
목이 아프나요?

Do you have lumps or swelling in the throat?
목안에 혹이 있거나 부었나요?

Do you have any difficulty swallowing?
삼키기 힘드나요?

Do you get sore throat quite often?
목안이 자주 아프나요?

How often do you get sore throat?
얼마나 자주 목이 아프죠?

Have you had your tonsils out?
편도선을 제거하셨나요?

Have you ever had any ulcer in your mouth or on your lips?
입안이나 입술에 궤양이 생긴 적은 없나요?

Have you notice any changes in your voice?
당신의 목소리가 변했나요?

Do you have a fever or cold symptom?
열이나 감기 증상이 있나요?

Do you catch cold easily?
쉽게 감기에 잘 걸리나요?

Are you taking any medication?
어떤 약을 먹고 있나요?

Do you have ---? or Do you feel ---?

Ear pain
Ear discharge
Ear itching
Reduced hearing
Fullness in the ear

Sensation of "speaking in a barrel".
Tinnitus or Noises in the ears
Ringing or whistling in ears
Continuous ear noise
Intermittent ear noise
Pulsing ear noises
Ear noises in time with heartbeat
Sinus pain
Tenderness over sinus region
Sore throat or Pain on swallowing
Vomiting or Diarrhea
Coughing
Sneezing or Runny nose
Tiredness
Aches or headache

Does your child have ---?

Irritability
Sleeping difficulty
Pulling at the ears
Crying or Screaming
Balance problems
Fever
Ear fluid draining
Common cold or Flu symptoms
Refusing to eat
Vomiting
Malaise
Loss of appetite
Earache
Red tonsils
Swollen tonsils
Whitened tonsils

Enlarged neck lymph glands
Enlarged jaw lymph glands
Epidemic outbreaks of tonsillitis

2) Otitis Media (중이염)

I'd like to examine your ear with my otoscope.
이경으로 당신의 귀를 검사하겠습니다.

Please tip the head slightly toward the shoulder.
머리를 어깨 쪽으로 기울여주세요.

Hearing test and tympanometry test are necessary.
청력 검사와 고막 운동 검사가 필요합니다.

Irrigation will be useful to remove cerumen and soft plastic curettes are necessary for a very hard block of cerumen.
귀지를 제거하기 위해 세척이 필요하고, 강하게 막힌 귀지를 위해 부드러운 플라스틱 귀쑤시개가 필요합니다.

Care should be taken to avoid perforation of the tympanic membrane.
고막이 뚫리지 않게 조심하세요.

Ear infections are usually characterized by a feeling of fullness in the ear and stabbing pains.
중이염은 귀가 꽉 막힌 것 같고, 찌르는 듯한 통증이 있습니다.

Underlying causes of middle ear infection are cold, flu, sinusitis, throat or adenoid or upper respiratory infections.
중이염의 원인은 감기, 독감, 부비동염, 목이나 상부 호흡기관의 감염입니다.

Allergy is the most common cause of recurrent ear infections in children.

알러지는 어린이에서 가장 흔한 중이염의 원인입니다.

Ear infections are usually caused by bacteria entering the middle ear through the eustachian tube.

중이염은 유스타키오관을 통해 중이로 들어 온 박테리아에 의해 원인이 됩니다.

The tube can swell and not function properly when allergies are present.

알러지 원인이 있을 때 튜브가 붓고 기능을 하지 못합니다.

Increased pressure can even cause the eardrum to rupture in severe cases.

심한 경우 압력이 증가되어 고막이 터집니다.

Acute otitis media lasts less than three weeks and produces a purulent exudate.

급성 중이염은 3주 이내까지 계속되며 고름이 나옵니다.

Chronic otitis media lasts longer than three months and produces a thick and tenacious secretion.

만성 중이염은 3개월 이상 지속되고 두텁고 끈적한 분비물을 냅니다.

Chronic otitis media is usually clinically asymptomatic.

만성 중이염은 임상적으로 항상 증상이 없습니다.

The tympanic membrane appears red and bulges outward.

고막이 붉고 바깥으로 부풀어올랐군요.

Tympanic membrane appears mildly infected and dull.

고막이 약간 감염되어 있고, 광택이 없군요.

There is a spontaneous rupture of the tympanic membrane.
고막의 자연 파열이 있군요.

I will prescribe broad ranged antibiotics for a period of ten days.
10일간의 광범위 항생제를 처방하겠습니다.

Antibiotics may work if the infection is bacterial, but not if viral.
항생제는 박테리아 감염에는 효과가 있지만, 바이러스에는 효과가 없습
니다.

Sterile effusion will not respond to antibiotics.
균이 없는 삼출액은 항생제에 반응하지 않습니다.

If there is not improvement within 2 days, antibiotics should be
discontinued.
만약 이틀 이내에 증상의 호전이 없으면 항생제를 끊어야 합니다.

Myringotomy surgery is needed to drain fluid in the ear if the
fluid has been present.
삼출액이 있으면 액을 빼기 위해 고막절개술이 필요합니다.

3) Tinnitus (이명)

I 'd like to do hearing test, balance tests and laboratory work.
청력검사, 균형검사, 실험실 검사가 필요합니다.

You have ruptured ear drum.
Your ear drum was ruptured.
고막이 파열되었군요.

The ruptured ear drum usually heals on its own in 2 weeks.
파열된 고막은 대개 2주안에 좋아집니다.

Hearing will be improved as the hole closes.

구멍이 막혀지면서 청력이 좋아질 것입니다.

If there is not improvement within a couple of months, you may
  need tympanoplasty.

만약 몇 달 이내에 증상의 호전이 없으면 고막성형술이 필요합니다.

Most tinnitus comes from damage to the endings of the hearing
  nerve in the inner ear.

대부분의 귀울림은 내이의 청신경 끝 부분의 손상으로 옵니다.

Advancing age is generally accompanied by a certain amount of
  hearing nerve impairment and tinnitus.

나이가 들면 대체적으로 청신경 이상과 귀울림이 옵니다.

Exposure to loud noise is probably the leading cause of tinnitus,
  and often damages hearing as well.

큰 소리에 노출되는 것이 귀울림과 청력에 손상을 주는 원인입니다.

Tinnitus can also be a symptom of stiffening of the middle ear
  bones.

귀울림은 중이의 뼈들이 딱딱해져도 증상이 생길 수 있습니다.

Tinnitus may also be caused by allergy, high blood pressure,
  diabetes and medications.

귀울림은 알러지, 고혈압, 당뇨, 약들에 의해 역시 생길 수 있습니다.

Treatments are quite different in each case of tinnitus.

치료는 귀울림 경우마다 틀립니다.

In most cases, there is no specific treatment for ear and head
  noise.

대부분 귀나 머리에서 들리는 잡음에 대한 특별한 치료는 없습니다.

Avoid exposure to loud sounds and noises.

큰 소리나 소음을 피하세요.

Exercise regularly and control your blood pressure.

규칙적으로 운동하고 혈압을 조절하세요.

Get adequate rest and avoid fatigue.

적당히 휴식을 취하고 피곤하지 않게 하세요.

Stop worrying about the noise and learn to ignore it as much as possible.

잡음에 대해 걱정을 그만하고 가능한 무시하는 법을 배우세요.

Concentration and relaxation can reduce the intensity of tinnitus.

정신 집중이나 휴식이 귀울림의 정도를 줄여줄 것입니다.

Hearing aid may reduce noise while your are wearing it.

보청기를 차는 동안 잡음이 줄어들 것입니다.

It is important not to set the hearing aid at excessively loud levels, as this can worsen the tinnitus in some cases.

귀울림이 악화되지 않도록 보청기의 볼륨을 높지 않게 하는 것이 매우 중요합니다.

4) Meniere's disease (메니어 병)

You may have meniere's disease or other problems on the hearing nerve.

당신은 아마도 메니어 질환이나 청신경에 문제가 있을 수 있습니다.

Meniere's disease is the name of a problem of the inner ear.

메니어 질환은 내이에 문제가 있을 때 불려지는 것입니다.

No one knows the cause.
원인은 밝혀지지 않았습니다.

It has something to do with fluid in canals of the inner ear.
그것은 내이의 터널에 있는 액체와 관계가 있습니다.

During an attack, rest in bed until the dizziness are gone.
이상이 생기면 어지러움이 없어질 때까지 침대에 누워계세요.

Don't drink a lot of fluids and avoid salty foods.
많은 물이나 짠 음식을 먹지 마세요.

5) Sinusitis (부비동염)

Your sinuses are infected and inflamed.
당신의 부비동들에 감염이 되어 염증이 있군요.

Acute sinisitis lasts for 3 weeks or less.
급성 부비동염은 3주 정도 갑니다.

Chronic sinusitis lasts for 3 to 8 weeks but can continue for months or even years.
만성 부비동염은 3내지 8주 가는데, 몇 달이나 몇 년이 갈 수도 있습니다.

Sinus pain is sometimes mistaken for tooth pain because of the close proximity of the sinus cavity to the upper jaw.
부비동염은 윗턱과 가까워 가끔씩 치통으로 오인될 수 있습니다.

Sinuses are hollow air spaces of four pairs of cavities.
부비동은 4개의 쌍으로 이루어진 좁은 공기를 가진 공간입니다.

Each sinus has an opening into the nose for the free exchange of air and mucus with the nasal passages.

각각의 부비동이 비강과 연결이 되어 공기와 점액이 자유롭게 왕래합니다.

Anything that causes a swelling in the nose such as infection, allergic reaction can affect the sinuses.

코에서 부종을 일으키는 감염이나 알러지와 같은 어떤 것들도 부비동에 영향을 미칠 수 있습니다.

Infection in the frontal sinuses can cause frontal headache.

전두동 감염은 전두부의 두통을 일으킵니다.

Infection in the maxillary sinuses can cause your upper jaw and teeth to ache and your cheeks to become tender to the touch.

상악동 감염은 윗턱과 이가 아프고 볼을 만지면 아프게 합니다.

Infection in the ethmoid sinuses causes swelling and pain around your eyes.

사상동 감염은 눈 주위가 붓고 아프게 합니다.

Infection in the sphenoid sinuses can cause earaches, neck pain, and deep aching at the top of your head.

접형동 감염은 귀나 목, 머리 위쪽이 아프게 합니다.

Most cases of acute sinusitis start with a common cold.

대부분의 급성 부비동염은 감기와 함께 시작됩니다.

Both the cold and the sinus inflammation usually go away without treatment in 2 weeks.

감기와 부비동 염증은 대부분 치료없이 2주 이내에 회복됩니다.

If you have allergic rhinitis, you may develop chronic sinusitis.

만약 당신이 알러지성 비염이 있다면 만성 부비동염이 올 수 있습니다.

I will prescribe decongestants, antibiotics and pain killers.
울혈 감소제, 항생제, 진통제를 처방해 드리겠습니다.

You may get some relief from your symptoms with a humidifier.
가습기로 증상이 조금 좋아질 것입니다.

Hot cup of water can soothe inflamed sinus cavities and might give you some comfort.
뜨거운 물이 염증난 부비동을 부드럽게하고 조금 안정을 줄 것입니다.

Air conditioning equipment are helpful in removing allergens from the air.
공기 청정기가 공기중의 알러지 원인을 제거해줄 것입니다.

Drinking alcohol causes nasal and sinus membranes to swell.
술을 마시면 코나 부비동이 붓게 만듭니다.

When medical treatment fails, surgery is needed for treating chronic sinusitis.
만약 약물치료가 안되면 만성 부비동염을 치료하기 위해서는 수술이 필요합니다.

Surgery is endoscopic sinus surgery which enlarge the natural openings of the sinuses to allow drainage.
수술은 부비동의 자연적인 입구를 넓혀서 고인 것들이 잘나오게 하는 내시경 수술입니다.

6) Sore throat (인후통)

I'd like to examine your throat.
당신의 목 안을 검사하겠습니다.

Say 'Ah' and stick out your tongue.
'아' 하고 말하며 혀를 내밀어 주세요.

Placing the stick at the back on the tongue may cause gag.
혀 뒤에 막대를 대면 구토가 날 수 있습니다.

Your tonsils are enlarged and inflamed.
당신의 편도가 커지고 염증이 있군요.

You have tonsillitis.
편도선염입니다.

Glands in the neck and at the angle of the jaw are swollen and
  tender.
목과 턱 주변도 부어있고 아프군요.

Tonsillitis usually occurs as part of a pharyngitis.
편도선염은 인후염의 일종입니다.

Tonsillitis may be caused by either viruses or bacteria.
편도선염은 바이러스나 박테리아에 의해 생깁니다.

Bacterial tonsillitis can be treated with antibiotics, but viral
  tonsillitis cannot.
박테리아에 의한 편도선염은 항생제로 치유되나 바이러스는 안됩니다.

I'd llke to differentiate between bacterial tonsillitis and viral
  tonsillitis by taking a throat culture.
박테이라에 의한 편도선염인지, 바이러스에 의한 것인지 알기 위해, 목안의
  균배양을 시행하겠습니다.

I will swab your child's throat to get a sample of throat
  secretions.
목안의 분비물 샘플을 얻기 위해 당신 아이의 목안을 긁겠습니다.

This sample is sent to a laboratory to see if bacteria grow.
이 검사물은 실험실로 보내어져 박테리아가 자라는 지 검사될 것입니다.

With antibiotic treatment, tonsillitis is usually cured within 1
  week, but it may take several weeks for the tonsils and swollen
  glands to return to normal size.
항생제로 편도선염은 1주일 이내에 치료가 되지만, 커진 편도선이 정상으
  로 되려면 몇 주일이 걸릴 수 있습니다.

I will prescribe antibiotics for a period of 7 days.
7일간의 항생제를 처방하겠습니다.

When tonsillitis is caused by group A streptococci, fever usually
  stops within 2 days, and the sore throat disappears soon
  afterward.
그룹 A 연쇄상구균에 의한 편도선염은 열이 2일 안에 떨어지고 목 아픈 것
  도 곧 좋아질 것입니다.

Drink plenty of fluids like tea, soup and juice.
차나 수프, 쥬스와 같은 물을 많이 드세요.

Use a cool humidifier.
가습기를 사용하세요.

Suck on a piece of hard candy.
캔디를 빠세요.

Try changing your child's diet to include more liquids and soft
  foods.
당신의 아이에게 죽이나 부드러운 음식을 먹이세요.

Gargling with warm and salty water can reduce the pain.
따뜻한 소금물로 입을 헹구면 통증을 줄여줄 것입니다.

Be sure that child spits out the salty water after he has finished.
헹구는 것이 끝나면 반드시 물은 뱉어내야 합니다.

Cool-mist humidifier will help soothe your child's sore throat.
찬 가습기는 어린이의 아픈 목을 부드럽게 해 줄것입니다.

A moist, warm towel around your child's neck will help soothe
swollen glands.
따뜻하고 젖은 수건을 어린이 목 주위에 감기면 부은 선들이 부드러워집
니다.

Most people are almost completely recovered within 1 week.
대부분의 사람들은 1주일 이내에 완쾌됩니다.

Since your child has frequent episodes of tonsillitis, I'd like to
suggest removing the tonsils with a surgical procedure called a
tonsillectomy.
당신의 아이가 자주 편도선염이 걸리므로, 수술로 편도선 절제술을 하기를
권합니다.

Because your tonsils keep getting infected and are causing
breathing problems, I recommend taking them out.
당신의 편도선이 자주 감염되고 호흡에 장해를 주기에 편도선을 제거하기
를 권합니다.

7) Dialogue

D : What seems to make your dizziness go away?
어떨 때 당신의 어지러움이 사라지죠?

P : I feel comfortable when I am in bed.
침대에 있을 때 편해져요.

D : Do you have cold symptoms and fever along with nausea and vomiting.

오심, 구토가 동반되는 열이나 감기 증상은 없습니까?

P : No.

없습니다.

D : Is there anything in your past history, such as diabetes, hypertension, tuberculosis, hepatitis and allergy?

당신은 과거에 당뇨병이나 고혈압, 결핵, 간염, 알러지 등을 앓은 적이 있습니까?

P : No.

아닙니다.

D : Do you suffer from any other disease?

다른 질환을 앓고 있는 것이 있나요?

P : No.

없습니다.

D : Is your vision normally OK?

시력은 정상인가요?

P : Yes, its fine.

예, 정상입니다.

D : Do you have ringing in the ears.

귀울림 같은 증상이 있었나요?

P : Yes. I have buzzing in the ears.

예. 귀 안이 윙윙거립니다.

D : Are you taking any medicine?

어떤 약을 먹고 있습니까?

A few medicine can cause hearing problems such as ringing.
어떤 약들은 귀울림과 같은 청각 장애를 일으킵니다.

P : No.
아닙니다.

D : I want to rule out other ear problems.
다른 귀 질환과 감별해야 될 것 같군요.

11 *Dentistry*
(치과)

1) 치과적 질문

Do you have toothache?
Do you have any pain with your teeth?
치통이 있나요?

Which tooth is painful?
어느 치아가 아프죠?

How long has it been bothering you?
언제부터 아프셨죠?

Do you feel pain in chewing?
씹을 때 아픈가요?

Do you have pain when you eat?
먹을 때 아프나요?

Do you feel pain when you drink cold water?
Does the tooth hurt when you drink cold water?
찬 물을 마실 때 아프나요?

Do you have tooth becoming loose?
흔들리는 치아가 있나요?

When did you have your teeth out?

언제 치아를 뽑았죠?

Do your gums bleed easily?

잇몸에서 쉽게 피가 나나요?

Do you have pain in your gums?

잇몸이 아픈가요?

Do you have any swelling in your gums?

잇몸이 부었나요?

Do you have difficulty in chewing?

씹기가 힘드나요?

How long has it been hurting you?

얼마나 오랫동안 아팠나요?

Do you have any discomfort with your mouth?

입안에 불편한 점이 있나요?

Do you have bad breath?

구취가 심하나요?

How often do you brush?

얼마나 자주 양치질을 하시죠?

Have you ever got dental treatment?

치과치료를 받은 적이 있나요?

Do you wear denture?

틀니를 사용하나요?

When did you start to use denture?

언제부터 틀니를 하셨죠?

2) Brushing (양치질)

How to brush and floss correctly is very important.
양치질 방법과 치실 사용법이 아주 중요합니다.

Brush three times a day for 2-4 minutes to remove plague.
프라그를 없애기 위해 하루에 3번 2-4분간 양치질하세요.

Gently brush the teeth on all sides with using a fluoride toothpaste.
불소가 있는 치약으로 치아의 모든 부분을 닦으세요.

Circular and short back-and-forth strokes work best.
둥글게 짧게 전후방으로 양치질하는 것이 좋습니다.

Take the time to brush along the gum line.
잇몸을 따라서 양치질도 하도록 하세요.

Lightly brushing your tongue also helps to remove plaque and food debris and makes your mouth feel fresh.
당신의 혀를 가볍게 닦아주는 것이 프라그와 음식물 찌꺼기 제거에 좋고 입 안을 상쾌하게 만듭니다.

Floss after brushing.
양치질 후 치실을 사용하세요.

Use a fluoride mouth rinse.
불소가 있는 구강청정제를 사용하세요.

Chew sugarless gum that contains xylitol
자이리톨이 있는 무설탕 껌을 씹으세요.

3) Caries (충치)

Open your mouth.
입을 벌려 주세요.

Open wide. More wider.
크게 벌리세요. 더 크게요.

It looks like you have a cavity.
충치를 가지고 있는 것 같군요.

Dental caries is a demineralization of the tooth surface caused by bacteria.
충치는 박테리아 때문에 치아 표면이 부식된 것을 말합니다.

Toothache can be treated with desensitizing treatments.
치통은 신경제거술 만으로도 치료가 가능합니다.

Dental restoration maybe needed if tooth has lost tooth structure.
치아 구조가 손상당하면 다시 회복시켜 주어야 합니다.

You need a temporary filling.
일시적으로 때워야 할 필요가 있습니다.

Caries is caused by bacteria that normally live in the mouth.
충치는 입안에 정상적으로 살고 있는 박테리아에 의해 생깁니다.

Because your tooth is damaged by decay, I will try to repair it and restore it with a filling.
치아가 썩어서 손상당했기 때문에 치료 후 땜질을 하겠습니다.

Tooth extraction is needed because the damage is too extensive for the tooth to be repaired.
치료되기에는 너무 손상이 커서 발치가 필요합니다.

Because the decay is extensive, there isn't enough tooth structure remaining to support a replacement filling.

너무 넓게 썩어서 땜질을 지지해줄 만한 충분한 구조물이 없군요.

An opening will be made through the crown of the tooth into the pulp which contains nerves, blood vessels.

구멍을 치관을 통해 신경과 혈관이 있는 치수까지 뚫겠습니다.

After removing the pulp and cleaning the root canal, a gold or porcelain crown will be placed over the tooth.

치수를 제거하고 치근관을 깨끗이 한 다음, 금이나 포세린으로 치아를 덮을 것입니다.

Your tooth have to be extracted.

당신의 치아를 뽑아야만 합니다.

Amalgams is a safe restorative material.

아말감은 안전한 대체물입니다.

Because composite resins are tooth-colored, it is difficult to distinguish them from natural teeth.

합성 레진은 치아 색이므로, 정상 치아와 구별하기 힘듭니다.

Dental carries can be successfully prevented by brushing your teeth three times daily and reducing number of intakes.

매일 하루에 세 번씩 양치질하고 음식을 자주 먹는 것을 피하면 충치를 예방할 수 있습니다.

Brushing your teeth after every meal is the best way to prevent tooth decay.

식후 양치질이 충치를 예방하는 최선의 방법입니다.

An abscessed tooth caused by tooth decay.

화농성 치아는 충치 때문에 옵니다.

An abscess can cause damage to the bone around the teeth.
농양은 치아 주위의 뼈에 손상을 일으킵니다.

When the infected pulp is not removed, pain and swelling can result.
감염된 치수를 제거하지 않으면 통증과 부종이 생깁니다.

4) Implant (이식)

Implant is an artificial tooth root to hold a replacement tooth.
임플란트는 교체된 치아를 지지해 줄 인공 치근입니다.

Implant is a good treatment to person who have lost a tooth.
임플란트는 치아를 잃은 사람들에게 아주 좋은 치료법입니다.

Implant is so natural-looking and feeling, you may forget you ever lost a tooth.
임플란트는 너무 자연스럽게 보이고 느껴져 치아를 잃지 않은 것처럼 느껴지실 겁니다.

Implants replace one or more teeth without affecting bordering teeth.
임플란트는 주위의 치아 손상 없이 1개 또는 여러 개 대치할 수 있습니다.

Implants can last a lifetime.
임플란트는 일생동안 쓸 수 있습니다.

Adequate bone in your jaw is needed to support the implant.
턱의 적당한 뼈가 임플란트 지지에 필요합니다.

A key to implant success is the quantity and quality of the bone where the implant is to be placed.
임플란트 성공의 열쇠는 임플란트가 이식될 부위의 뼈의 질과 정도입니다.

Because you missed a single tooth, one implant can replace it.
치아 한 개를 잃었기 때문에 한 개의 임플란트만 필요합니다.

Because you missed several teeth, an implant-supported bridges
  can replace them.
치아를 여러 개 잃었기 때문에 임플란트 지지대가 필요합니다.

Implants are like your own teeth and will require the same care.
임플란트는 당신의 치아와 똑같으므로 같은 방법으로 돌봐야 합니다.

5) Dialogue

D : Do you have any discomfort?
  불편한 점이 있으세요?

P : I am suffering from toothache.
  저는 치통을 앓고 있어요.

D : Tell me abut your symptom.
  증상을 말해 주세요.

P : I have pain when I chew and drink cold water.
  씹을 때나 찬 물을 마시면 아파요.

D : OK. Let me have a look.
  알겠습니다. 잠깐 볼까요.

P : OK.
  알겠습니다.

D : You have dental caries.
  당신은 충치를 앓고 있군요.

P : Should I have to get a decayed tooth pulled?
충치를 뽑아야만 하나요?

D : I will try to save that tooth.
살리도록 노력해 볼께요.

P : Can you give me a filling?
때워 주실건가요?

D : Yes. Which filling do you want to choose? porcelain, gold?
예. 필링을 어떤 것으로 하실래요? 포셀린, 아니면 금으로 하실래요?

P : Gold.
금으로요.

D : OK.
알겠습니다.

Try to relax.
긴장을 푸세요.

Open wide for me.
입을 벌려 주세요.

I will give you an injection for local anesthesia.
국소마취를 위해 주사를 놓을 것입니다.

Don't move.
움직이지 마세요.

We are done.
끝났습니다.

I'll give you a prescription.
처방전을 드리겠습니다.

12 *Dermatology*
(피부과)

1) 피부과적 질문

Do you have any skin problem?
피부에 어떤 문제가 있나요?

Do you feel itching?
가려운가요?

Where is it most severe?
어디가 가장 심하죠?

Do you get any spots?
점들이 있나요?

Do you have any rashes?
Do you get the rash?
Do you have hives?
발진이 있나요?

When did the rash start?
When did you have?
언제 발진이 있었죠?

Where did it start?
어디서 시작하던가요?

Did the rash spread?
발진이 퍼지던가요?

When does your skin feel itchy?
언제 피부가 가렵죠?

Is there anything that aggravates your eczema?
습진을 악화시키는 것이 있나요?

What have you tried for your eczema?
습진치료를 위해 어떻게 하셨죠?

Do you have any allergies?
Do you have any history of allergy?
알러지 병력이 있나요?

Do you have any history of a similar rash?
비슷한 발진이 있었나요?

Have you ever experienced any skin eruptions on your body?
몸에 피부 발진이 일어난 적이 있나요?

Is your skin dry?
피부가 건조하나요?

Are you on any medication?
어떤 약을 복용하고 있나요?

Did you eat something special?
특별한 음식을 먹었나요?

Does anyone in your family suffer from skin problem?
가족 중에 피부 문제를 가지고 있는 사람이 있나요?

Do you have---? or Do you feel---?

Itchy skin
Scaly skin
Inflamed skin
Skin rash
Skin spots
Skin patches
Skin redness
Skin swelling
Skin cracking
Weeping
Crusting
Scaling
Blisters
Hyperpigmented skin
Leathery skin
Papules
Bumps
Urticaria
Pimples
Pustules
Skin ulcer
Skin lump
Green nails
Grey nails
Thickening nails
Brittle nails

2) Acne (여드름)

The exact cause of acne is unknown.
여드름의 정확한 원인은 알려져 있지 않습니다.

Acne results from several related factors.

여드름은 여러 가지 관련된 요소로 생깁니다.

One important factor is an increase in hormones called androgens (male sex hormones).

중요한 원인은 남성 호르몬인 안드로젠의 증가 때문입니다.

Trigger factors for acne are skin rubbing, skin picking, pollution, high humidity, menstrual periods and stress.

여드름을 악화시키는 이유들은 피부를 긁거나 짜거나 오염되거나 습기가 너무 많거나, 생리기간이거나 스트레스 때문입니다.

The goals of treatment are to heal existing lesions, stop new lesions from forming, prevent scarring.

치료의 목적은 지금의 부위를 낫게 하고, 새로운 곳이 생기지 않게 하며, 흉터를 방지하는 것입니다.

Simple treatments and preventive measures are washing skin, avoiding rubbing, avoid sun exposure.

간단한 치료와 예방법은 피부를 씻고, 문지르지 않고, 햇빛을 피하는 것입니다.

You should avoid rubbing and touching your skin lesions.

당신의 피부 병변 부위를 문지르거나 만지지 마세요.

Don't scratch.

긁지 마세요.

You need to change some of the cosmetics which is oil free.

기름기가 없는 화장품으로 교체해야 합니다.

Gently wash your face with a mild soap, once in the morning and once in the evening and after exercise.

얼굴을 아침에 한 번, 저녁에 한 번, 운동 후에 부드러운 비누를 이용하여 씻으세요.

Laser or dermabrasion therapy can treat scars left by acne.

레이저나 박피술이 여드름에 의해 생긴 흉터를 치료할 수 있습니다.

3) Dermatitis (피부염)

You seem to have atopic dermatitis.

아토피성 피부염인 것 같습니다.

Atopy is a word that is used to describe an allergic condition.

아토피란 알러지 상태를 말하는 단어입니다.

Overacting immune system cause the manifestation of an atopic dermatitis.

과도한 면역반응이 아토피성 피부염을 일으킬 수 있습니다.

Atopic dermatitis appears to run in families.

아토피성 피부염은 가족에서 잘생깁니다.

Don't rub the itching spot.

가려운 곳을 긁지 마세요.

Scratching and rubbing in response to itching increases inflammation.

가려워 피부를 긁는 것이 염증을 증가시킵니다.

Atopic dermatitis affects approximately 10 percent of children.

아토피성 피부염은 어린이의 10%에 발생합니다.

A spontaneous resolution occurs in about 80-90% of cases.

80-90%에서는 자연적으로 좋아집니다.

Avoid things that trigger the symptoms.

증상을 악화시키는 것들을 피하세요.

Keep the skin from drying out by the application of moisturizers.

보습제를 발라 피부가 건조해지는 것을 막으세요.

I will prescribe oral antihistamines to provide relief from itching.

가려움을 줄이기 위해 항히스타민제를 처방해 드리겠습니다.

Topical corticosteroids can be used to decrease the inflammation and ease the itching.

국소 스테로이드는 염증을 줄이고 가려움을 줄여줍니다.

It looks like contact dermititis.

접촉성 피부염 같습니다.

Contact dermatitis is inflammation of the skin resulting from contact with an irritant.

접촉성 피부염은 자극제에 접촉할 때 피부에 염증이 생기는 것입니다.

Cosmetics, fragrances, preservatives are common causes of allergic contact dermatitis.

화장품, 방향제, 방부제가 알러지성 접촉성 피부염의 흔한 원인들입니다.

Cortisone cream will clear it right up.

코티손 크림이 바로 치료해 줄 것입니다.

Symptomatic treatments are the use of moisturizers, antihistamines and topical or systemic corticosteroids.

증상치료는 보습제와 항히스타민, 국소 또는 전신 스테로이드를 사용하는 것입니다.

You have got hives.

두드러기이군요.

I'll write a prescription for oral antihistamines.

항히스타민제를 처방해 드리겠습니다.

Seborrheic dermatitis occurs in areas produce a high amount of
  sebum.

지루성 피부염은 비지가 많은 곳에 잘 생깁니다.

Seborrheic dermatitis may persist for a prolonged period of time.

지루성 피부염은 오랫동안 지속됩니다.

The goal of treatment is to control the symptoms.

치료의 목적은 증상을 조절하는 것입니다.

I'll give you this lotion.

이 로션을 드리겠습니다.

This lotion is a good remedy for eczema.

이 로션은 습진에 좋은 치료약입니다.

Just apply on the affected area.

병변 부위에 단지 바르기만 하세요.

4) Skin Cancer (피부암)

We have some very serious matters to discuss regarding your
  skin problem.

당신의 피부병에 대해 상의할 중요한 문제가 있습니다.

You have a skin cancer.

당신은 피부암을 가지고 있습니다.

UV radiation from the sun is the main cause of skin cancer.

태양의 자외선이 피부암의 가장 중요한 원인입니다.

Excessive and chronic sun exposure is a major risk factor for melanoma.

햇빛에 지나치게 만성적으로 노출되는 것이 흑색종의 가장 큰 위험요소입니다.

A suspicious lesion should be biopsied to determine proper treatment.

의심되는 부분은 적절한 치료를 결정하기 위해 조직검사를 해야 합니다.

I will remove part of the growth to check for cancer cells.

암 세포가 있는 지 알기 위해 자란 곳 일부를 절제하겠습니다.

Basal cell carcinoma seldom metastasizes, although it may invade lymph or blood vessels.

기저 세포암은 비록 임파선이나 혈관들을 침범하더라도 잘 전이되지 않습니다.

Early treatments of basal cell carcinoma are curettage, electrocautery, cryosurgery, radiotherapy, topical chemotherapy, laser surgery, or surgical excision.

기저세포암의 치료는 소파술, 전기 소작술, 냉동 소작술, 방사선 치료, 국소 화학치료, 레이저 치료, 수술적 제거술입니다.

Squamous cell carcinoma is capable of metastasizing to other areas of the body if not treated early.

상피세포암은 초기에 치료하지 않으면 몸의 다른 곳으로 전이될 수 있습니다.

Sometimes you continue to have problem even after removal.

때때로 제거 후에도 계속적인 문제가 발생되기도 합니다.

5) Dialogue

D : Do you have any allergies?

알러지가 발생한 적은 없습니까?

P : I am allergic to mold.

곰팡이에 알러지가 있어요.

D : How did you know that?

어떻게 그것을 알았지요?

P : I suffered with sneezing, runny nose and watery eyes when I was exposed it.

곰팡이에 노출되면 재치기를 하고, 콧물과 눈물이 납니다.

D : How can you avoid allergens?

어떻게 원인물질을 피하고 있죠?

P : I am trying to reduce the mold in my home by removing house-plants and frequently cleaning my house.

저는 집에 있는 화분을 제거하고 집을 자주 청소하여 곰팡이를 줄이려고 노력합니다.

D : Do you have any medication?

어떤 약을 먹고 있나요?

P : Anti-histamines help reduce the symptoms.

항히스타민이 증상을 줄이는데 도움을 주더군요.

D : Did you take allergy shots?

알러지 면역 치료는 받으셨나요?

P : No.

아닙니다.

D : You need to have allergy shots when you can't avoid them.
원인물질을 피하기 힘들 때는 알러지 면역 치료가 필요합니다.

P : Well, it's still on the drawing board.
글쎄요, 아직은 생각중입니다.

13 *Urology*
(비뇨기과)

1) 비뇨기과적 질문

How about your urination?
How is the water?
How are the water works?
Do you have any problems passing water?
Do you have any difficulties in voiding your urine?
Urination?
Water?
소변보는 것은 어떤가요?

Do you have pain or burning with urination?
Do you have any pain or burning while urinating?
소변을 눌 때 아프거나 화끈거리나요?

Do you ever experience any pain in your penis when you urinate?
소변을 볼 때 음경이 아프지는 않나요?

Is your urine cloudy?
소변이 탁하나요?

Have you noticed any changes in size or the force of the stream of urine?
소변의 양이나 힘에서 변화가 있습니까?

Where does your belly hurt you?
배 어느 부위가 아프죠?

Do you get pain in your side?
옆이 아픕니까?

Do you have a fever and flank pain?
열이 나고 옆구리가 아프나요?

Do you have any pain in your abdomen, side or back?
배나 옆구리, 허리가 아프지는 않나요?

Do you have pain into the groin?
서혜부 안쪽이 아프나요?

Is there pain behind the scrotum?
음낭 뒤쪽으로 통증이 있나요?

Do you feel like urinating often?
소변을 자주 보고 싶나요?

Do you ever feel pain in your bladder?
방광이 아팠던 적이 있나요?

Do you have a discharge from the tip of the penis?
끝부분에서 뭐가 나오나요?

Did you see pus in your urine?
소변에서 고름을 보았나요?

Did you see blood in your urine?
소변에서 피를 보았나요?

Have you ever had any veneral diseases?
성병에 걸린 적이 있나요?

Have you ever had a kidney or bladder infection?
신장염이나 방광염을 앓은 적이 있습니까?

Do you leak when you cough?
기침을 하면 소변을 흘리나요?

When do you have leakage?
언제 요실금이 있죠?

How many pads do you use per day?
하루에 몇 개의 패드를 쓰죠?

Do you have problems starting the urine stream?
소변을 볼 때 처음에 문제가 있나요?

Do you have a weak urinary stream?
소변이 약하나요?

Do you dribble urine after you urinate?
소변을 본 다음에도 소변이 뚝뚝 떨어지나요?

Do you wake many times at night to urinate?
소변을 보기 위해 밤에 자주 일어나나요?

How often have you had a sensation of not emptying your bladder completely after you have finished urinating?
소변을 다 눈 후에도 얼마나 자주 방광이 빈 것 같지 않은 느낌이 들죠?

How often have you had to urinate again less than two hours after you finished urination?
소변을 본 다음에 2시간 이내에 다시 소변을 보는 경우가 얼마나 자주 있나요?

433

How often have you found you stopped and started again several
  times when you urinated?

얼마나 자주 소변을 보다가 멈추었다가 다시 보곤 합니까?

How often have you found it difficult to postpone urination?

소변을 보지 않기 어려울 때가 얼마나 자주 있습니까?

Do you have---? or Do you feel---?

Urinary hesitancy
Weak urination
Urinary blockage
Urinary urgency
Urinary leakage
Urinary dribbling
Difficulty starting urination
Unsteady urine stream
Frequent urination
Night urination
Painful urination
Burning urination
Blood in urine
Cloudy urine
Urine that smells bad
Renal colic
Sharp pain in the back
Cramping pain in the flank.
Reduced urine
Loss of urine
Abdominal pain
Abdominal discomfort
Chronic urine retention
Erection difficulty
Painful ejaculation

Blood in semen
Fever and chills

2) Renal disease (신장 질환)

I'm going to get some blood tests done to see what is causing the symptom.

증상의 원인이 무엇인지 알기 위해 혈액 검사를 하겠습니다.

You will feel tired and weak because your body needs clean blood to function properly.

당신의 몸이 혈액을 적절하게 기능할 수 있도록 깨끗이 하지 못하므로 피곤하고 약하게 느껴지실 겁니다.

Your kidneys cannot filter wastes from your blood very well.

당신의 신장이 당신 핏속의 대사물들을 잘 제거하지 못합니다.

Early kidney disease is a silent problem, so you don't feel sick.

초기 신장질환은 증상이 없어 당신은 아픔을 느끼지 못합니다.

To detect the disease, the level of creatinine in your blood and the level of protein in your urine should be checked.

병을 발견하기 위해 당신의 혈액 크레아티닌 농도와 소변의 단백질 농도를 검사해야 합니다.

Kidney disease often cannot be cured.

신장 질환은 종종 치료하지 못합니다.

Because you are in the early stages of a kidney disease, you can be able to make your kidneys last longer by treatment.

당신의 신장 질환은 초기이므로, 당신은 치료에 의해 당신의 신장이 계속 괜찮을 수 있습니다.

Because your kidneys stop working completely, your body fills
with extra water and waste products.
당신의 신장 기능이 완전히 멈추었기 때문에 당신의 몸에는 과다한 수분과
대사물이 축적되어 있습니다.

This condition is called uremia.
이 상태를 요독증이라 합니다.

Your hands or feet may swell.
당신의 손과 발이 부을 것입니다.

Untreated uremia may lead to seizures or coma and will
ultimately result in death.
치료하지 않은 요독증은 발작이나 혼수를 일으킬 수 있고, 사망할 수도 있
습니다.

You need to undergo dialysis or kidney transplantation.
당신은 투석이나 신장이식이 필요합니다.

There are two major forms of dialysis.
투석에는 2종류가 있습니다.

In hemodialysis, your blood is sent through a machine that filters
away waste products.
혈액투석은 당신의 혈액을 기계로 보내어 대사물을 제거합니다.

Hemodialysis should be   performed at a dialysis center three
times per week for 3 to 4 hours.
혈액투석은 투석실에서 일주일에 3번 3-4시간동안 행해져야 합니다.

In peritoneal dialysis, a fluid is put into your abdomen to capture
the waste products from your blood.
복부투석은 액체를 복부에 넣어 피속의 불순물을 잡아내는 것입니다.

After a few hours, the dialysate containing your body's wastes is
  drained away.
몇 시간 후 당신 몸의 불순물이 포함된 투석액이 배출될 것입니다.

You can give yourself treatments at home, at work, or on trips.
당신은 스스로 집이나, 직장에서나, 여행중 치료를 할 수 있습니다.

Reducing dietary intake of phosphorus is one of the most
  important steps in preventing bone disease.
인이 함유된 유제품을 줄이는 것이 뼈 질환을 막는 중요한 것입니다.

I will prescribe a calcium supplement in addition to Vitamin
  D(calcitriol) to prevent osteoporosis.
골다공증을 방지하기 위해 칼슘과 비타민 D를 처방해 드리겠습니다.

Diabetes and hypertension can damage the small blood vessels
  in your kidneys.
당뇨병과 고혈압이 당신의 신장에 있는 혈관들을 손상시킬 수 있습니다.

3) Urinary Stone (결석)

I'd like to scan your urinary system using a special X-ray test
  called an IVP (intravenous pyelogram).
IVP란 X-선 촬영을 통해 배뇨계를 검사해 보겠습니다.

You have an ureteral stone.
요로결석이군요.

Most kidney stones spontaneously pass out of the body without
  being noticed.
대부분의 신장 결석은 느낌 없이 자연스레 몸밖으로 배출됩니다.

A stone is a hard mass developed from crystals that separate from the urine.

결석은 소변에서 분리된 결정들이 덩어리를 만든 것입니다.

Normally, urine contains chemicals that prevent the crystals from forming.

정상적으로 소변에는 결정을 만드는 것을 방지하는 화학물이 있습니다.

These inhibitors do not seem to work for everyone.

이 억제제가 모든 사람들에게 적용되는 것은 아닌가 봅니다.

If the stone is tiny, it will pass out of the body in the urine without causing too much pain.

만약 돌이 작으면, 큰 통증 없이 몸밖으로 나올 수 있습니다.

A larger stone may get stuck in a ureter, the bladder, or the urethra.

큰돌은 요관, 방광, 요도에 걸릴 수 있습니다.

A problem stone can block the flow of urine and cause great pain.

문제를 일으키는 돌은 소변의 흐름을 막아 큰 통증을 일으킵니다.

Fortunately, surgery is not usually necessary.

다행스럽게도 대부분은 수술이 필요하지 않습니다.

Most stones can pass through the urinary system with plenty of water to help move the stone along.

대부분의 돌은 많은 양의 물을 마셔 스스로 움직이도록 하면 나올 수 있습니다.

Drink plenty of water.

많은 양의 물을 마시세요.

If you have a stone that will not pass by itself, I need to use a machine to send shock waves directly to the stone.
만약 돌이 스스로 나오지 않으면, 기계를 이용해 돌에 직접 충격파를 가하겠습니다.

The shock waves break a large stone into small stones that will pass through your urinary system with your urine.
충격파는 큰돌을 부수어 작은 돌로 만들어 배출되게 합니다.

This method is extracorporeal shockwave lithotripsy.
이 방법은 체외 충격파 쇄석술입니다.

I will insert ureteroscope into your urethra, pass it up through the bladder, and direct it to the ureter for destroying the stone.
돌을 깨기 위해, 요관내시경을 요도로 넣은 다음, 방광을 통과하여, 요관으로 직접 갈 것입니다.

Drink lots of water to prevent more stones from forming.
돌이 더 생기지 않도록 물을 많이 드세요.

Try to drink 12 full glasses of water every day.
매일 12컵의 물을 마시세요.

The most common type of stone contains calcium.
대부분의 돌은 칼슘을 포함하고 있습니다.

Recent studies have shown that foods high in calcium, including dairy foods, help prevent calcium stones.
최근의 연구에서 유제품을 포함하여 칼슘이 든 음식은 칼슘으로 생긴 돌을 막는데 도움이 된다고 합니다.

Taking calcium in pill form may increase the risk of developing stones.
칼슘을 정제로 먹는 것은 돌을 더 만들 위험이 있습니다.

You need to cut back on certain foods, such as chocolate, coffee, tea, cola, nuts.

당신은 초콜릿이나 커피, 차, 콜라, 호두 등을 먹는 것을 줄여야합니다.

4) Prostate Hyperplasia & Cancer (전립선 비대, 암)

I will insert a gloved finger into the rectum to check the size of the prostate.

전립선 크기를 측정하기 위해 글러브를 낀 손가락을 직장 안에 넣겠습니다.

We'll do ultrasonogram on your prostate.

전립선에 초음파 검사를 할 것입니다.

Your prostate is enlarged.

당신의 전립선이 커져있습니다.

It is common for the prostate gland to become enlarged as a man ages.

남자들은 나이가 듦에 따라 일반적으로 전립선이 커지게 됩니다.

Some drugs can either prevent progression of growth of the prostate or shrink the prostate.

어떤 약들은 전립선의 증식을 막거나 줄일 수 있습니다.

I'd like to recommend removal of the enlarged part of the prostate.

커진 전립선의 일부를 제거할 것을 권유하고 싶군요.

Minimally invasive surgery or transurethral microwave procedures is needed to relieve BPH symptoms.

최소 침습 수술이나 요도를 통한 마이크로웨이브 시술은 전립선 비대중의 증상을 완화시켜 주는데 필요합니다.

We can reach the prostate by inserting an instrument through the urethra.

우리는 요도를 통해 기구를 넣어 전립선에 도달할 수 있습니다.

Transurethral resection of the prostate is less traumatic than open forms of surgery.

요도를 통한 전립선 절제술은 일반 개복술보다 덜 손상을 입습니다.

Open surgery is needed because the prostate gland is greatly enlarged.

전립선이 너무 커서 개복술이 필요합니다.

A special catheter will be inserted through the opening of the penis to drain urine from the bladder into a collection bag.

특별한 도뇨관이 방광에 있는 소변을 빼내기 위해 요도로 삽입될 것입니다.

This catheter will be left in place for several days.

도뇨관은 며칠 동안 둘 것입니다.

After surgery, you will probably notice some blood or clots in your urine as the wound starts to heal.

수술 후, 당신은 상처가 아물 때까지 혈뇨를 볼 것입니다.

Some bleeding is normal, and it should clear up in several days.

약간의 출혈은 정상이고, 며칠 내 좋아지게 됩니다.

It is important to drink a lot of water to help flush out the bladder and speed healing.

방광을 씻어주고 빨리 낫기 위해서는 많은 물을 마시는 것이 중요합니다.

Eat a balanced diet to prevent constipation.

변비를 예방하기 위해 균형적인 식사를 하세요.

Don't do any heavy lifting.

무거운 물건을 들지 마세요.

In the years after your surgery, it is important to continue having a rectal exam once a year.

수술 후 몇 년간은 일 년에 한 번, 직장 검사를 하는 것이 중요합니다.

I will do Prostate Specific Antigen (PSA) blood test to rule out cancer.

암을 감별하기 위해 **PSA** 혈액검사를 하겠습니다.

Treatment methods for prostate cancer are radical prostatectomy, radiation therapy or hormonal therapy.

전립선암의 치료는 광범위 전립선 절제술, 방사선 치료, 호르몬 요법입니다.

Radical prostatectomy is a surgical procedure to remove the entire prostate gland and nearby tissues.

광범위한 전립선 절제술은 전체 전립선과 주위의 조직을 제거하는 수술입니다.

Sometimes people continue to have problem even after surgery.

때때로 수술 후에도 계속적인 문제가 발생되기도 합니다.

Radiation therapy uses high-energy X-rays to kill cancer cells.

방사선 치료는 암세포를 죽이기 위해 고에너지 방사선을 이용합니다.

Hormonal therapy keeps cancer cells from getting the male hormones they need to grow.

호르몬 요법은 암세포가 자라는데 필요함 남성호르몬을 억제하는 것입니다.

Combination treatment with chemotherapy and radiation therapy is needed to relieve symptoms and to destroy cancer cells that may remain in the area.

항암제와 방사선 치료 요법이 증상을 완화시키고, 남은 부위의 암세포를 죽이기 위해 필요합니다.

5) Dialogue 1.

P : I urinate frequently.
소변을 자주 봅니다.

I have to get out of bed to urinate in the night.
밤에 소변을 보기 위해 잠에서 일어나야 합니다.

D : How many times in the night?
밤에 얼마나 자주 그러시죠?

P : Up to four times lately.
최근엔 네 번까지 그랬습니다.

D : Have you noticed any change in your urine?
소변에서 이상한 점은 없나요?

P : My urine is dark and reddish.
검고 붉은 색입니다.

D : Do you have burning sensation with urination?
소변을 볼 때 화끈거리지는 않나요?

P : No.
아닙니다.

D : Do you have problems starting the urine system?
소변을 보려할 때 처음에 잘 나오지 않나요?

P : No.
아닙니다.

D : Do you have a fever and backache?
열이 나고 등이 아프지는 않나요?

P : My flank hurts.

옆구리가 아픕니다.

D : Have you noticed any swelling in your legs?

다리가 붓지는 않습니까?

P : I've noticed my legs are puffed up in the evening.

밤에는 다리가 붓습니다.

My face, legs, feet are sometimes swollen after I arise in the morning.

얼굴과 다리가 아침에 일어나면 가끔씩 부어요.

D : Let me look at your feet.

발을 한 번 볼까요?

Slip off your shoes and socks.

신발과 양말을 벗으세요.

When did this all start?

언제부터 그랬죠?

P : Well, just since the weather has been cold.

날씨가 추워지면서부터 그랬습니다.

D : I want you to have an ultrasound examination of the kidneys.

신장 초음파 검사를 해보아야 할 것 같군요.

Also renal function test and some blood tests are needed.

그리고 신장 기능검사와 혈액 검사 역시 필요합니다.

P : Is the test painful?

검사가 아픈가요?

D : No. Test is a simple procedure.

아뇨. 검사는 간단한 것입니다.

Normal daily rate of urinary protein excretion averages less than 150 milligrams per 24 hours.

24시간 소변에서 평균적인 단백질 배출은 150 mg이하입니다.

Proteinuria exceeding 750 milligrams per 24 hours occurs commonly in kidney disease.

24시간에 750mg을 넘는 단백뇨는 신장에 문제가 있을 때 자주 나타납니다.

I want you to collect your urine for 24 hours.

24시간 소변을 모아주세요.

P : How can I get an urine specimen?

어떻게 소변을 모으죠?

D : Nurse will tell you exactly how to do it.

간호사가 어떻게 하는지 가르쳐 줄 것입니다.

I will make an appointment for an ultrasound examination.

초음파 검사는 예약을 해드리겠습니다.

D : Hematuria and proteinuria are detected.

혈뇨와 단백뇨가 검출되었습니다.

P : What is hematuria?

혈뇨가 무엇이죠?

I can't see the blood when I urinate.

소변볼 때 피를 보지 못했는데요?

D : Sometimes hematuria can only be seen through a microscope.

혈뇨는 때때로 현미경을 통해서만 볼 수 있습니다.

Red blood cell casts were seen in your urine specimen.

적혈구 덩어리가 당신의 소변에서 보여졌습니다.

A lot of protein was also found in your urine.

그리고 당신의 소변에서 많은 양의 단백질도 발견되었습니다.

P : Can you tell me what is wrong with my kidneys?

신장이 어떻게 잘못되었는지 말해 주실래요?

D : I think your problem is due to acute glomerulonephritis.

제 생각에 당신의 문제는 급성 사구체신염 때문인 것 같습니다.

P : How are kidney diseases treated?

신장질환을 어떻게 치료하죠?

D : Symptoms of sodium retention such as hypertension and edema can be managed with careful sodium restriction, but diuretics and antihypertensive drugs maybe used if necessary.

고혈압이나 부종과 같은 고농도 염분에 의한 증상은 소금 섭취량을 줄이면 되고, 필요시 이뇨제나 고혈압 약을 사용합니다.

Sometimes dialysis maybe required temporarily.

때론 일시적인 복막투석이 필요할 수 있습니다.

P : How long will I have to take medicines?

얼마나 오랫동안 약을 복용해야 하죠?

D : Treatment length depends on your overall health.

치료 기간은 당신의 전체 건강 상태에 따라 다릅니다.

You will have to continue bearing up even though you feel
  so bad.

당신의 상태가 좋지 않더라도 계속 참아야 할 것입니다.

P : OK. I will try.

알겠습니다. 노력하겠습니다.

6) Dialogue 2.

D : Tell me about your pain.

당신의 통증에 대해서 말해 주세요.

P : I have a pain in my left flank.

저의 왼쪽 옆구리가 아픕니다.

It's already as serve as I can stand.

지금까지는 참을 만치 참았어요.

D : Do you have abdominal pain in the middle or lower right
  side?

배 중간이나 우측 아래부위 배가 아픈가요?

P : No.

아닙니다.

D : What does your pain feel like?

통증이 어떻게 느껴지죠?

P : I have sharp mid-back pain.

허리 중간에 날카로운 통증이 있어요.

D : Has the pain moved or spread?

통증이 옮겨다니거나 방사통을 일으키지는 않습니까?

P : No.

아닙니다.

D : Is the pain associated with eating?

통증이 먹는 것과 관련이 있습니까?

P : No.

아닙니다.

D : Can't you pass your urine?

소변을 볼 수 없습니까?

P : It passes all right, but I have pain in urination.

잘 나옵니다. 하지만 소변 볼 때 아픕니다.

D : Does any position help you?

어떤 자세가 통증을 줄여주던가요?

P : No. I can't find any comfortable position.

아뇨, 어떤 자세를 해도 좋아지지 않습니다.

D : Is your flank very tender to touch?

옆구리 부분을 만지면 아주 아픈가요?

P : No.

아닙니다.

D : I think that you maybe have kidney stone.

제 생각에 당신은 신장 결석인 것 같군요.

Actually the better term is an ureteral stone.

좀 더 정확하게 말하면 요로 결석이죠.

P : Stone? What can I do?

돌이라구요? 어떻게 해야 하죠?

D : Now what I think you should do is taking some blood and urine tests.

지금 당신이 할 수 있는 것은 제 생각에 피검사와 소변 검사를 하는 것입니다.

Typical symptom is blood in the urine.

전형적인 증상은 소변에 피가 보이는 것입니다.

And then send you X-ray department to do an IVP.

그리고 나서 당신을 방사선실로 보내 **IVP**를 하도록 하겠습니다.

P : IVP?

아이 브이 피라뇨?

D : That's an X-ray of the kidney.

그것은 신장에 대한 **X-ray**입니다.

P : OK. But I don't want to have surgery.

알겠습니다. 하지만 전 수술은 받고 싶지 않습니다.

D : If you have a small stone, I will observe a few more days to see if it passes byitself.

만약 당신의 결석이 작을 경우엔, 그것이 저절로 빠져나가도록 며칠을 기다릴 것입니다.

Drink at least 10 glasses of water every day.

매일 물을 10잔 이상씩 마시십시오.

Keeping active may help the stone pass.

활동을 하면 돌이 나오는데 더 도움이 됩니다.

Don't stay in bed.

침대에만 있지 마세요.

Walk as much as possible.
가능한 많이 걸으세요.

P : OK.
알겠습니다.

D : And there also may be some infection.
그리고 약간의 감염도 있을 것입니다.

I would want to treat you with an antibiotic and with some
pain medicines.
약간의 항생제와 진통제로 치료할 것입니다.

Take it exactly as directed.
지침대로 정확히 드세요.

P : OK.
알겠습니다.

D : Let me review your medical history now.
이제 당신의 병에 대한 과거력을 물어보겠습니다.

14 *Psychiatry*
(신경정신과)

1) 신경정신과적 질문

How has your mood been lately?
What sort of mood have you been recently?
How would you describe your general mood now?
최근 기분이 어떤가요?

Why don't you tell me something about what's bothering you?
당신을 괴롭히는 것에 대해 말해줄래요?

Do you feel sad or depressed?
Do you feel blue?
슬프거나 우울함을 느끼나요?

Do you feel worried?
걱정거리가 있나요?

What's your concern?
걱정거리가 무엇이죠?

How have your spirits been?
요즘 기분은 어떠했습니까?

Are you optimistic?
낙천주의자입니까?

Are you pessimistic?
염세주의자입니까?

Do you get angry more easily than usual?
Do you become easily irritated?
보통 때 보다 더 자주 화를 내나요?

Do you feel life isn't worth living any more?
삶이 더 살 가치가 없다고 느끼나요?

Do emotional problems at work seem to make it worse?
직장에서의 감정이 증상을 더 나쁘게 만들던가요?

How have you been sleeping?
잠자는 것은 어떤가요?

Do you have any difficulty falling asleep?
잠드는 것에 문제가 있나요?

Are you able to sleep when you want to sleep?
잠자고 싶을 때 잠을 잘 수 있나요?

How long does it take you to fall asleep?
잠자려면 얼마나 시간이 걸리죠?

What is your usual bed time?
보통 몇 시에 자죠?

What time do you usually get up?
언제 보통 일어나죠?

Do you wake up early than usual?
보통보다 일찍 일어나나요?

What is your average total sleep time?
평균 수면시간이 얼마나 되죠?

Does anything interrupt your sleep?
수면을 어떤 것이 방해하나요?

How long have you had difficulty sleeping?
수면장애가 얼마나 오래되었죠?

Have you ever taken some medicine for sleep?
Do you take sleeping pills sometimes?
잠을 자기 위해서 약을 먹은 적이 있나요?

Are you very nervous?
아주 예민한 편인가요?

What stress do you experience in your relationship?
타인과의 관계에서 어떤 스트레스를 느끼나요?

Do you have any problems with your work?
Do you have any problem with your working?
일하는 데 어떤 문제가 있나요?

Do you enjoy your work?
일하는 것이 즐겁나요?

Have you been having any problems with your memory?
기억에 문제가 있지는 않나요?

Do you have a good appetite?
식욕은 좋나요?

Are you losing weight?
체중이 줄었나요?

Have you ever had a seizure?
발작이 있었던 적이 있습니까?

Do you have--? or Do you feel---?

Sleep problems
Difficulty falling asleep
Frequent night waking
Difficulty returning to sleep
Waking too early
Sleep pattern changes
Oversleeping
Daytime tiredness or Fatigue
Drowsiness
Difficulty concentrating
Increased irritability, anger, or hostility
Losing your temper
Anxiety
Depressed mood and other emotional problems
Persistent sadness
Feelings of worthlessness or Hopelessness
Empty feeling
Misery
Inappropriate guilt
Loss of confidence
Loss of interest in activities
Loss of interest in activities once enjoyed
Thoughts of death or suicide
Appetite loss or Weight loss
Overeating or Weight gain
Mental changes
Forgetfulness
Difficulty thinking

Alcohol problems or Drug problems

Sex problems or Physical problems

Aches and pains that just won' t go away

Difficulty remembering, or making decisions

Persistent sad or irritable mood

Frequent absences from school or poor performance in school

Talk of or efforts to run away from home

Outbursts of shouting, complaining, unexplained irritability, or crying

Social isolation, poor communication

Extreme sensitivity to rejection or failure

Reckless behavior

Difficulty with relationships

2) Insomnia (불면증)

Common triggers for insomnia are stress, anxiety, depression, environment change, shift work, jet lag, caffeine, alcohol, medications, nighttime activity or disease.

불면증의 원인들은 스트레스와 걱정, 우울증, 환경변화, 직업변경, 시차, 카페인, 알코올, 약들, 밤 작업이나 질병 등입니다.

Insomnia may result from either psychological or physical causes.

불면증은 정신적 혹은 육체적 원인에 의해 생길 수 있습니다.

The amount of melatonin produced by your body seems to decrease as you get older.

나이가 듦에 따라 멜라토닌의 분비가 감소될 수 있습니다.

Melatonin may improve sleep.

멜라토닌이 잠을 잘 자게 해 줄 것입니다.

I will prescribe some medicine.
약간의 약을 처방해 드리겠습니다.

Mild cases may require no treatment.
가벼운 경우엔 치료가 필요 없습니다.

Go to sleep and get up at the same time.
같은 시간에 잠을 자고 일어나세요.

Avoid daytime naps
낮잠을 자지 마세요.

Avoid stress and worrying about not sleeping
스트레스를 피하고 잠을 자지 않는 것에 대해 걱정을 하지 마세요.

Avoid caffeine, nicotine and alcohol.
카페인과 니코틴, 알코올을 피하세요.

Avoid nosing environment or cold environment.
소란스럽거나 차가운 환경을 피해야 한다.

Create a safe and comfortable place to sleep.
잠을 자기 위한 안정되고 안락한 장소로 만드세요.

Try to get some natural light in the afternoon each day.
매일 오후에 자연광을 쬐세요.

You should exercise in the early part of the day regularly and
avoid strenuous activity before bedtime.
매일 일찍 규칙적으로 운동하고 자기 전에는 무리한 운동은 하지 마세요.

Avoid large meals and excessive fluids before bedtime.
자기 전에 많은 음식이나 물을 먹지 마세요.

3) Depression (우울증)

Everybody feels sad or blue now and then.
모든 사람이 때때로 슬픔을 느낍니다.

It's part of life.
그것은 생활의 일부입니다.

Depression can be caused by a combination of genetic, biological, and psychosocial factors.
우울증은 유전적, 생물학적, 정신사회학적 요소들의 조합으로 생깁니다.

Depression lasts weeks or months, sometimes years if you don't seek treatment.
만약 우울증을 치료하지 않으면 몇 주, 몇 달, 몇 년이 갈 수도 있습니다.

The first step to getting help is to overcome negative attitudes.
도움이 되는 첫 번 째 단계는 부정적인 자세를 극복하는 것입니다.

Try to focus on activities that make you feel better.
당신을 더 기분 좋게 해주는 활동에 집중하도록 노력하세요.

Don't isolate yourself.
당신을 홀로 고립시키지 마세요.

Take part in activities even when you may not want to.
당신이 원하지 않을 때라도 활동에 참가하세요.

Talk with your friends and family and consider joining a support group.
친구나 가족들과 이야기하고 당신을 도와줄 단체와 함께 하는 것을 고려해 보세요.

Communicating your feelings will help your recovery.
당신의 감정에 대해 대화하는 것은 회복에 도움이 됩니다.

Try to maintain a positive outlook.
긍정적인 면을 보려 하세요.

Having a good attitude can be beneficial.
긍정적인 자세는 도움을 줍니다.

You can try to transform your mind from negative to positive.
당신의 마음을 부정적인 것에서 긍정적인 것으로 바꾸도록 노력하세요.

Regular exercise and proper diet are essential to good health.
규칙적인 운동과 적절한 식사는 좋은 건강에 필수적입니다.

Try to get enough rest and maintain a regular sleeping pattern.
충분한 휴식을 취하고, 규칙적인 수면습관을 유지하세요.

Avoid drinking alcohol or using any illicit substances.
알코올과 금지된 약물은 피하세요.

Most people with depression can be helped with psychotherapy,
  medicine, or both together.
우울증에 걸린 사람들은 정신치료, 약, 또는 두 가지로 함께 치료합니다.

Antidepressant medications, especially when combined with
  psychotherapy, can be very effective treatments.
항우울제를 정신치료와 병행할 때 아주 효과가 좋습니다.

Treatment can help most depressed people start to feel better in
  just a few weeks.
치료는 대부분의 우울증 환자들을 몇 주 내에 좋아지게 합니다.

Talking with a trained therapist can also be effective in changing
  the relationships, thoughts, or behaviors that contribute to
  depression.
훈련된 치료사와 대화를 나누는 것은 우울증을 야기한 관계나 생각, 행동
  등을 변화시키는 효과가 있습니다.

Antidepressant drugs can improve mood, sleep, appetite, and concentration.

항우울제는 기분이나 수면, 식욕, 집중력을 좋아지게 합니다.

It is important to take antidepressant drugs in the proper dose and on the right schedule.

항우울제를 적당한 용량과 적절한 스케줄로 쓰는 것이 중요합니다.

Although some improvements may be seen in the first few weeks, antidepressant medications must be taken regularly before the full therapeutic effect occurs.

비록 몇 주 내로 증상이 조금 좋아졌더라도, 효과가 완전히 나타날 때까지 약을 계속해서 먹어야 합니다.

Some medications must be stopped gradually to give the body time to adjust, and many can produce withdrawal symptoms if discontinued abruptly.

어떤 약들은 몸이 적응되도록 점차 줄여나가야 하며, 갑자기 끊으면 많은 경우에 부작용이 있을 수 있습니다.

4) Dialogue 1.

D : This doctors are medical students.
이 의사선생님들은 의과대학 학생들입니다.

They are going to listen into our conversation.
그들은 우리들의 대화를 들을 것입니다.

P : No problem.
괜찮습니다.

D : Tell me about your symptom.
당신의 증상에 대해서 말해 주세요.

P : I get these headaches.
두통이 있어요.

D : When did they start?
언제부터 시작되었죠?

P : I started getting them about 2 days ago.
2일 전부터 시작되었어요.

D : Is that the first time you ever had these headaches?
두통을 갖게 된 게 그 때가 처음인가요?

P : Yes. My wife insisted I come here.
그렇습니다. 집사람이 이곳으로 오도록 강요했죠.

D : When does this symptom seem to come on?
증상이 언제 발생되는 것 같아요?

P : It can be any time.
아무 때나 발생됩니다.

D : When you get these headaches, where does it hurt?
두통이 있을 때면 어디가 아프던가요?

P : They start on the back side of my head and they just go around.
머리 뒷부분에서 시작하여 주위로 퍼져나가요.

D : Tension headache is usually felt most in the back of the head and neck.
긴장성 두통은 주로 머리와 목 뒤에서 느껴지죠.

P : Headache kept me from doing much of anything.
두통은 내가 많은 것을 못하게 합니다.

D : It starts for no apparent reason.

특별한 이유 없이 시작되죠.

I think that headaches are part of a disturbed inner health
state.

저는 두통은 내적 건강상태의 이상에서 올 수 있는 부분이라고 생각합
니다.

We can try to find the focus.

원인을 찾도록 노력해보죠.

Is there anything you can think of that triggers these
headaches?

두통을 자극하는 어떤 것들이 있다고 생각하나요?

P : No.

없습니다.

D : How has your mood been lately?

최근 기분은 어떻습니까?

P : Not so good.

별로 좋지 않습니다.

D : Any other problems?

다른 문제는 없나요?

P : I am so tired of hearing all about people's personal lives
through their cell phone conversation.

많은 사람들이 핸드폰으로 그들의 사생활에 대해서 이야기를 할 때면
정말 피곤해 집니다.

I want to take medicine to relieve headache.

두통을 감소시키기 위해 약을 먹기를 원합니다.

D : OK. I'd like to ask several questions before writing a prescription.

알겠습니다. 처방전을 쓰기 전에 몇 가지를 묻고 싶군요.

5) Dialogue 2.

D : How much do you smoke?

담배를 얼마나 많이 피시죠?

P : I smoke a couple of packs a day.

하루 2-3갑 피웁니다.

D : Is that as much as you have always smoked?

그 양이 당신이 항상 피우는 양입니까?

P : Sometimes more, sometimes less.

어쩔 때는 많이 피고, 어쩔 때는 적게 핍니다.

When I was under pressure, I used to smoke more.

스트레스가 있을 때는 더 피웁니다.

But I am trying to reduce smoking.

하지만 줄이려고 노력하고 있습니다.

What's the best way to quit smoking?

금연의 가장 좋은 방법이 무엇이죠?

D : You try to quit.

끊을려고 노력해야 합니다.

You start smoking again, you try to quit again.

담배를 다시 피게되면 다시 끊을려고 노력하는 것입니다.

To reduce smoking withdrawal symptoms, improve your concentration by planning your work.
금단 증상을 줄이려면 일에 더 집중을 하여야 합니다.

Reduce headache pain by drinking water and practicing relaxation techniques.
물을 마시고, 휴식을 취해 두통을 줄이도록 하세요.

Are you a heavy drinker?
술을 많이 마시나요?

P : Yes, I still drink about 5 cocktails a day.
예, 저는 여전히 하루에 칵테일 5잔씩 마십니다.

D : And more some days?
어떤 날은 더 마시나요?

P : When I went out in the weekend, I used to drink a bottle of whisky.
주말에 밖에 나간 경우엔 항상 위스키 한 병씩 마셨었습니다.

D : Wow!
굉장하군요.

Do you have any drinking problem?
술로 문제가 있던 적이 있습니까?

P : Absolutely not.
절대 아닙니다.

D : Alcohol is best known as a cause of liver cirrhosis.
알코올은 간경화의 가장 큰 원인입니다.

It can also cause stomach pain due to a bleeding ulcer or irritated stomach lining.
또한 출혈성 궤양이나 위점막 자극으로 위통을 일으킬 수 있습니다.

You should keep off alcohol if you want to have good health.
당신은 건강을 위해 술을 끊어야 할 것 같군요.

15 *Complementary Medicine*
(보완의학)

1) Active Physical Therapy (Exercise - 운동)

Active physical therapy like exercise is important in the management of the pain.

운동과 같은 능동적인 치료가 통증 관리에 중요합니다.

Adequate exercises help you lead a healthy life.

적절한 운동은 당신을 건강한 생활로 이끕니다.

Exercise is able to build strength and create a perfect harmony between mind and body.

운동은 힘을 길러주고 마음과 몸 사이의 완벽한 균형을 만들어 줍니다.

Modern lifestyles have grown increasingly less active, affecting the condition of our bodies.

현대의 생활은 덜 능동적으로 가며, 우리 몸 상태에 영향을 주고 있습니다.

Regular excercise would bring back the natural balance and harmony in our bodies.

규칙적인 운동은 우리 몸의 자연적인 균형과 조화를 가져옵니다.

You must be aware of every movement that is part of an exercise and trying to have mind and body working as a team.

모든 활동이 운동의 하나이며, 몸과 마음이 하나가 되도록 노력해야합니다.

If exercise performed at the proper intensity, duration and frequency, you will achieve significant improvements in physical working activity.

만약 운동을 적당한 강도와 시간, 빈도에 맞추어 한다면, 당신은 육체적인 활동 능력이 의미 있게 증가될 것입니다.

Walking is good for your health

걷는 것이 당신의 건강에 좋습니다.

Walking strengthens the leg muscles and makes your bones stronger.

걷는 것은 다리의 근육을 강화시키고 당신의 뼈를 튼튼하게 합니다.

Running can cause trouble for your knees if you are overweight or have arthritis.

달리기는 당신이 과체중이거나 관절염이 있을 때 문제를 일으킬 수 있습니다.

Walking may be better than running in some ways.

걷는 것이 어떤 때는 달리는 것보다 좋습니다.

Try to walk 6 km an hour, about 3 or 4 time a week to make it a regular exercise.

규칙적인 운동이 되기 위해서는, 한 시간에 6 km 정도, 일주일에 3, 4번하도록 하세요.

Power center should be formed by the abdomen, low back and the buttocks which supports the spine and posture.

힘의 중심은 척추와 자세를 잡아주는 복부와 허리, 둔부이어야 합니다.

Adequate breathing is important to keep the bloodstream pure by oxygenating the blood.

적절한 호흡은 혈액에 산소를 보내 순혈을 유지하도록 하는데 중요합니다.

Proper position of the head, neck and back is very important to avoid the prolong contraction of the muscles causes pain.
머리, 목, 허리의 적당한 자세가 통증을 일으키는 오랜 근육 수축을 피하는 데 중요합니다.

You should try to maintain a moderate exercise, such as stretching, strengthening and aerobic conditioning.
스트레칭, 근력강화운동, 에어로빅 운동 등의 중등도의 운동을 유지하도록 해야합니다.

(1) Neck Pain

Try to avoid movements which aggravate your pain.
통증을 유발시키는 운동을 하지 마세요.

Try an adequate pillow which keeps the curve in your neck in its proper position while you sleep.
잠자는 동안 목의 자세가 적절한 베개를 사용하세요.

Let your neck bend to the side, and with your hand apply a little pressure to your head to help bring it into the same direction.
목을 옆으로 돌리고 손으로 같은 방향으로 눌러 주세요.

Let your head hang forward, as if you are touching your chin to your chest.
머리를 앞으로 숙여 턱이 가슴에 닿는 것처럼 하세요.

With your shoulders relaxed, turn your head to side as if you were looking over your shoulder.
어깨의 힘을 빼고, 머리를 돌려 어깨 뒤를 보는 것처럼 돌리세요.

Repeat this three times.
이런 것들을 3번 반복하세요.

(2) Shoulder Pain

React to shoulder pain by not moving your shoulder can lead to complete loss of shoulder mobility.

어깨에 통증이 있다고 움직이지 않는 것은 어깨의 움직임을 완전히 잃게 만듭니다.

You should try to keep your shoulder in motion.

어깨가 항상 움직이도록 하세요.

Good active exercise can improve shoulder motion and decrease pain.

올바른 능동적인 운동이 어깨의 운동을 증가시키고 통증을 줄여 줍니다.

Pendulum exercise of shoulder is useful to be performed in a prone lying position.

어깨의 시계추 운동은 엎드린 자세로 하는 것이 효과적입니다.

Lie on your stomach close to the edge of the bed and let your weak arm hang over the edge of the bed.

엎드린 다음 테이블 가장자리에서 팔이 매달리도록 하세요.

Relax your shoulder, arm and hand and gently swing your arm forward and back.

어깨와 팔에 힘을 뺀 다음, 팔을 앞뒤로 부드럽게 움직이세요.

As pain decreases, increase your swing.

통증이 줄어들수록 움직임을 증가시키세요.

Bend forward at the waist and relax your weak arm to let it drop.

허리를 숙인 다음, 아픈 팔의 힘을 빼고 떨어뜨리세요.

Use body motion to swing your arm in small circles.

몸을 이용하여 팔이 작은 원을 그리도록 하세요.

(3) Elbow Pain

Elbow pain is generally caused by overuse of the extensor or flexor tendons of the forearm.

팔꿈치의 통증은 전완부의 신전근 및 굴곡근의 과사용으로 옵니다.

To decrease inflammation and pain, promote tissue healing, and retard muscle atrophy, follow the RICE principle.

염증과 통증을 줄이고, 조직 치유가 잘 되고, 근 위축을 지연시키기 위해서는 RICE 요법을 해야합니다.

Rest means avoiding further overuse, not absence of activity.

쉰다는 것은 과사용을 피하라는 것이지 쓰지 말라는 것이 아닙니다.

You should maintain as adequate activity level as possible while avoiding activities that aggravate the pain.

통증을 일으키는 운동을 피하는 동안에도 적절한 활동은 유지를 하세요.

Absolute rest should be avoided as it encourages muscle atrophy and decreases blood supply to the area.

완전히 쉬는 것은 근 위축을 일으키고 그 부위에 혈액공급을 줄이므로 피하여야합니다.

Gentle elbow stretching exercise with wrist flexion, extension and rotation is needed.

손목을 구부리고 피고 돌려주는 것과 함께 부드러운 팔꿈치의 스트레칭이 필요합니다.

The elbow should be extended and not flexed to increase the amount of stretch.

팔꿈치는 스트레칭이 증가하면서 구부리지 않고 펴야 합니다.

These stretches should be held for 20-30 seconds and repeated 5-10 times, at least twice a day.

이런 스트레칭을 하루에 2번 이상, 20-30초간, 5-10번하여야 합니다.

Do not stretch to the point of pain that reproduces your symptoms.

당신의 증상을 다시 만드는 정도까지 통증이 오도록 스트레칭을 하면 안됩니다.

Place 1 lb. weight in hand with palm facing downward after supporting forearm on your knee and raise hand up slowly and lower slowly to strengthen the tendons.

1 파운드의 무게를 손에 들고 전완부를 무릎에 받치고 바닥을 향한 다음, 건들이 강해지도록 느리게 손을 위 아래로 올렸다가 내리세요.

Place 1 lb. weight in hand with palm facing upward after supporting forearm on your knee and bend hand up slowly, and then lower slowly.

1 파운드의 무게를 손에 들고 전완부를 무릎에 받치고 위를 향한 다음, 건들이 강해지도록 느리게 손을 위아래로 올렸다가 내리세요

Continue the stretching and strengthening exercises emphasizing the motion of wrist flexion and extension.

손목을 구부리고 피는 운동을 강조한 스트레칭과 근육 강화 운동을 계속하세요.

(4) Back Pain

Stretching and flexibility exercises can be beneficial for your back.

스트레칭과 굴곡운동이 허리에 좋습니다.

Every individual who has suffered from back pain should stretch
their hamstring muscles and strengthen the back muscles.

요통을 호소하는 사람들은 오금 근육을 스트레칭 해주고 등 근육을 강화시
켜 주어야 합니다.

Active physical therapies like exercises are typically necessary
to strengthen the spine and help reduce severity and duration of
potential future episodes of back pain.

운동과 같은 능동적인 물리치료가 척추를 강화시키고, 향후 올 수 있는 요
통의 정도나 기간을 줄여주는데 도움을 줍니다.

Stretching the back and hamstring muscles typically helps
decrease the intensity of back pain.

허리와 오금을 스트레칭 하는 것이 요통의 정도를 줄여줍니다.

The most common stretching technique is to simply bend
forward at the waist, with legs relatively straight, and try to
touch the toes and hold this position.

가장 흔한 스트레칭 방법은 허리를 숙이고 다리를 곧게 핀 다음 다리를 잡
고 있는 것입니다.

And then slowly stand up, place your palms on your back just
above your buttocks, and lean gently backward.

천천히 일어선 다음, 손바닥을 엉덩이 바로 위 허리에 대고 뒤로 젖히세요.

Repeat several times.

여러 차례 반복하세요.

Lie on back, knee bent, tighten abdomens and buttocks.

누워서 무릎을 굽힌 다음 복부와 엉덩이에 힘을 주세요.

Raise one leg with knee straight and hold 3 seconds, repeat 10
times.

한쪽 다리를 무릎을 편 상태로 올려 3초간 있도록 하고, 10번 반복하세요.

Repeat with the other leg.
다른 쪽 다리도 반복하세요.

(5) Knee and Ankle Pain

The most common type of knee and ankle pain is a sprain.
가장 흔한 무릎과 발목 통증은 염좌입니다.

Tears of the anterior or posterior cruciate ligament and meniscus are common in knee injuries.
전방 또는 후방 십자인대와 연골 파열이 무릎 손상에서 흔합니다.

A sprain results from the stretching and tearing of small ligaments.
염좌란 작은 인대들이 늘어나거나 파열된 것을 의미합니다.

To decrease inflammation and pain, promote tissue healing, and retard muscle atrophy, follow the RICE principle.
염증과 통증을 줄이고, 조직의 치유를 높이고, 근 위축을 늦추려면 RICE 요법을 따르세요.

Usually requires some form of immobilization in a stable position lasting several days.
며칠 동안 안정된 자세로 어떤 방법으로든 못 움직이게 하는 것이 필요합니다.

Allow injured joint to rest for approximately a couple of days after the injury
손상 후 며칠 간 손상된 관절이 쉬도록 해야 합니다.

Early walking is essential, since weight bearing inhibits contractures of tendons, which may lead to tendonitis.
체중부하가 건염을 일으키는 건들의 구축을 막아주므로 조기 보행이 꼭 필수입니다.

2) Passive Physical Therapy (PT, Massage, Chiropractic - 물리치료, 마사지, 카이로프랙틱)

You need to focus on decreasing pain with passive physical therapy.
수동적인 물리치료로 통증을 줄이는데 중점을 두는 것이 필요합니다.

Physical therapies help restore function, improve mobility, relieve pain suffering from injuries or disease.
물리치료는 기능을 회복시키고, 운동을 증가시키고, 손상이나 질병으로 인한 통증을 완화시켜 줍니다.

Physical therapist can use electrical stimulation, hot packs or cold compresses, traction or deep-tissue massage, and ultrasound to relieve pain.
물리치료사들은 통증을 줄이기 위해 전기자극이나 뜨거운 찜질, 얼음 찜질, 견인요법, 심부 마사지, 초음파 등을 쓸 수 있습니다.

Heat or ice are easily available and helps reduce muscle spasm and inflammation.
뜨거운 찜질이나 얼음찜질은 근 경련과 염증을 줄여주는 아주 쉬운 방법입니다.

Take a nice hot shower and let the water run on your pain lesion.
뜨거운 물에 목욕을 하고, 물이 아픈 부위 위를 흐르도록 하세요.

Place a heating pad on your pain site and keep it on long enough to allow your skin to turn a little red and warm up.
찜팩을 아픈 곳 위에 놓고, 피부가 약간 빨개지거나 따뜻해질 때까지 충분히 기다리세요.

Ice packing is recommended as long as inflammation is present.
염증이 있는 동안은 얼음찜질이 필요합니다.

Ice packing can be used to reduce nervous system response, making the area easier and more comfortable to work.

얼음찜질이 신경시스템의 반응을 줄이고, 치료에 도움이 되도록 사용될 수 있습니다.

Ice decreases the inflammatory process, slows local metabolism and helps relieve pain and muscle spasm.

얼음찜질은 염증과정을 줄여주고, 대사를 느리게 하며, 통증과 근 수축을 좋아지게 합니다.

Ice packing may be done throughout the entire rehabilitation process and return to sports.

얼음찜질은 스포츠를 할 수 있는 재활 과정 내내 해도 좋습니다.

Compression and elevation help venous return and minimize swelling.

압박과 올려 주는 것은 정맥 순환을 높여 부종을 줄여 줍니다.

A transcutaneous electrical nerve stimulator (TENS) unit uses electrical stimulation to modulate the sensation of pain by overriding the painful signals that are sent to the brain.

TENS는 뇌로 가는 통증 신호를 교란시켜 통증감각을 조절하는 전기자극 입니다.

Ultrasound is a form of deep heating in which sound waves are applied to the skin and penetrate into the soft tissues.

초음파는 피부와 심부 조직에 열을 가해주는 방법입니다.

Ultrasound is especially useful in relieving acute episodes of pain and may enhance tissue healing.

초음파는 급성 통증을 줄이고 조직의 치유를 높여주는 데 유용합니다.

Massage can be used for removing tension and pain.

마사지는 긴장과 통증을 줄이는데 쓸 수 있습니다.

Massage therapy is a hands-on manipulation to help reduce the
soft tissue discomfort associated with chronic muscular
overuse which causes chronic pain.
마사지 치료는 만성 통증을 일으키는 만성적인 근육의 과사용에 의한 연부
조직의 불편함을 줄여주는 수기입니다.

Massage improves the circulation of blood through the body and
speed the removal of metabolic waste products from muscles.
마사지는 몸으로 가는 혈액순환과 근육으로부터 생긴 대사 물질의 배출을
도와줍니다.

Benefits of massage are reducing muscular tension, enhancing
tissue elasticity.
마사지의 장점은 근육의 긴장을 줄여주고, 조직의 탄력을 높여주는 것입
니다.

Trigger point pressure methods help reducing spasm and
inducing new blood flow into the affected area.
아픈 곳의 압박은 경련을 줄이고 새로운 혈액이 흐르도록 해줍니다.

Pressure should be applied to trigger points between about 7 to
10 seconds per point, several times.
압박은 아픈 곳에 한 번에 7-10초 간, 여러 번 해주어야 합니다.

Mobilizing the spine joints through manipulations can decrease
back pain.
수기를 통한 척추 관절의 운동은 요통을 줄여줍니다.

The overall philosophy for chiropractic manipulations is that
joint dysfunction in the spine can produce back pain.
카이로프랙틱 수기는 요통을 일으키는 척추의 관절 기능이상에 개념을 두
고 있습니다.

Chiropractic focuses on adjustments to correct spinal malfunctions, called subluxations, in order to remove interference to the spinal nerves that exit between the bones of the spine.

카이로프랙틱은 척추 뼈 사이에서 나오는 척추 신경의 방해를 제거하기 위해 아탈구와 같은 척추의 기능 이상을 교정하는데 중점을 둡니다.

The objective of the chiropractic treatment is to reduce the subluxation of spine, which results in an increased range of motion, reduced nerve irritability and improved function.

카이로프랙틱 치료의 목적은 척추의 아탈구와 같은 것들을 줄여 운동 범위를 증가시키고, 신경 자극을 줄이고, 기능을 향상시키는 것입니다.

3) Meditation (명상)

Meditation is complementary medical care by encouraging healing of the body, mind, and spirit.

명상은 몸과 마음과 정신의 치유를 도와주는 보완적인 의료행위입니다.

Modern people feel stressed under over-worked condition.

현대인들은 과도한 일 때문에 스트레스를 느끼고 있습니다.

Our stress and tiredness make us unhappy and affect our health.

우리들의 스트레스와 피곤함은 우리를 불행하게 하고, 우리의 건강에 영향을 줍니다.

Meditation make your mind comfortable.

명상은 당신의 마음을 안락하게 합니다.

Meditation make you feel good naturally.

명상은 당신이 자연스럽게 행복해지게 합니다.

Meditation make you more spiritual.
명상은 당신을 좀 더 영성적으로 만듭니다.

Understanding the mind-body relation is important to enhance
  the mind's capacity to affect bodily function and symptoms.
마음과 몸과의 관계를 이해하는 것이 몸의 기능과 증상에 영향을 주는 마음
  의 능력을 높여주는 데 중요합니다.

To feel the bio-energy give you a chance of self discovery.
생명에너지를 느끼게 되면 자신의 내면을 발견하게 됩니다.

Cultivating constructive thoughts is the purpose of the
  meditation.
건설적인 생각을 만드는 것이 명상의 목적입니다.

Meditation is needed for all who desire to maintain health of
  mind and body.
명상은 마음과 몸의 건강을 유지하려는 사람들에게 필요한 것입니다.

I highly recommend it to anyone who needs relaxation.
저는 여유로움이 필요한 사람들에게 이것을 강하게 추천합니다.

Medication can help you to understand your mind.
명상은 당신이 당신의 마음을 이해하도록 도와줍니다.

Open your heart toward the world and whole system of the
  nature.
세계와 자연의 전체 시스템에 대한 개방된 마음을 가지세요.

We should find the universe within us.
우리는 우리들 안에 있는 우주에 대해 발견해야 합니다.

The universe open the door for the spiritual human being who
  realize the natural secret.
우주는 자연의 비밀을 깨달은 정신적으로 성숙된 사람들에게 문을 엽니다.

We try to live out our dreams and to transform them into action.
우리는 우리의 꿈을 현실로 실현시키기 위해 노력해야 합니다.

Meditation, breathing exercise, praying, and therapies that use creative outlets such as art, music, or dance can help promoting health.
명상이나 호흡운동, 기도, 예술, 음악, 춤과 같은 창조적인 배출활동들이 건강을 증진시키는데 도움을 줍니다.

Meditation if done properly is beneficial to your health and keep you calm and relaxed.
적절히 행해진 명상은 당신의 건강에 좋고 고요함과 안정을 줍니다.

Bio-energy training like meditation and breathing excercise affect internal energy condition.
명상이나 호흡법과 같은 생체에너지 훈련은 내적 에너지 상태에 영향을 줍니다.

4) Breathing Exercise - Dahn, Zen, Ki and Yoga (호흡법 - 단, 선, 기, 요가)

A simple couple of minutes meditation with breathing exercise can help you to overcome stress and find inner peace and balance.
호흡운동과 더불어 하는 몇 분간의 명상은 당신의 스트레스를 없애주고, 내면의 평화와 균형을 찾게 해줍니다.

There were many ancient secrets of the method of meditation in Asia.
아시아에는 명상의 방법에 관한 많은 고대의 비밀이 있습니다.

Dahn(Korea), Yoga(Indo), Zen(Japan) and Ki(China) are similar methods which make someone to feel more energized and more relaxed.

한국의 단, 인도의 요가, 일본의 선, 중국의 기와 같은 것들은 사람들에게 충만된 에너지를 느끼게 하며, 여유롭게 만듭니다.

These are the similar training methods of the biological energy that maintains the health.

이것들은 건강을 유지하는 생물학적인 에너지를 훈련시키는 비슷한 방법들입니다.

Most meditation practices, yoga and breathing exercise encourage breathing from the lower abdomen.

모든 명상활동이나 요가, 호흡운동 등은 복부 아래의 호흡을 권유합니다.

Focusing attention on the lower abdomen help harmonizing the body and mind, helping you to feel more grounded.

복부 아래에 주의를 집중하는 것은 몸과 마음을 조화롭게 하고, 더 구심점이 되게 합니다.

If we breathe well, we can increase our vitality and feel a sense of well-being.

만약 호흡을 잘하면, 우리는 생명력을 증가시키고, 웰빙 감각을 느낄 수 있습니다.

I will introduce the precise, scientific method of breathing excercise.

제가 간결하고 과학적인 호흡법을 소개해 드리겠습니다.

Lie on the ground or sit in a position where your spine is straight.

허리가 반듯하도록 바닥에 눕거나 앉으세요.

Close your eyes and relax all your body.
눈을 감고 몸 전체에 긴장을 푸세요.

Inhale with nose only, mouth closed.
입은 다물고 코로만 쉬세요.

Inhale very slowly through your nose and send your breath to go
deep down into your abdomen.
코를 통해 느리게 쉬고 숨이 복부 깊은 곳으로 가게끔 하세요.

Push out your abdomen gently and try to move your chest as
little as possible.
복부를 부드럽게 내밀고 가슴은 가능한 움직이지 마세요.

Tense abdominal muscles as you inhale and gradually let the
muscles go as you exhale.
들이쉴 때 복부 근육에 힘을 주고, 내 쉴 때 자연스럽게 힘을 빼세요.

Focus your attention on the movement of your abdomen as you
inhale and exhale.
숨을 들이쉬고 내쉴 때, 복부에 집중을 하세요.

Pay attention to your depth of breath and its rhythm and pace.
숨쉬는 시간과 리듬과 속도에 주의하세요.

Repeat and try to let go and relax totally.
전체적으로 자연스럽게 진행되도록 반복하세요.

As you continue to do this regularly, you will have a feeling of
letting go and well being sensation.
규칙적으로 반복할 경우, 당신은 안정됨과 웰빙을 느낄 것입니다.

Bio-energy discipline means to combine individual human spirit into universal spirit.

생체 에너지 훈련은 개인의 정신이 우주의 정신과 융합되는 것을 의미합니다.

This can improve mental clarity, greater self-understanding, stress control and general well-being.

이것은 의식을 명료하게 하고, 스스로 깨닫게 만들고, 스트레스 조절과 웰빙을 느끼게 합니다.

10 minutes breathing excercise a day will improve the functioning of the digestive, circulatory and respiratory systems.

하루에 10분 호흡 운동하는 것이 소화기, 순환기, 호흡기의 기능을 향상시킵니다.

Gradually increase your schedule to 30 minutes a day.

하루에 30분이 되도록 점차 스케줄을 높이세요.

5) Acupuncture (침)

Oriental medicine is based on the fact that disease is present when the flow of bio- energy through the channels is disrupted.

동양의학은 채널을 통한 생체에너지의 흐름이 파괴될 때 질병이 생긴다는 것에 근거를 두고 있습니다.

If the internal balance of bio-energy is seriously disrupted, then there will be an abnormal flow of bio-energy representing the diseased organ.

만약 생체 에너지의 내적 균형이 깨진다면, 질병을 의미하는 생체에너지의 비정상적인 흐름이 생깁니다.

The existence of bio-energy channels has not yet been scientifically proven.

생체 에너지 채널들은 아직 과학적으로 입증된 것은 아닙니다.

Bioelectromagnetic energy is a normal and subtle energy in living creature.

생체전자기장의 에너지는 모든 생명체에 정상적으로 있는 작은 에너지입니다.

Acupuncture is based on the assumption that bio-energy courses through the body just as streams and rivers.

침술은 생체에너지의 흐름이 강처럼 몸을 통해 흐른다는 가정에 기초를 두고 있습니다.

Acupuncture points are located in the gates of the body which communicate from the outside to the inside.

침술의 부위는 외부와 내부를 연결하는 몸의 문과 같은 곳입니다.

Acupuncture points represent points of maximum influence on the flow of bio-energy through the channels

침술의 부위는 채널을 통한 생체에너지의 흐름에 가장 큰 영향을 주는 곳입니다.

Acupuncture is a helpful methods which can relieve pain.

침술은 통증을 줄여주는 방법입니다.

Acupuncture stimulates the nerves in skin and muscle, and can produce a pain control effect.

침술은 피부와 근육에 있는 신경들을 자극하여 통증을 조절하는 효과가 있습니다.

Acupunture may increase the body's release of natural painkillers such as endorphin and serotonin which reduce pain and improve sense of well-being.

침술은 통증을 줄여주고 웰빙을 느끼게 하는 자연 진통제인 엔돌핀이나 세로토닌의 분비를 증가시킬 수 있습니다.

A small stimulus is probably more effective than a large one.

작은 자극이 큰 자극보다 효과적입니다.

The emphasis in acupuncture therapy is to select a minimal number of acupuncture points.

침술의 중요한 점은 가장 작은 수의 침을 놓는 것입니다.

Many people find that they feel better after acupuncture treatment, even if there is no real improvement in their medical condition.

많은 사람들은 비록 의학적인 진정한 치료효과는 없어도 침술 치료 후 기분이 좋아집니다.

6) Aroma Therapy (향기 요법)

Smells and fragrances can affect mood and emotions, and trigger the production of hormones in the body.

냄새와 향기는 기분과 감정에 영향을 주고, 몸의 호르몬 분비를 자극합니다.

Aroma-therapy works on the simple basic principle of enjoying the fragrance.

향기 요법은 향기를 즐기는 단순한 기본적인 원칙에서 시작합니다.

Using the essential oils of aromatic plants, trees and flowers can uplift the spirit, clear the mind and relax the body.

향기 있는 식물, 나무, 꽃들의 기본 오일을 사용하면 기분이 상쾌해지고, 마음이 맑아지며, 몸의 긴장이 풀립니다.

The aromas are perceived by the nerve endings at the nose, and signals are passed to the brain which controls hormone release.

향기는 코의 후각 끝에서 흡수되어 호르몬을 조절하는 뇌로 전달됩니다.

During the massage with an aromatherapy, the very small molecules of essential oils penetrate the skin to get into the bloodstream and the immune system to work in a physiological method.

아로마 마사지를 하는 동안 미세한 오일입자가 피부를 뚫고 혈액과 면역 시스템으로 가서 생리적으로 자극을 줍니다.

The warmth of a bath with fragrant oil relaxes you.

방향제로 따뜻한 목욕을 하는 것은 당신의 긴장을 풀어줍니다.

16 APPENDIXES
(부록)

병원 영어 및 영문 문서

1. Reception Desk (접수처)

Hi.
안녕하세요.

I am open down here.
이쪽으로 오세요.

Can I help you?
무엇을 도와드릴까요?

What's your name?
이름이 어떻게 되지요?

What's your last name?
성이 무엇이지요?

What's your first name?
이름은 무엇이지요?

Could you spell it out for me?
철자를 말해 줄래요?

Do you have medical insurance?
의료보험은 가지고 계십니까?

I would like to verify your identity.
당신의 신원을 확인하고 싶군요.

Do you have any identification card?
어떤 신분증이 있나요?

What department do you want to make an appointment?
어느 과 예약을 원하십니까?

Is there a doctor you want to see?
보시길 원하는 선생님이 계십니까?

What's your symptom?
증상이 무엇이지요?

You'd better make an appointment in orthopaedic department.
정형외과로 예약하시는 것이 좋을 것 같습니다.

We need you to write this form.
이 양식에 적어주세요.

What's your current address?
주소가 어떻게 되죠?

What's your telephone number?
전화번호가 어떻게 되지요?

What's your date of birth?
생일이 언제이지요?

Your appointment is 11 O'clock.
당신의 예약은 11시입니다.

Please go to there 5 minutes before your appointment time.
예약 시간 5분전까지 그곳으로 가세요.

Sorry to have kept you waiting.
기다리게 해서 죄송합니다.

If you come with me, we'll get you admitted.
저를 따라 오시면 입원을 시켜 드리겠습니다.

We need you to sign some papers.
서류에 사인이 필요합니다.

2. Reservation (예약)

Do you want to make an appointment?
예약을 원하십니까?

Who is your doctor?
담당 선생님이 누구시죠?

Do you want to make an appointment with Dr. Kim?
김 선생님에게 예약하시기를 원하나요?

What's your name?
성함이 어떻게 되죠?

How do you spell it?
철자가 어떻게 되지요?

Do you have medical insurance card?
의료보험은 가지고 계십니까?

May I see your insurance card?
보험카드를 볼 수 있을까요?

What date do you want?

어느 날짜를 원하시죠?

Let me see.

잠깐 살펴볼께요.

We have June 18, at 3 p.m. open.

오후 3시가 비어있군요.

Will that be a good time?

괜찮습니까?

2 p.m. is filled.

2시는 예약이 다 예약되었습니다.

2 : 20 p.m. open.

2시 20분이 비어있습니다.

Will you take it?

이것으로 예약하시겠습니까?

Your appointment is at 2 : 20 p.m. on June 18.

당신의 예약 시간은 6월 18일 오후 2시 20분입니다.

What's your phone number?

전화번호가 몇 번이죠?

Charge is 12,000 won.

비용이 12,000원입니다.

How do you want to pay?

어떻게 지불을 하실건가요?

By cash or credit card?

현금인가요, 신용카드인가요?

When is your appointment?

예약이 언제입니까?

What's the reason for the cancellation?

취소 이유가 무엇이지요?

I will cancel it for you.

취소하겠습니다.

Do you reschedule your appointment?

예약을 변경하시겠습니까?

The doctor is not available at that time.

그 시간은 안됩니다.

Can you make it at another time?

다른 시간을 말해 주실래요?

Your appointment has been changes to -.

당신의 예약이 -로 변경되었습니다.

If you arrive more than 30 minutes late, you may have to rebook
to avoid delaying other patients.

30분 이상 늦게 오시면 다른 환자가 늦어지지 않도록 다시 예약하셔야 합
니다.

3. 외래환자 (Outpatient)

Please register at the reception desk in the main entrance
lobby.

정문 로비에 있는 접수처에 가서 접수해 주세요.

Please register at the front desk.

앞에서 접수해 주세요.

Please go to the admission desk and check in.
입원계로 가서 수속해 주세요.

Staff will assist in making your admission easy and comfortable.
직원이 입원을 쉽고 편하도록 도와 줄 것입니다.

Please come in and have a seat.
안으로 들어오셔서 자리에 앉으세요.

Take a seat over there and I'll let you know.
저기에 앉아 계시면 알려 드릴께요.

Please take a seat until you are called.
부르실 때까지 앉아 계세요.

Doctor will call you soon.
의사선생님이 곧 부르실 겁니다.

After paying at the reception desk, go to the X-ray and blood lab.
접수처에서 계산을 한 다음에 X-ray실과 혈액 검사실로 가세요.

Follow the yellow line to the X-ray department.
방사선과로는 노란색을 따라 가세요.

X-ray is around the corner.
X-ray실은 모퉁이에 있습니다.

You need to go to the toilet before examination.
검사 전에 화장실을 다녀오세요.

The staff are familiar with this examination.
직원들은 이 검사를 잘합니다.

Please ask the staff any question about the procedure that you
  may have.
당신이 받아야할 시술에 대해서는 직원에게 물어보세요.

I'll make an appointment for you.
예약을 해드리겠습니다.

Your appointment is ---.
당신의 예약은 ---입니다.

Please come to here 5 minutes before your appointment time.
예약 시간 5분전까지 이곳으로 오세요.

Your appointment has been changes to -.
당신의 예약이 -로 변경되었습니다.

Since you arrived late, you have to wait to avoid delaying other
  patients.
늦게 오셨기 때문에 다른 환자가 늦어지지 않도록 기다리셔야 합니다.

You can leave when you are done.
다 끝나시면 가셔도 됩니다.

4. 입원환자 (Inpatient)

Hi. I'm nurse Kim.
안녕하세요. 김 간호사입니다.

Are you a Mr. Brown?
브라운씨죠?

Where are you come from?
어느 나라에서 오셨죠?

Race : White, Colored, Oriental
인종 : 백인, 흑인, 아시아인

How old are you?
몇 살이시죠?

What's your main problem?
주 증상이 무엇이지요?

I'll take your vital signs.
Let me take your vital signs.
활력징후를 측정하겠습니다.

I'll take your blood pressure.
Let me check your blood pressure.
혈압을 측정하겠습니다.

Please roll up your sleeve.
소매를 걷어올리세요.

Your blood pressure isn't that high.
혈압이 그리 높지는 않군요.

I will check your pulse.
맥박을 측정하겠습니다.

I'll check your temperature.
Let me take your temperature.
체온을 측정하겠습니다.

Please hold the thermometer under your tongue.
Put the thermometer under your tongue.
체온계를 혀 아래에 물고 계세요.

Put the thermometer under your armpit.

체온계를 겨드랑이에 넣으세요.

Place the thermometer under your armpit and fold arm across chest.

체온계를 당신의 겨드랑이에 놓고 팔을 가슴 쪽으로 붙이세요.

How much do you weigh?

몸무게는 얼마나 나가지요?

I'll check your body weight.

몸무게를 측정하겠습니다.

Please, step on the scale.

체중계 위로 올라가 줄래요?

Okay, step off.

됐습니다. 내려오세요.

You weigh - kilogram.

- Kg 나가는군요.

How tall are you?

키가 얼마죠?

Are you married?

결혼은 했나요?

Married, Divorced, Widow, Bachelor.

기혼, 이혼, 과부, 독신.

How many people are there in your family?

가족이 모두 몇 명이지요?

Do you have any children?
아이들이 있나요?

How old are they?
몇 살이지요?

What's your occupation?
직업이 무엇이지요?

What religion do you have?
종교가 무엇이지요?

Catholic, Protestant, Buddhist.
카톨릭, 신교도, 불교.

Do you have any medical conditions?
어떤 질환이 있나요?

Have you ever had any serious illnesses or operations?
과거에 아프거나 수술했던 적이 있나요?

Have you ever been in hospital for any reason?
어떤 이유로 입원한 적이 있나요?

Do you remember what the diagnosis was?
진단이 무엇이었는지 기억하십니까?

When were you hospitalized?
언제 입원하셨죠?

What kind of operations have you had?
어떤 종류의 수술을 받으셨죠?

When was the date of operation?
수술 날짜가 언제죠?

Have you ever been told that you have high blood pressure, diabetes, allergy or any other disease?

고혈압이나 당뇨병, 알러지 같은 어떤 질환이 있다고 진단을 받은 적이 있습니까?

Have you ever had an allergic reaction to any drug?

어떤 약에 부작용이 있었던 적이 있나요?

Are you taking any medication?

어떤 약을 먹고 있나요?

What medications are you currently taking?

지금 어떤 약을 먹고 계시죠?

How much alcohol do you consume?

술을 얼마나 많이 드시죠?

Do you smoke?

담배도 피우시나요?

Are you on any special diet?

특별히 먹는 음식이 있나요?

Fill out this paper and return it.

이 설문지를 채우시고 돌려주세요.

Could you put your signature here?

이곳에 사인해 주실래요?

The doctor will be here soon.

의사 선생님이 곧 오실 것입니다.

5. 병동에서 (Ward)

How are you feeling?
How is it going?
조금 어떠세요?

You are looking much better.
You look great.
더 좋아진 것 같군요.

You seem to be in a good mood.
기분이 좋으신 것 같군요.

Don't you feel well?
어디 안 좋으세요?

You look so down.
어디 안 좋으신 것 같군요.

Do you have any pain?
어디가 아프세요?

Did you take your medicines?
약은 드셨나요?

Pain pills didn't help?
진통제가 효과가 없던가요?

Is it a piercing sort of pain?
찌르는 것 같은 통증인가요?

We'll get you something as soon as we can.
가능한 빨리 조치해 드리겠습니다.

Doctor is with an other patient right now.
의사선생님은 지금 다른 환자와 함께 있습니다.

Doctor is gonna be here.
의사선생님이 곧 이곳에 올 것입니다.

Doctor will come here and you can converse any further concerns with doctor.
의사 선생님이 이곳으로 오면 당신이 걱정하는 것에 대해 이야기할 수 있을 것입니다.

Did you eat your meal?
식사를 하셨나요?

You don't seem to have much of an appetite yet.
아직 식욕이 없으신가보군요.

How many times did you have bowel movements and urination?
대변과 소변을 몇 번 보셨죠?

We need to put a catheter in to get urine.
소변을 받으려 도뇨관을 넣을 것입니다.

Take this medication after meal.
식사 후 이 약을 드세요.

You'll feel better in a couple of hours.
몇 시간 뒤면 좋아질 것입니다.

If you feel any discomfort, just let me know.
만약 불편한 느낌이 들면 저에게 알려 주세요.

Call me when the family arrives.
가족들이 오면 알려주세요.

If you want to call me, please press this button.
저를 부르시려면 이 버튼을 눌러 주세요.

Will you let me know if anything changes?
변화가 있으면 알려 줄래요?

If you need anything, just press the button.
필요한 것이 있으면 이 버튼을 눌러 주세요.

I am on my way.
I am coming.
I'll be right there.
곧 갈께요.

I'll be over to see you in a few minutes.
당신을 보러 몇 분 안에 가겠습니다.

What happened?
무슨 일이죠?

Do you need anything?
무엇이 필요합니까?

We're gonna have to draw some blood.
약간의 혈액을 빼겠습니다.

I'll do a blood sampling.
혈액 채취를 하겠습니다.

I'll start the intravenous(IV) injection.
정맥 주사를 놓겠습니다.

Will you roll up your sleeve?
소매를 올려 줄래요?

It'll hurt a bit.
약간 아플 것입니다.

Grip your hand.
손을 쥐어주세요.

You haven't get a vein anywhere.
어느 곳에도 정맥이 없군요.

I got it.
됐습니다.

Let's take the IV out.
혈관 주사를 뺄게요.

I'll give you the intramuscular(IM) injection.
근육 주사를 놓겠습니다.

Could you turn on your side?
옆으로 누워 줄래요?

We are done.
다 됐습니다.

May I see you for a minutes?
잠간 볼까요?

Would you come with me?
저를 따라 오실래요?

Can I ask you something?
무엇 좀 물어봐도 되나요?

Did you notify family of your operation schedule?
당신 가족들에게 수술 스케줄에 대해 이야기했습니까?

Excuse me for a second.
잠깐 실례합니다.

I'll be right back.
곧 돌아오겠습니다.

Sorry to keep you waiting.
기다리게 해서 죄송합니다.

Did you sleep well?
잘 주무셨어요?

Did you get any sleep?
잠 좀 주무셨어요?

Get some sleep.
잠 좀 주무세요.

I'll give you extra blanket.
여분의 담요를 드리겠습니다.

I will change your sheet.
시트를 바꾸어 주겠습니다.

Dr. Kim. The family has arrived.
김 선생님 가족들이 왔습니다.

Please come to nurse station.
간호사 스테이션으로 와 주세요.

Dr. Kim. There is a call from a Dr. Choi.
김 선생님. 최 선생님에게서 전화 왔습니다.

Dr. Phone is for you.
선생님 전화 왔습니다.

Dr. Kim. Call on nurse station phone.
김선생님. 간호사 스테이션에 전화입니다.

Can I give Mr. Kim more prn injection?
김씨에게 prn 주사를 더 주어도 될까요?

You need to get an X-ray.
X-ray를 찍어야 합니다.

You'll be going to X-ray in a few minutes.
곧 X-ray실로 갈 것입니다.

Would you excuse us for a moment?
잠시 자리를 좀 비워줄래요?

Let's get a foley in.
도뇨관을 하도록 하죠.

We'll insert catheter into your bladder.
도뇨관을 방광에 삽입하겠습니다.

It doesn't hurt.
아프지 않습니다.

You're going to operation room.
수술실로 갈 것입니다.

Everything is going to be fine.
모든 것이 잘 될 것입니다.

Orderly. Take this patient to OR.
오더리. 이 환자를 수술실로 데려가세요.

Be careful of her legs.
다리를 조심하세요.

Watch the line.
선을 조심하세요.

Let's move on my count. One. Two. Three.
제가 셋 셀 때 옮기세요.

Coming through.
Clear the way.
길 좀 비켜주세요.

Orderly took the patient to the operation room 30 minutes ago.
오더리가 환자를 30분전에 수술실로 데려갔습니다.

Orderly. Please bring a wheelchair to admitting.
오더리. 휠체어를 병실로 가져오세요.

I will show you how to use a wheelchair.
휠체어를 어떻게 타는 지 가르쳐 드리겠습니다.

You can move around as much as you like.
당신이 하고 싶은 만큼 돌아다녀도 됩니다.

Movement is good for you.
움직이는 것이 당신에게 좋습니다.

It's good to see you you're healing.
당신이 나은 것을 보니 좋군요.

You will be discharged tomorrow.
내일 퇴원하게 될 것입니다.

Does ICU have any bed?
중환자실에 남은 베드가 있나요?

We have 2 discharges and 1 admit.
우리는 2명 퇴원하고 1명 입원했습니다.

We have 1 open bed.
베드 한 개가 있습니다.

Suture removal's 7 days.
실밥 뽑는 것은 7일째입니다.

1500 cc's input, 700 cc's output.
1500cc 들어가고 700cc 나왔습니다.

Vitals are stable.
활력징후는 괜찮습니다.

Try and stay calm. Relax.
진정하세요.

You just have a major surgery.
방금 당신은 큰 수술을 받으셨습니다.

Lie still.
계속 누워 계세요.

You need to calm down.
진정하세요.

Take a deep breath and cough in order to free your lungs of any
fluid build up that may occur due to the general anesthesia.
전신마취 때문에 당신의 폐에 액체가 고이지 않도록 숨을 크게 쉬고 기침을
하세요.

Doctor. Would you come immediately?
선생님 빨리 좀 와 주실래요?

Patient is having trouble breathing.
환자가 숨을 잘 쉬지 못합니다.

Patient is not in good shape.
환자 상태가 좋지 못합니다.

The breathing difficulty has been going on for 20 minutes.
호흡곤란이 20분간 지속되었습니다.

Doctor. An arrest. There is an arrest.
선생님. 심장마비입니다.

Come quickly.
빨리 와주세요.

Residents are on call.
레지던트 선생님들을 불렀습니다.

Can I talk to you outside?
밖에서 이야기 좀 할까요?

Family have to stay outside.
가족들은 저기 밖에서 기다려야합니다.

I need you to go with the kid to the wait room.
어린이와 함께 대기실로 가 주시길 원합니다.

We will take care of patient.
우리가 환자를 돌볼 것입니다.

Doctor is gonna explain it all to you when he gets here.
의사선생님이 이곳에 오면 당신에게 모든 것을 설명해 줄 것입니다.

I'm sorry to cut you off.
말을 끊어서 미안해요.

Stop pestering me.
저를 너무 귀찮게 하지 마세요.

I'm sorry. I'm busy at the moment.
지금 바쁩니다.

I've got another patient. Excuse me.
다른 환자를 보아야 합니다. 미안합니다.

Please give us room to work.
일할 공간을 좀 주세요.

We need you to sign this paper.
이 서류에 사인을 부탁드립니다.

6. 안내

Can I help you?
무엇을 도와드릴까요?

Follow the red line to emergency room.
빨간색을 따라 응급실로 가세요.

Follow the arrows on the wall.
벽에 있는 화살표를 따라 가세요.

I'll show you to emergency room.
응급실로 안내해 드리겠습니다.

Come this way, Please.
이 쪽으로 오세요.

There is a rest room in the west wing.
화장실은 서쪽 건물에 있습니다.

Down this hallway.

이 복도를 따라 가세요.

Rest room is around the corner.

화장실은 모퉁이에 있습니다.

The pharmacy is in the main hospital building.

약국은 병원 본부 건물 안에 있습니다.

Go through this door and turn right.

이 문을 지나 오른쪽으로 가세요.

I'll show you.

제가 가르쳐 드리지요.

Please, follow me.

저를 따라 오세요.

Come right this way.

이쪽으로 오세요.

Smoking is not permitted in the hospital.

흡연은 병원에서 금지되어 있습니다.

You can't smoke here.

여기서는 담배를 못 피우십니다.

Do not leave your cell phone on in hospital.

병원에서는 핸드폰을 켜 놓지 마세요.

Are you looking for someone?

누구를 찾으세요?

You have to wait outside.

밖에서 기다리셔야 합니다.

Please wait in the wait room.

대기실에서 기다려 주세요.

The patient was discharged 2 hours ago.

환자는 2시간 전에 퇴원하셨습니다.

7. Medical Certificate (진단서)

(1) Personal Information

Last name :   First name :

Sex :   Date of Birth :

Address :

Health insurance number :

(2) Doctor's Diagnosis

Diagnosis :

Onset :

Is the person incapable of carrying out his or her normal activities(work or studies)?   Yes,   No

Approximate extent of disability :   Light,   Moderate, Severe

Date of beginning of disability : ( )

Expected date of the end of disability : (   )

Has the person been hospitalized?   Yes, No

If yes, indicate when : from ( ) to ( )

Has the person had an operation?   Yes, No

If yes, operation name :

Comments : In view of the medical history, physical examination, X-ray and blood test report, it is my opinion that he/she suffers from ---.

(3) Doctor identification and signature

Last name :   First name :

Doctor's licence number :   Address of hospital :

Date :   Signature :

8. To Whom It May Concern
(통원치료 확인서 - 관계자에게)

To whom it may concern.

This is to certify that ＊＊＊ was seen at our hospital,

on ＊＊＊, for treatment of his/her problem or for doctor's appointment.

If you have any questions,

please feel free to contact us at ＊＊＊＊ - ＊＊＊＊.

Sincerely,

Attending Clinician : Dr. ＊＊＊

Address of hospital :

Date :   Signature :

관계자에게

환자 ＊＊＊ 분께서 ＊년 ＊월 ＊일

병을 치료하기 위해서, 또는 의사와의 진료예약으로.

본원에서 다녀갔음을 확인하여 드립니다.

만약 의문사항이 있으시면, 이 곳으로 연락을 주시기 바랍니다.

진료 의사 : Dr. ＊＊＊

9. Medical Certificate for healthy person (건강 진단서)

I certify that I have carefully examined him/her.

Based on the examination, I certify that he/she is good mental and physical
  health.

He/She is free from any physical defects which may interfere with his/her
work including the active outdoor duties required of a professional.

Doctor :　　　　(Doctor's licence number: 　　　　)

Address of hospital :

Date :　　　Signature :

이 사람을 정밀 검사하였음을 확인합니다.

검사 상 이 사람은 정신적으로나 육체적으로 건강합니다.

이 사람은 외부 활동을 포함하여 직업상 요구되는 어떤 일을 방해할 만한
육체적인 장애가 없습니다.

10. Death Certificate (사망 진단서)

Name of the deceased :　　　　Age :

Sex :　　　　　　　　　　Date of Birth :

Nationality :

Address :

Date of Death :

Place of Death :

Date last seen by the doctor :

1. Cause of Death

I.　Primary cause of death :

II.　Significant conditions not related to primary cause of death :
　　(can be more than one)

2. Manner of Death

(1) Natural (2) Accidental

(3) Suicidal (4) Undetermined (5) Homicidal

Name of physician :

(Doctor's licence number:)

Date of issue :

Date :   Signature :

CF) The doctor can circle one or more of the following statements

1. This certificate takes account of information obtained from post-mortem

2. Information from post-mortem may be available later

3. Post-mortem not being held

4. I have reported this death to the coroner for further action

CF) The doctor can circle one of the following statements

1. Seen after death by me

2. Seen after death by another medical practitioner but not by me

3. Not seen after death by a medical practitioner

다음 관련된 사항에 표시해 주세요.

1. 이 진단서는 사후 얻은 정보를 고려한 것입니다.

2. 사후 정보는 추후 얻도록 하겠습니다.

3. 사후 정보가 없습니다.

4. 검시관에게 향후 평가를 위해 보고하는 바입니다.

다음 관련된 사항에 표시해 주세요.

1. 사망후 저에게 확인되었습니다.

2. 사망후 제가 아닌 다른 의료 종사자에게 확인되었습니다.

3. 의료종사자들에게 확인되지 않았습니다.

11. Birth Certificate (출생 증명서)

This certificates that (   ) was born in this hospital.

1. Name of child :   Sex :

Date of birth :   Hour of birth :

Place of birth :

Home address :

2. Name of farther :

Date of birth :   Place of birth :

3. Name of mother :

Date of birth :   Place of birth :

4. Name of physician :   (Doctor's licence number:)

Address of hospital :

Date :   Signature :

12. Certificate of Immunization (면역 접종 증명서)

Name :

Date of birth :   Sex :

Social security number :

Address :

Required immunization

1. BCG (   ) (Month/Day/Year)

2. DTP (Tetanus, Diphtheria, Pertussis)

(1) Completed primary series of DTP immunizations

   Dose 1. (   ) (Month/Day/Year)

   Dose 2. (   ) (Month/Day/Year)

   Dose 3. (   ) (Month/Day/Year)

   Dose 4. (   ) (Month/Day/Year)

   Dose 5. (   ) (Month/Day/Year)

(2) Received DTP booster within last ten years

   Dose 6. (   ) (Month/Day/Year)

3. IPV or OPV (Inactivated Poliovirus Vaccine or Oral Polio Vaccine)

   Dose 1. (   ) (Month/Day/Year)

Dose 2. (　　　　　) (Month/Day/Year)

Dose 3. (　　　　　) (Month/Day/Year)

Dose 4. (　　　　　) (Month/Day/Year)

4. MMR (Measles, Mumps, Rubella)

Received MMR vaccinations since the age of twelve months.

Dose 1. (　　　　　) (Month/Day/Year)

Dose 2. (　　　　　) (Month/Day/Year)

5. Chicken pox (　　　　　) (Month/Day/Year)

Doctor or Health care provider

Name :

Address :　　　　　(Phone :　　)

Signature

CF) 1. Medically contraindicated because of allergy to vaccine, etc.

　　　Must list reason(s) :

　　2. Refused immunization because of religious objections.

　　　Attach statement :

13. Advance Beneficiary Notice (보험과 관련된 사전 설명서)

You need to make a choice about receiving these health care items or services.

당신은 치료를 위해 다음과 같은 의료 아이템이나 서비스를 선택하실 수 있습니다.

We expect that medical insurance will not pay for the items or services that are described below.

아래의 아이템이나 서비스는 의료 보험이 되지 않습니다.

Medical insurance does not pay for all of your health care costs.
의료보험은 치료비용을 모두 지급하지 않습니다.

Medical insurance only pays for covered items and services when medical insurance rules are met.
의료보험에서는 의료보험으로 지정된 것만 지불하게 되어있습니다.

The fact that medical insurance may not pay for a particular item or service does not mean that you should not receive it.
의료보험에서 지급하지 않는 아이템이나 서비스를 당신이 꼭 받지 않아야 한다는 뜻이 아닙니다.

There may be a good reason your doctor recommended it.
당신의 의사가 권하는 것은 좋기 때문입니다.

Right now, in your cases, medical insurance will not pay for (items or services).
지금 당신의 경우엔 다음 것들이 의료보험이 안됩니다.

Please choose one option, check one, sign and date your choice.
옵션을 선택하고 하나를 선택해 사인해 주세요.

Option 1. ( )

Yes. I want to receive these items or services.
예 나는 이 아이템이나 서비스를 받기를 원합니다.

I understand that medical insurance will not decide whether to pay unless I receive these items or services.
나는 내가 이들 아이템이나 서비스를 받지 않을 경우, 의료보험에서 지불하지 않는 것을 이해합니다.

I understand that you may bill me for items or services and that I
   may have to pay the bill.
나는 내가 지불해야할 아이템이나 서비스에 대해 당신들이 청구하는 것을
   이해합니다.

Option 2. ( )

No. I have decided not to receive these items or services.
아닙니다. 나는 이 아이템이나 이 서비스를 받지 않겠습니다.

I will not receive these items or services.
나는 이들 아이템이나 서비스를 받지 않을 것입니다.

Date :

Signature of patients or person acting on patient's behalf :

14. Consent to Simple Procedure
(간단한 시술에 대한 승낙서)

It has been fully explained to me the nature and purpose,
   risks, benefits, and alternative treatment methods and their
   risks and benefits of the procedure.
시술에 대한 성질과 목적, 위험성과 이점 그리고 여러 가지 치료방법들에
   대해 충분한 설명이 제게 이루어졌습니다.

I have not had allergic reaction to any medication.
나는 어떤 약에도 알러지 반응을 보인 적이 없습니다.

I do hereby consent to and authorize Doctor ＊＊＊ to perform
   the following procedure : ＊＊＊ ＊＊＊
나는 의사에게 다음과 같은 시술을 맡깁니다.

I also consent and authorize the Doctor in case of local anesthesia, to make use of such anesthetizing agents as shall be deemed advisable or necessary.

나는 의사에게 국소마취에 필요한 마취제 사용을 맡깁니다.

The usual risks and hazards of anesthetic procedure were made known to me.

마취과정의 위험성에 대해서 들었습니다.

I consent to the disposal of any tissue or body parts removed.

나는 제거된 조직이나 몸의 일부의 처리를 의뢰합니다.

(Woman : To the best of my knowledge, I am not pregnant.)

여성인 경우 : 지금 임신중이 아닙니다.

Date :

Signature of patient or person acting on patient's behalf :

15. Consent to Operation (수술 승낙서)

I hereby authorize and direct Dr. * * *, and whomever he/she may designate as his/her assistants, to perform the following operation upon me.

나는 의사에게 이 수술과 조력자들에 대한 모든 것을 맡깁니다.

Operation : * * * * * * (수술명)

And to any additional procedure that in his/her judgment may be deemed necessary or different from those now contemplated, whether or not arising from presently unforeseen conditions, which he/she may consider necessary or advisable in the course of the operation.

그리고 의사의 판단에 의해 예기치 못했던 어떤 추가적 시술에 대해서도 맡깁니다.

I hereby authorize the doctors to use his/her discretion in the disposal of any removed tissue.

나는 제거된 조직의 처리에 대해 의사에게 자유롭게 맡깁니다.

For the purpose of advancing medical education, I consent to the admittance of observers to the operating room.

의학교육의 발전을 위해 나는 수술실의 참관자에 대해 허락합니다.

I consent to the photographing of the operations or procedures performed for medical scientific, or educational purposes, providing my identity is not revealed by pictures or descriptive text accompanying them.

나는 나의 개인 정보가 책의 사진이나 그림에 나타나지 않는다면, 과학과 의학적 교육을 위해 수술이나 행해진 과정들의 사진촬영을 허락합니다.

The doctor has explained alternative forms of treatment and I understand that this operation is elective or optional.

의사는 내게 치료의 여러 형태를 설명하였으며, 이 수술이 선택적임을 이해합니다.

I accept and certify that I have read and had explained to me by the doctor, in terminology that I fully understand.

나는 이 것들을 읽고 의사에게 충분히 설명 들었음을 서약합니다.

The usual risks and hazards of operation were made known to me.

일반적인 수술의 위험성과 합병증에 대해 주의를 받았습니다.

Date :

Signature of Patient :

Person acting on patient's behalf :

16. Consent to Possible Complications
(합병증에 대한 설명서)

It has been explained to me that satisfactory results are anticipated.

만족할만한 결과들이 기대된다는 설명을 들었습니다.

However, complications or after effects could occur.

하지만 합병증이나 부작용이 생길 수 있습니다.

These include anesthetic reactions, infections, scarring, phlebitis, prolonged swelling, prolonged pain, prolonged hospital stay, delay in wound healing, delay in return to normal activity, numbness and tingling, nerve damage, reduction in range of motion or stiffness in the joints, recurrence of the original condition, need for further surgery, and others as follows : *** ***.

이것들은 마취 반응, 감염, 흉터, 정맥염, 지속적인 부종, 지속적인 통증, 장기 입원, 상처 치유 지연, 정상 생활 지연, 무감각이나 저리는 것, 신경 손상, 관절 운동의 제한이나 강직, 재발, 추가 수술 등이 해당됩니다.

I accept and certify that I have read and had explained to me by the doctor, in terminology that I fully understand.

나는 이와 같은 것들을 읽고 의사에게 충분히 이해가 되도록 설명을 들었습니다.

The usual complications of treatment made known to me.

치료의 일반적인 합병증에 대해 알게 되었습니다.

Date :

Signature of Patient :

Person acting on patient's behalf :

17. Consent to Anesthesia
   (마취 승낙서)

I hereby authorize the doctors to perform the following anesthesia.

나는 다음 마취 시술에 의사에게 맡깁니다.

I consent to the administration of such anesthetics as may be considered necessary or advisable by the physician responsible for this procedure.

이 시술을 받기 위해 필요한 마취제의 투약을 의사에게 맡깁니다.

I have not had allergic reaction to any medication.

나는 어떤 약에도 알러지가 있었던 적이 없습니다.

I am aware of the danger of food or liquid in my stomach during anesthesia and I certify that I will have had nothing to eat and drink after midnight on the evening before surgery.

나는 위에 음식이나 액체가 있으면 위험하다는 것을 알고, 수술 전날 밤 12시 이후에 아무 것도 먹지 않을 것임을 확약합니다.

I consent to the use of intravenous fluids when necessary.

나는 필요할 경우, 정맥 내 수액 투여를 허락합니다.

I consent to the use of medical laboratory and X-ray services as needed.

나는 필요한 의학적 검사나 방사선 검사를 허락합니다.

I accept and certify that I have read and had explained to me by the doctor, in terminology that I fully understand.

나는 이것을 읽고, 의사에게 충분히 설명을 들었습니다.

I also understand that the risk of complications is always present, including shock, brain damage, and permanent nerve injury.

나는 합병증이 생길 수 있고, 쇼크나 뇌 손상, 신경 손상 등의 위험성에 대해 이해합니다.

The usual risks and hazards of anesthetic procedure were made known to me.

마취 과정의 일반적인 위험성에 대해 주의를 받았습니다.

Date :

Signature of Patient :

Person acting on patient's behalf :